ADVANCED MATHS FOR AQA

Statistics

S1

Graham Upton Ian Cook

Course consultant: John White

Coursework guidance: Craig Simms

OXFORD
UNIVERSITY PRESS

Great Clarendon Street, Oxford OX2 6DP

Oxford University Press is a department of the University of Oxford.
It furthers the University's objective of excellence in research, scholarship, and education by publishing worldwide in

Oxford New York

Auckland Cape Town Dar es Salaam Hong Kong Karachi
Kuala Lumpur Madrid Melbourne Mexico City Nairobi
New Delhi Shanghai Taipei Toronto

With offices in

Argentina Austria Brazil Chile Czech Republic France Greece
Guatemala Hungary Italy Japan South Korea Poland Portugal
Singapore Switzerland Thailand Turkey Ukraine Vietnam

Oxford is a registered trade mark of Oxford University Press
in the UK and in certain other countries

First published 2004

British Library Cataloguing in Publication Data

Data available

ISBN 9780199149377

20 19 18 17 16 15

Typeset by Tech-Set Ltd, Gateshead, Tyne and Wear
Printed and bound in Great Britain by Ashford Colour Press Ltd, Gosport, Hants

Acknowledgements
The publishers would like to thank AQA for their kind permission to reproduce past paper questions. AQA accept no responsibility for the answers to the past paper questions which are the sole responsibility of the publishers.

The publishers would also like to thank James Nicholson for his authoritative guidance in preparing this book.

The publishers and authors are grateful to the following:
Office of National Statistics; Centre for Environment, Fisheries and Aquaculture Science; Department for Transport

The photograph on the cover is reproduced courtesy of Photodisc.

About this book

This Advanced level book is designed to help you get your best possible grade in the AQA S1 module for first examination in 2005. This module can contribute to an award in GCE A-level or AS-level Mathematics or Statistics.

Each chapter starts with an overview of what you are going to learn and a list of what you should already know. The 'Before you start' section contains 'Check in' questions, which will help to prepare you for the topics in the chapter.

You should know how to ...	Check in
1 Represent data on a scatter diagram.	**1** Plot the following data on a scatter diagram.

x	1	2	3	4	5	6	7	8
y	−4	−1	0	5	3	7	7	9

Key information is highlighted in the text so you can see the facts you need to learn.

> A random variable having a $B(n, p)$ distribution has a mean of np and a variance of $np(1-p)$.

Worked examples showing the key skills and techniques you need to develop are shown in boxes. Also hint boxes show tips and reminders you may find useful.

Example 14

Two events, A and B, are such that $P(A) = 0.7$, $P(B) = 0.4$, and $P(A|B) = 0.3$. Determine the probability that neither A nor B occurs.

From Equation (2.10):

$$P(B \cap A) = P(B) \times P(A|B) = 0.4 \times 0.3 = 0.12$$

From Equation (2.3), you can now obtain $P(A \cup B)$:

$$P(A \cup B) = P(A) + P(B) - P(A \cap B) = 0.7 + 0.4 - 0.12 = 0.98$$

But, looking at a Venn diagram, you will see that:

$$P(\textbf{Neither } A \textbf{ nor } B) = 1 - P(A \cup B)$$

The required probability is therefore $1 - 0.98 = 0.02$.

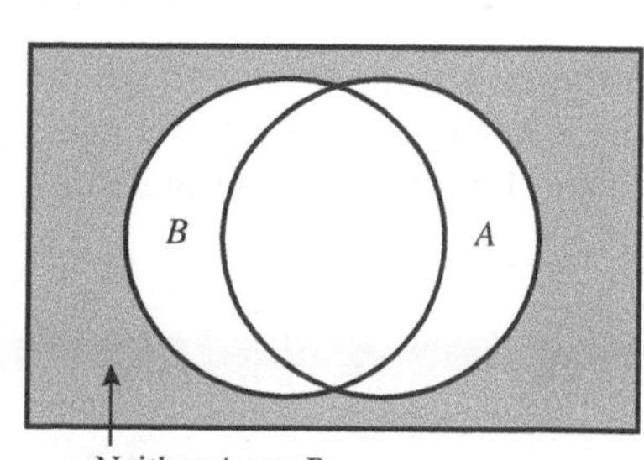

This result was used in Example 7 (page 45).

'Calculator practice' boxes suggest ways in which you can use your calculator more effectively in handling data.

Calculator practice

Some calculators have special routines for dealing with frequency distributions and grouped frequencies. Check whether your calculator is one that has. If it is, then use it to check the answer in Example 22.

The questions in the exercises are carefully selected to provide basic practice at the beginning, and harder questions towards the end.

At the end of each chapter there is a summary. The 'You should now know' section is useful as a quick revision guide, and each 'Check out' question identifies important techniques that you should remember.

You should know how to ...	Check out
1 Calculate a probability when the possible outcomes are equally likely.	**1** A fair twelve-sided die has faces labelled 1, 2, …, 12. Determine the probability that, when rolled, it comes to rest on a face that is a multiple of 4.

Following the summary you will find a revision exercise with past paper questions from AQA. These will enable you to become familiar with the style of questions you will see in the exam.

Towards the end of the book there are two Practice Papers, one for Option A (with coursework) and one for Option B (without coursework). These will directly help you to prepare for your exams.

The last chapter is entitled 'Coursework Guidance', and is for students taking the MS1A unit (with coursework). The chapter tells you what you have to do for your coursework, and contains advice from a senior moderator to help you improve your grade.

At the end of the book you will find numerical answers, statistical tables, a list of formulae you need to become familiar with, and a list of useful mathematical notation.

Contents

1 Numerical measures

This chapter will show you how to

- ✦ Find measures of location
- ✦ Find measures of spread
- ✦ Use linear scaling
- ✦ Choose an appropriate numerical measure

Before you start

S1

You should know how to ...	Check in
1 Represent a frequency distribution using a bar chart or line graph.	**1** Represent these data by using either a bar chart or a line diagram.
2 Use linear interpolation.	**2** The quantities x and y are linearly related. Find the values of p, q and r.

Check in 1:

a)

x	1	2	3	4	5	6
f	8	13	22	14	9	4

b)

Value	10	11	12	13	14
Frequency	3	12	24	17	9

Check in 2:

a)

x	44	50	68
y	10	p	30

b)

x	27	30	42
y	9.5	q	19.5

c)

x	63	75	83
y	5	r	9

1.1 The mode, median and mean

Statistics, with a capital 'S', involves transforming a lot of bewildering numerical information into a few simple facts. The individual pieces of numerical information are called **observations** or **data**. By studying a set of values – called the **sample** – drawn from a much larger set of values – called the **population**, you can often gain information about the values of the population. The first step is usually to calculate the values of quantities derived from the data, which are called **statistics** – with an initial small 's'. Here are some statistics which you should have met before.

The mode

The two most obvious questions to ask about a set of numbers are 'What are their typical values?' and 'How variable are they?'. The statistics used to answer the first question are called **measures of location**. The simplest of these is the **mode**.

> The mode is the value that occurs most frequently.

When there are two values which occur with equal frequency, there is no unique mode and the data is described as being **bimodal**. When there are three or more values which occur with equal frequency, the data is called **multimodal**. Note that you are sometimes asked to find the modal value or modal class.

S1

Example 1

At the supermarket, I buy eight cans of soup. According to the information on the cans, four weigh 400 grams, three weigh 425 grams and one weighs 435 grams. Find the mode.

The mode is 400 grams because 400 grams is the most common value.

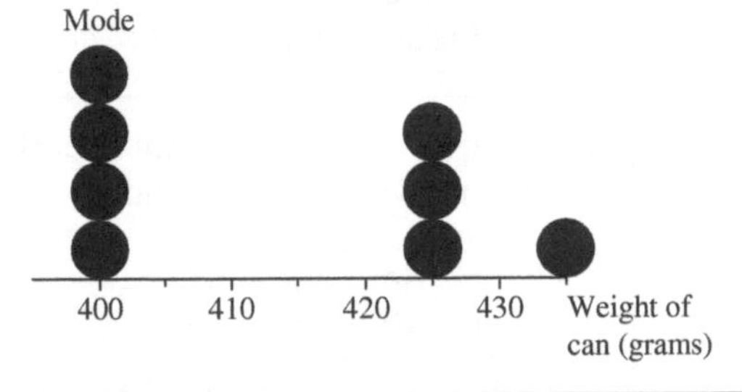

Example 2

After unpacking the shopping, I feel hungry and have soup for lunch. I choose one of the 400-gram cans bought in the previous example. What is an appropriate description of the frequency distribution of the remaining seven weights?

There are now two modes, one at 400 grams and one at 425 grams. The frequency distribution is described as 'bimodal'.

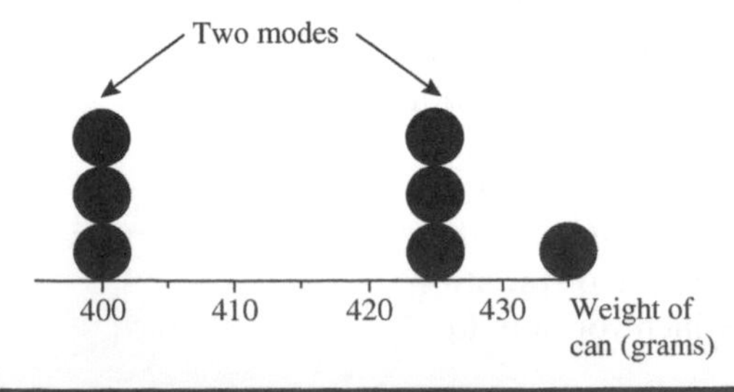

Example 3

After lunch, I examine the money in my piggy bank (with a view to buying more soup). The ages of the coins are summarized in the table.

Age (years)	0–4	5–9	10–14	15–19	20–24	25–29
Number of coins	12	15	10	8	12	10

Determine the modal class.

The classes have equal width. The modal class is 5–9 years, because 15 is the largest of the class frequencies.

With classes of unequal width, you need to take the class-widths into account. The modal class is then the class for which the value of the ratio

$$\text{Frequency density} = \frac{\text{Class frequency}}{\text{Class width}}$$

is greatest.

Calculator practice

When used to plot a bar chart or a line diagram, a graphical calculator may also indicate the value of the mode and the associated frequency. Use a calculator to determine the mode of the cans of soup data in Example 1. What happens if the 435-gram can is replaced by a 425-gram can?

The median

'Median' means 'mid-point' or 'middle value'.

After the observations have been collected, they can be arranged in a row in order of magnitude, with the smallest on the left and the largest on the right (or vice-versa). The **median** of the data is the middle value of this set of ordered values. For example, suppose the observed values are 13, 34, 19, 22 and 16. Arranged in numerical order, you would get:

13, 16, <u>19</u>, 22, 34

Here, the middle value, 19, is the median.

When there is an even number of observations, there are two middle values. Conventionally, the median is taken as their average. For example, for the eight cans of soup in Example 1, the values are:

400, 400, 400, <u>400</u>, <u>425</u>, 425, 425, 435

The value of the median is taken to be:

$$\frac{1}{2}(400 + 425) = 412.5$$

With n observations arranged in order of size, the median is calculated as follows.

- When n is odd, the median is the $\frac{(n+1)}{2}$th ordered value.
- When n is even, the median is the average of the $\frac{n}{2}$th and the $\left(\frac{n}{2}+1\right)$th ordered values.

Example 4

A chemistry professor has an accurate weighing machine. He also has two sons, Charles and James, who are keen on playing conkers. One day, Charles and James collect some new conkers. On their return home, following a dispute over who has the heaviest conkers, they use their father's weighing machine to determine the weights of the conkers (in grams). Their results were:

Charles: 31.4, 44.4, 39.5, 58.7, 63.6, 51.5, 60.0
James: 60.1, 34.7, 42.8, 38.6, 51.6, 55.1, 47.0, 59.2

Which boy's collection of conkers has the higher median weight?

First, arrange each set of observations in ascending order. Then highlight the central value(s):

Charles: 31.4, 39.5, 44.4, 51.5, 58.7, 60.0, 63.6
James: 34.7, 38.6, 42.8, 47.0, 51.6, 55.1, 59.2, 60.1

The median for James's conkers is the average of 47.0 and 51.6, which is 49.3. This is less than the median for Charles's conkers, which is 51.5.

You can determine the median of a frequency distribution in a similar way, as Example 5 shows.

Example 5

Each student in a class is asked how many brothers and sisters they have. The results are summarized in the table. Determine the median of the data.

Number of brothers and sisters	0	1	2	3	4 or more
Frequency	6	11	8	3	3

There are 31 students in the class. So:

$$\frac{n+1}{2} = 16$$

If you imagine the 31 numbers arranged in increasing order, then you would see six 0s followed by eleven 1s. So, the 16th of the ordered numbers would be a 1. The median of the data is 1.

For small data sets, one simple method of locating the median is to use a stem-and-leaf diagram. However, with more data, it is easier to work with class frequencies. With grouped data, for n observations, the value corresponding to the $\frac{n}{2}$th largest observation must be estimated.

Working with class frequencies, you do not need to consider whether n is even or odd.

One method of determining a value for the median is to plot the data on a **cumulative frequency diagram**.

Cumulative frequencies are obtained by summing the frequencies for all classes up to and including the class under consideration. In a cumulative frequency diagram, cumulative frequency is plotted against the upper class boundary. The median is then determined by reading off the graph. The procedure is illustrated in Example 6.

S1

Example 6

The data summarize the distances travelled by a fleet of 190 buses before experiencing a major breakdown.

Distance, x '000 miles	0–	60–	80–	100–	120–	140–220
Frequency, f	32	25	34	46	33	20

By constructing a cumulative frequency diagram, estimate the distance exceeded by half the buses.

Begin by tabulating the data using cumulative frequencies and upper class boundaries.

Distance, x '000 miles	<60	<80	<100	<120	<140	<220
Cumulative frequency	32	57	91	137	170	190

The upper class boundaries are the values 60, 80, …, 220, so that the graph joins the successive points (60, 32), (80, 57), …, (220, 190). The graph starts with a cumulative frequency of 0 at the lowest possible value of x, which, in this case, is 0. The resulting graph is as shown.

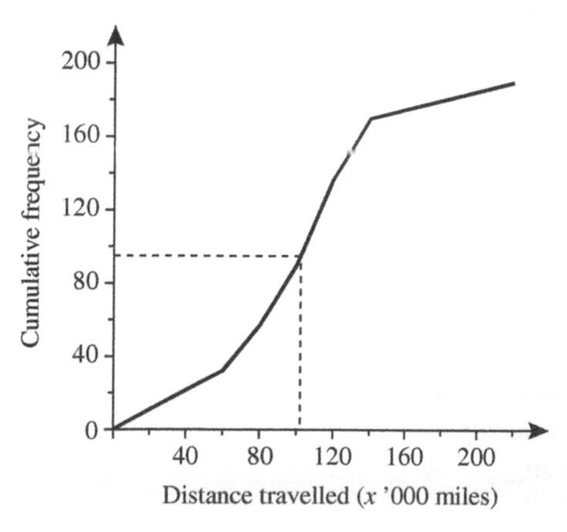

Using the graph, the median can be estimated as about 100 000 miles.

This graphical method is likely to give a rather imprecise answer. A more precise answer is provided by **linear interpolation**. The procedure is illustrated in Example 7.

Example 7

Use linear interpolation to estimate the median distance travelled for the data in Example 6.

To use linear interpolation, begin by noting that there are 190 buses and that $\frac{190}{2} = 95$. Since 95 falls between 91 and 137, the median distance falls between 100 and 120 thousand miles. There were 46 buses whose distance travelled fell in this class. Since $95 - 91 = 4$, you need to estimate the fourth largest of the 46 distances in this class.
Using linear interpolation, the median is therefore estimated as:

$$100 + \frac{4}{46} \times (120 - 100) = 102 \quad \text{(to 3 sf)}$$

Hence, linear interpolation gives a value for the median of about 102 000 miles.

S1

With grouped data, the median is taken to be the value of the $\frac{n}{2}$th observation, preferably calculated using linear interpolation.

Calculator practice

Some calculators will report the median value. You may need to delve deeply into your calculator manual in order to find the correct sequence of key-strokes. You should check that your calculator reports the correct value for the median, both in the case of an even number of data items and in the case of an odd number. Use the data in Example 4 (page 4) as a check.

The mean

This measure of location is also called the **average**. The mean of a set of values is equal to the sum of the values divided by the number of values. Thus the mean weight (in grams) of the cans of soup in Example 1 (page 2) is:

$$\frac{400 + 400 + 400 + 400 + 425 + 425 + 425 + 435}{8} = 413.75$$

If there are n values sampled from a population, then, denoting the values by $x_1, x_2, \ldots, x_n$, the **sample mean,** $\bar{x}$, is given by:

$$\bar{x} = \frac{x_1 + x_2 + \cdots + x_n}{n} \qquad (1.1)$$

entire population, their average is the
ally denoted by the Greek letter μ

ge stones from the beach. Their
5 and 545. Determine their

340 grams

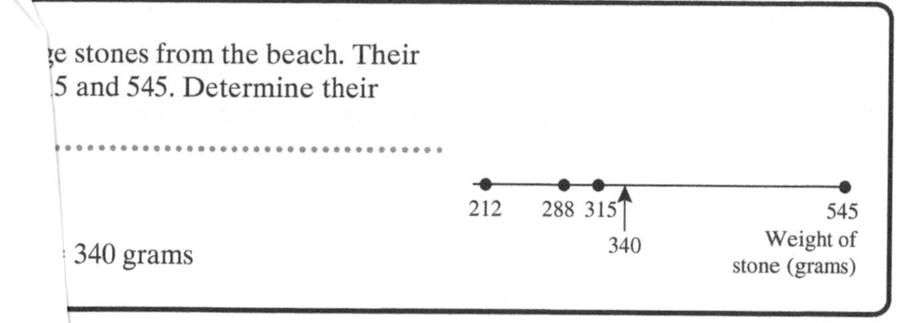

S1

olar system. Their typical
kilometres) are given as

aturn	Uranus	Neptune	Pluto
1427	2870	4497	5893

al distances. How many
the sun?

of major planets, which is
value is given by:

0 (to 3 sf)

ly 1780 million kilometres.
reater distance from the

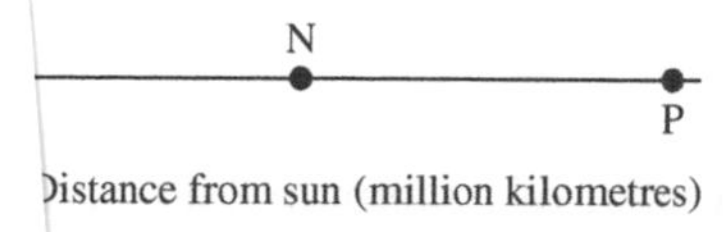

g the mean for a set of
riate sequence of key-
own calculator.
memories have been set

Exercise 1A

1 A gardener classifies a potato having a weight over 100 grams as being 'large'. The gardener grows a number of potato plants and, for each plant, he counts the number of large potatoes, obtaining the following results:

8, 5, 7, 10, 8   6, 5, 6, 4, 8   10, 9, 8, 7, 3   10, 11, 6, 9, 8

Find: a) the mode, b) the median, c) the mean, of the numbers of large potatoes.

2 The heights, in metres, of 12 walnut seedlings, after 20 years growth, were:

4.3, 5.2, 4.1, 3.5   5.2, 4.8, 5.3, 4.8   3.7, 4.1, 4.5, 5.0

S1

Find the mean height.

3 Sarah's bank balance at the end of each month was recorded in pounds sterling. A negative quantity denotes an overdraft. The figures were as follows:

341.32	97.53	−57.44	255.93	5.89	−83.33
152.81	−23.11	−105.73	−204.50	−150.46	−85.39

Find Sarah's mean end-of-month bank balance, giving your answer to the nearest penny.

4 The weights, in kilograms, of the oarsmen in a Cambridge Boat Race crew were:

90.7   89.4   93.4   92.1   82.6   92.5   94.4   89.8

The weights of the oarsmen in the corresponding Oxford crew were:

86.9   90.3   94.8   97.5   89.6   89.8   91.9   89.1

Find the mean weight of each crew and verify that the Oxford crew is heavier than the Cambridge crew by an average of 0.63 kilograms per man.

5 A baker keeps a count of the number of doughnuts sold each day for three working weeks, each of six days. The numbers were:

35, 47, 34, 46, 55, 82   41, 35, 47, 51, 56, 75
38, 41, 44, 51, 45, 74

Find the median number of doughnuts sold per day.

6 The marks obtained in a mathematics test (marked out of 50) were:

35, 42, 31, 27, 48, 50, 24, 27, 21, 37, 41, 34, 12, 18, 27

Find: a) the mean mark, b) the median mark.

7 The boot sizes of the members of a football team are:

10, 10, 8, 11, 10, 9, 9, 10, 11, 9, 10

Find: a) the mean boot size, b) the median boot size, c) the modal boot size.

8 Most people have more than the average number of legs! Explain.

Sigma ($\sum$) notation

Expressions such as $(x_1 + x_2 + \cdots + x_n)$ are tedious to write. Instead, the following notation is used:

$$\sum_{i=1}^{n} x_i = x_1 + x_2 + \cdots + x_n \qquad (1.2)$$

$\sum$ is the Greek equivalent of capital 'S' and is pronounced 'sigma'.

There are three particularly useful results that involve the manipulation of $\sum$:

$$\sum_{i=1}^{n} (x_i + y_i) = \sum_{i=1}^{n} x_i + \sum_{i=1}^{n} y_i \qquad (1.3)$$

$$\sum_{i=1}^{n} cx_i = c\sum_{i=1}^{n} x_i \qquad (1.4)$$

$$\sum_{i=1}^{n} c = nc \qquad (1.5)$$

In each of these results, c is a constant. Result (1.5) should be particularly noted. It follows immediately from result (1.4) by putting all the x-values equal to 1. All three results are easily proved by writing out the various summations in full.

Often the limits of the summation are obvious, in which case they may be dropped from the formula. For example, the mean of n observations $x_1, x_2, \ldots, x_n$ may be written:

$$\bar{x} = \frac{\sum x_i}{n}$$

or, more simply still:

$$\bar{x} = \frac{\sum x}{n} \qquad (1.6)$$

The sample mean, $\bar{x}$, for a sample of size n is given by:

$$\bar{x} = \frac{\sum x}{n}$$

Exercise 1B

1 A set of data for ten observations has $\sum x = 365$. Find the mean.

2 For a set of observations, $n = 60$, $\sum y = 74\,400$. Find the mean value of y.

3 The results of 30 experiments to find the value of the acceleration due to gravity are summarized by $\sum g = 294.34$. Find the mean value.

4 Eight numbers have a mean of 17. Given that the first seven numbers have a total of 130, determine the value of the eighth number.

5 A set of 25 observations was found to have a mean of 15.2. It is subsequently found that one item of data has been wrongly recorded as 23 instead of 28. Find the revised value of the mean.

S1

The mean of a frequency distribution

Data are often represented by a frequency distribution. For example, for the cans of soup in Example 1 (page 2):

Reported weight, x grams	400	425	435
Observed frequency, f	4	3	1

The sum of the frequencies $(4 + 3 + 1)$ is equal to n, the total number of observations. The sum of the three products 4×400, 3×425 and 1×435, is equal to the sum of the eight observations, and so the mean weight is:

$$\frac{1600 + 1275 + 435}{4 + 3 + 1} = 413.75 \text{ grams}$$

which is the result obtained on page 6.

The formula for the sample mean of a frequency distribution is:

$$\bar{x} = \frac{\sum fx}{\sum f} \qquad (1.7)$$

The sum of the frequencies is denoted by $\sum f$. Similarly, the sum of the products of f and x is denoted by $\sum fx$.

For a frequency distribution, the sample mean, $\bar{x}$, is given by:

$$\bar{x} = \frac{\sum fx}{\sum f}$$

where f is the frequency of the value x.

Example 10

The number of people in each household on a housing estate are summarized in the frequency table. Determine the mean number per household.

Household size, x	1	2	3	4	5	6	7	8	9
Number of households, f	3	2	5	8	4	1	1	0	1

$$\sum fx = (3 \times 1) + (2 \times 2) + \cdots + (1 \times 9) = 3 + 4 + \cdots + 9 = 96$$
$$\sum f = 3 + 2 + \cdots + 1 = 25$$

Hence, the mean number of people per household is:

$$\frac{96}{25} = 3.84$$

The mean household size is a little less than four people.

S1

Calculator practice

Most calculators with statistical functions have some special key sequence for dealing with the input of frequencies. Investigate how this can be done with your calculator and test the procedure using the cans of soup data (Example 1 on page 2), or the data in Example 10.

The mean of grouped data

The formula for the mean of a frequency distribution can also be used to calculate a value for the sample mean of a set of grouped data. With grouped data, the individual x-values are not known. However, the mean can be estimated by using the mid-point of each class, which is often denoted simply by x.

If x_L is the lower class boundary and x_U is the upper class boundary, the mid-point is:

$$\frac{x_L + x_U}{2}$$

For grouped data, an estimate of the sample mean, $\bar{x}$, is given by:

$$\bar{x} = \frac{\sum fx}{\sum f}$$

where f is a class frequency and x is a class mid-point.

Grouped data are often represented by a **histogram**, in which area is proportional to frequency. Brief details on the construction of histograms are given in Examples 11 and 12.

Example 11

A botanist measures the lengths of willow leaves, obtaining the results summarized in the table.

Length, x cm	2–	4–	6–	8–10
Frequency, f	12	25	37	12

a) Draw a histogram representing the data.

b) Estimate the mean leaf length, giving your answer to one decimal place.

a) In this case, drawing the histogram is easy, since each class has a width of 2 cm. You simply draw rectangles with heights $\frac{12}{2}, \frac{25}{2}, \frac{37}{2}, \frac{12}{2}$.

Note that the vertical axis of a histogram is usually labelled **Frequency density**.

These heights ensure that the rectangle areas are equal to the frequencies that they represent.

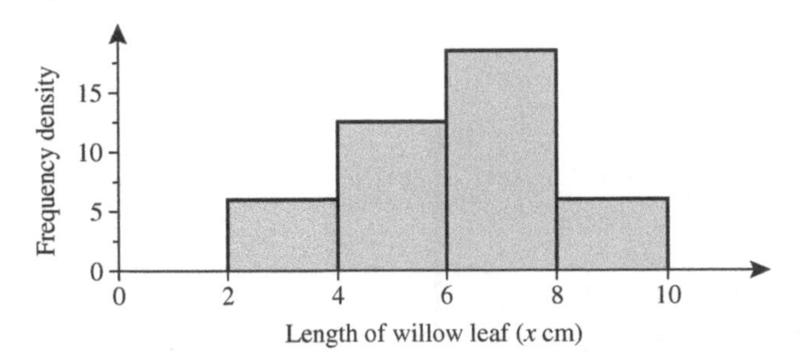

Note that it is important to leave no gap between the end of one rectangle and the start of the next.

b) Consider the 12 leaves with lengths between 2 cm and 4 cm. A sensible estimate of their average length is 3 cm, the mid-point of that class. The other class mid-points (in cm) are 5, 7 and 9. Therefore:

$$\begin{aligned}\sum fx &= (12 \times 3) + (25 \times 5) + (37 \times 7) + (12 \times 9)\\ &= 36 + 125 + 259 + 108 = 528\\ \sum f &= 12 + 25 + 37 + 12 = 86\end{aligned}$$

The mean leaf length is given by:

$$\bar{x} = \frac{\sum fx}{\sum f} = \frac{528}{86} = 6.1 \text{ (to 1 dp)}$$

The mean leaf length is estimated as 6.1 cm.

In a histogram, a class frequency is represented by the area of a rectangle, with

$$\text{Height} = \text{Frequency density} = \frac{\text{Class frequency}}{\text{Class width}}$$

Example 12

The data in the table summarizes the distances travelled by a fleet of 190 buses before a major breakdown occurred.

Distance, '000 miles	0–	60–	80–	100–	120–	140–220
Frequency, f	32	25	34	46	33	20

a) Draw a histogram to represent these data.
b) Estimate the mean distance travelled.

a) Extend the table to include class width and frequency density:

Distance, '000 miles	0–	60–	80–	100–	120–	140–220
Class width, w	60	20	20	20	20	80
Class frequency, f	32	25	34	46	33	20
Frequency density, $\frac{f}{w}$	0.53	1.25	1.70	2.30	1.65	0.25

Now draw the histogram with the vertical axis labelled 'Frequency density'.

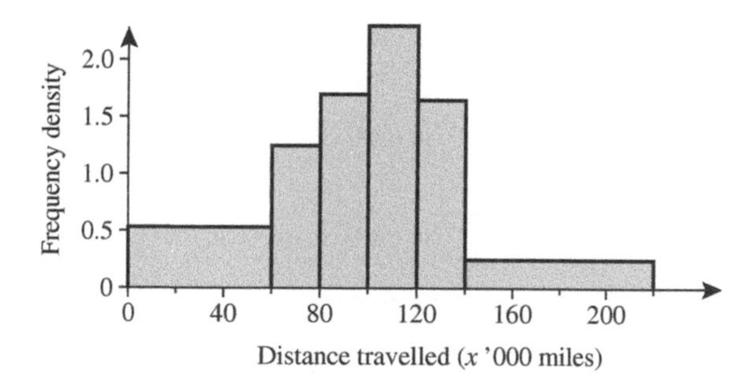

b) Begin by computing the class mid-points.

Distance, x '000 miles	0–	60–	80–	100–	120–	140–220
Class mid-point, x	30	70	90	110	130	180
Class frequency, f	32	25	34	46	33	20

Working in units of a thousand miles, you have:

$$\sum fx = (32 \times 30) + \cdots + (20 \times 180) = 18\,720$$

Now $\sum f = 190$. So:

$$\bar{x} = \frac{18\,720}{190} = 98.5 \quad \text{(to 3 sf)}$$

The estimate of the mean distance travelled is 98 500 miles. This value is reassuringly close to the rough estimate based on the histogram.

This is an extension of Example 6, page 5.

Beware: in this case, the first and last classes are wider than the others.

The diagram suggests that the sample mean, $\bar{x}$, will be at about 100 thousand miles. If the calculated answer turns out to be very different from this, it should be checked for a possible error.

S1

Exercise 1C

1 A marine biologist is studying the population of limpets on a rocky coast. The numbers of a rare type of limpet which are found in 1 m square sections of the undercliff are summarized in the table.

Number of limpets	0	1	2	3	4
Number of squares	73	19	5	2	1

Calculate the mean number of limpets per square metre of undercliff.

2 A proofreader reads through a 250-page proof of a book. The numbers of mistakes found on each page are summarized in the table.

S1

Number of mistakes	0	1	2	3	4
Number of pages	61	109	53	23	4

Determine the mean number of mistakes found per page.

3 Construct a frequency distribution for the following data:

5, 7, 5, 3   1, 4, 5, 4   3, 2, 1, 3   4, 5, 7, 6
8, 4, 3, 1   5, 3, 5, 7   3, 2, 4, 2   6, 5, 2, 2

Find: a) the mean, b) the median.

4 A sales representative records his daily mileage (in completed miles) for a period of four weeks. Here is his record:

153, 127, 142, 82, 91   125, 113, 105, 93, 105
88, 122, 96, 145, 136   115, 107, 125, 98, 94

Group the data using the classes 80–, 100–, etc.

a) Determine the mean of the grouped data.

b) Find the modal class.

5 Each day the number of diners in a restaurant was recorded and the following grouped frequency table was obtained.

Number of diners	16–20	21–25	26–30	31–35	36–40
Number of days	67	74	38	39	42

a) Estimate the mean number of diners.

b) Find the modal class.

6 The weights (in grams) of a random collection of offcuts taken from the floor of a carpenter's shop are summarized in the table.

Weight	0–20	–40	–60	–80	–100
Frequency	12	25	42	18	6

a) Represent the data using a histogram.

b) Determine the modal class.

c) Estimate the median.

d) Estimate the mean.

7 The lengths of telephone calls, in minutes, are summarized in the table.

Length	0–1	–3	–5	–10	–30
Number of calls	15	37	33	25	10

a) Represent these data using a cumulative frequency diagram.

b) Hence estimate the median length of a telephone call.

c) Estimate the mean length of a telephone call.

1.2 The standard deviation and variance

The standard deviation and variance are both **measures of spread**. That is, they tell you about the variability of the data. Before looking at these new measures, two other measures are considered.

Range

The **range** of a set of numerical data is the difference between the highest and lowest values.

The range is the simplest possible measure of spread. It cannot be used with grouped data and it ignores the distribution of intermediate values. A single very large or very small value would give a misleading impression of the spread of the data.

Example 13

The numbers of words in the 18 sentences of Chapter 1 of *A Tale of Two Cities* by Charles Dickens are:

118, 39, 27, 13, 49, 35   51, 29, 68, 54, 58, 42   16, 221, 80, 25, 41, 33

The numbers of words in the first 17 sentences of Chapter 1 of *Not a Penny More, Not a Penny Less* by Jeffrey Archer are:

8, 10, 15, 13, 32, 25   14, 16, 32, 25, 5, 34   36, 19, 20, 37, 19

Determine the range of each data set.

For the Dickens data, the minimum and maximum sentence lengths are respectively 13 and 221, giving a range of $221 - 13 = 208$.

For the Archer data, the minimum and maximum are respectively 5 and 37, giving a range of just 32.

The 208 gives a rather distorted impression because of the unusually long sentence.

Interquartile range

More useful than the range is the **interquartile range (IQR)**. The **semi-interquartile range**, which is half the interquartile range, is also used.

While the median is a value that subdivides the ordered data into two halves, the **quartiles** subdivide the data into quarters. There are three quartiles: the **lower quartile**, Q_1, the **median** (Q_2) and the **upper quartile**, Q_3. A study of the values of the quartiles gives an idea of the spread of the data.

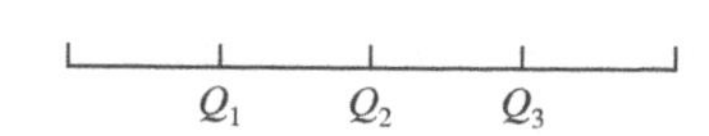

The lower quartile is the median of the lower half of ordered data.
The upper quartile is the median of the upper half of ordered data.

For n data values, alternative definitions of the lower and upper quartiles are:

$$\text{the } \frac{n}{4}\text{th and } \frac{3n}{4}\text{th observations}$$

or:

$$\text{the } \frac{n+1}{4}\text{th and } \frac{3(n+1)}{4}\text{th observations.}$$

There are no universally agreed formulae for the quartiles. There is, therefore, no virtue in reporting their values to great accuracy. They should be reported using at most one more decimal place than that given in the original data.

S1

Example 14

Determine the median and the quartiles for the Dickens and for the Archer sentence lengths given in Example 13, page 15.

Rearranging the Dickens data in order of magnitude:

13 16 25 27 29 33 35 39 41 42 49 51 54 58 68 80 118 221

$Q_1 = 29$ $Q_2 = 41.5$ $Q_3 = 58$

There are 18 observations, nine in each half. The median is the average of the 9th and 10th ordered observations: $\frac{41 + 42}{2} = 41.5$.

There are nine observations to the left of the median. The median of these is the 5th observation, which has the value 29. There are also nine observations to the right of the median. The median of these has the value 58. So the lower and upper quartiles of the Dickens data are 29 and 58, respectively.

Rearranging the Archer data in order:

5 8 10 13 14 15 16 19 19 20 25 25 32 32 34 36 37

$Q_1 = 13.5$ $Q_2 = 19$ $Q_3 = 32$

Since $\frac{17+1}{2} = 9$, the median is the 9th largest observation, namely 19.

There are eight observations to the left of the median. The median of these eight is:

$$\frac{13 + 14}{2} = 13.5$$

The median of the eight observations to the right of the median is:

$$\frac{32 + 32}{2} = 32$$

Thus, the lower and upper quartiles of the Archer data are 13.5 and 32, respectively.

For data given in the form of a frequency distribution, the quartiles can be estimated as shown in Example 15.

S1

Example 15

Determine the lower and upper quartiles for the data given in Example 5 on page 4, and reproduced in this table.

Number of brothers and sisters	0	1	2	3	4 or more
Frequency	6	11	8	3	3

There are 31 numbers summarized in the table. The median is the 16th of the ordered numbers, which is a 1.

If you imagine the numbers laid out in a row from left to right, there would be 15 numbers to the left of the median and 15 to the right.

The numbers to the left are:

0 0 0 0 0 0 1 $\underline{1}$ 1 1 1 1 1 1 1

↑ $Q_1 = 1$

and those to the right are:

1 2 2 2 2 2 2 $\underline{2}$ 2 3 3 3 4+ 4+ 4+

↑ $Q_3 = 2$

The medians of these two sets are 1 and 2, respectively.

The full set of 31 observations has both the lower quartile and the median equal to 1. The upper quartile is 2.

With grouped data, where the individual values are unknown, the quartiles can be estimated either by using a cumulative frequency diagram or by using linear interpolation.

5 The following table gives the ages at first marriage of males and females in the United Kingdom in 2001. Entries are percentages.

	14–19	20–24	25–29	30–34	35–39	40–44	45–
Males	1	14	37	29	12	4	3
Females	4	25	38	21	8	2	2

Source: *Office of National Statistics*

a) Using the same graph, draw cumulative (percentage) diagrams for males and for females.

b) Estimate the median, the quartiles, and the interquartile range, for males and for females.

c) Comment on the differences that you observe.

S1

Deviations from the mean

Suppose you wish to measure the spread of the following values:

0 99 99 100 100 100 100 100 101 101 200

$Q_1 = 99$ $Q_2 = 100$ $Q_3 = 101$

This set of values has mean, median and mode equal to 100, quartiles equal to 99 and 101, and range equal to 200. You should check that the same is true for this second set of values:

0 0 99 99 100 100 100 101 101 200 200

$Q_1 = 99$ $Q_2 = 100$ $Q_3 = 101$

However, this second set has four extreme observations, compared with only two in the first set. This extra variability can be quantified by calculating the **deviation** of each observation from the mean.

Set 1:	−100	−1	−1	0	0	0	0	0	1	1	100
Set 2:	−100	−100	−1	−1	0	0	0	1	1	100	100

$0 - 100 = -100$
$99 - 100 = -1$
$99 - 100 = -1$
$100 - 100 = 0$, and so on.

Although the two sets of differences are very different from each other, their sums are both zero. In fact, it is always the case that:

$$\sum(x - \bar{x}) = 0$$

whatever the values of $x_1, x_2, \ldots, x_n$.

If the summation is over all the values in a population, then:

$$\sum(x - \mu) = 0$$

where μ is the population mean.

The positive and negative deviations cancel each other out. The proof of this important result is as follows.

$$\begin{aligned}\sum(x - \bar{x}) &= \sum x - \sum \bar{x} \\ &= \sum x - n\bar{x} \\ &= \sum x - n \times \frac{1}{n}\sum x \\ &= 0\end{aligned}$$

The variance

The sum of the deviations from the mean is no use as a measure of spread, since it is always zero. A possible measure is the sum of the squares of the differences.

In the case of a population with mean μ, this is:

$$\sum(x - \mu)^2$$

In the case of a sample of n observations, $x_1, x_2, \ldots, x_n$, with sample mean $\bar{x}$, it becomes:

$$\sum(x - \bar{x})^2 = (x_1 - \bar{x})^2 + \cdots + (x_n - \bar{x})^2$$

The more variation there is in the x-values, the greater this sum will be. However, the sum might be large simply because of the number of x-values. This is taken into account by using suitable divisors. The resulting quantities are called **variances**.

S1

The **population variance** is denoted by σ^2. It is given by:

$$\sigma^2 = \frac{1}{n}\sum(x - \mu)^2 \qquad (1.8)$$

The Greek letter σ is the lower-case version of Σ, and is therefore also called 'sigma'.

The **sample variance** is denoted by s^2, and is given by:

$$s^2 = \frac{1}{n-1}\sum(x - \bar{x})^2 \qquad (1.9)$$

Notice that the divisor here is $(n - 1)$ and not n. This ensures that the mean value of s^2 is σ^2. For this reason, s^2 is often referred to as the **unbiased estimate of the population variance**.

Since s^2 and σ^2 are positive multiples of a sum of squares, two consequences are:

- They cannot have negative values.
- They have units which are squares of the units of x.

The standard deviation

The **standard deviation** is the square root of the variance.

One reason for quoting the standard deviation rather than the variance is that its units are those of the values whose variability is being assessed.

The **population standard deviation,** σ, is given by:

$$\sigma = \sqrt{\frac{1}{n}\sum(x - \mu)^2} \qquad (1.10)$$

and the **sample standard deviation,** s, is given by:

$$s = \sqrt{\frac{1}{n-1}\sum(x - \bar{x})^2} \qquad (1.11)$$

Statistical calculators take the hard work out of these calculations.

On some calculators, the quantity σ is indicated by σ_n, s_n or σ_x, and the quantity s by σ_{n-1}, s_{n-1} or s_x.

Calculator practice

Check which symbols are used on your calculator and practise using the calculator to find the standard deviations and variances for the following examples.

Example 17

My three books on travel in South Africa have respectively 272, 316 and 405 pages. Determine the standard deviation, σ, of the length of these books.

The total length of the three books is 993 pages. Hence, the mean length, μ, is 331 pages. Thus:

$$\sigma = \sqrt{\frac{1}{3}\{(272 - 331)^2 + (316 - 331)^2 + (405 - 331)^2\}}$$
$$= 55.3 \quad \text{(to 3 sf)}$$

The standard deviation of this population of three books is approximately 55 pages.

S1

Example 18

A random sample of five travel books are chosen from those on a library book shelf. They are found to have lengths of 100, 347, 212, 388 and 262 pages, respectively. Determine the sample standard deviation.

The total length of the five books is 1309 pages, giving a mean length, $\bar{x}$, of 261.8. Thus:

$$s = \sqrt{\frac{1}{5-1}\{(-161.8)^2 + 85.2^2 + (-49.8)^2 + 126.2^2 + 0.2^2\}}$$
$$= 114 \quad \text{(to 3 sf)}$$

The sample standard deviation is approximately 114 pages.

Without a calculator, applying Equations (1.10) and (1.11) can be tedious. By manipulating the algebra, it is possible to rewrite the formulae in the following forms:

$$\sigma = \sqrt{\frac{1}{n}(\Sigma x^2) - \mu^2} \qquad (1.12)$$

$$s = \sqrt{\frac{1}{n-1}\left\{\Sigma x^2 - \frac{(\Sigma x)^2}{n}\right\}} \qquad (1.13)$$

For the calculation of s^2 use:

$$s^2 = \frac{1}{n-1}\left\{\Sigma x^2 - \frac{(\Sigma x)^2}{n}\right\}$$

Example 19

Use the formula involving $\sum x^2$ and μ to confirm that the standard deviation of the page lengths of my three South African travel books in Example 17 is approximately 55 pages.

First, calculate $\mu = \dfrac{\sum x}{3}$
$= 331$

and $\sum x^2 = 337\,865$.

Since $n = 3$:

$$\sigma = \sqrt{\frac{1}{3}(337\,865) - 331^2}$$
$$= \sqrt{\frac{1}{3}(337\,865 - 328\,683)}$$
$$= \sqrt{\frac{9182}{3}} = 55.3 \quad \text{(to 3 sf)}$$

The standard deviation is indeed approximately 55 pages.

Example 20

Use the formula involving $\sum x^2$ and $\sum x$ to determine an unbiased estimate of the variance of the lengths of the travel books in a library, based on the random sample of five books whose lengths are given in Example 18.

First, calculate $\sum x = 1309$ and $\sum x^2 = 394\,541$. Since $n = 5$:

$$\frac{(\sum x)^2}{n} = 342\,696.2$$

from which:

$$s^2 = \frac{1}{4}(394\,541 - 342\,696.2)$$
$$= 12\,961.2 = 13\,000 \quad \text{(to 3 sf)}$$

This is the square (to 3 sf) of the sample standard deviation found in Example 18.

Approximate properties of the standard deviation

The following statements are true for many sets of data.

- About two-thirds of values lie within one standard deviation of the mean.
- About 95% of values lie within two standard deviations of the mean.
- Almost all the values lie within three standard deviations of the mean.

A useful check that your calculations have not gone hopelessly wrong is provided by noting that the standard deviation will usually have a value which is between a third and a sixth of the range.

As an example, suppose that the observed data includes values ranging between 0 and 30. You would expect a mean of about 15 (since this is half-way between 0 and 30) and a standard deviation of between 5 and 10. If your calculations find a standard deviation of 4, this should not worry you, but if you have calculated a value of 40, you have certainly made a mistake.

Example 21

An office manager wishes to get an idea of the number of phone calls received by the office during a typical day. A week is chosen at random and the numbers of calls on each day of the five-day week are recorded. They are as follows:

15, 23, 19, 31, 22

a) Determine the sample mean, $\bar{x}$, and the sample standard deviation, s.

b) Use the approximate properties of the standard deviation to make statements concerning the likely numbers of daily phone calls that will be received in the next week.

a) Using a calculator, the mean is 22 and the standard deviation is 5.92 (to 3 sf).

b) For the next week, the office manager can conclude that on about two-thirds of days the office will receive between $22 - 6 = 16$ and $22 + 6 = 28$ calls. (There is no point in using great precision, since these are only very rough approximations.)

Assuming no major business changes, the office is unlikely to receive less than $22 - (3 \times 6) = 4$ calls, or more than $22 + (3 \times 6) = 40$ calls during a five-day week.

It is a sound idea always to check for errors. Note that the values range between 15 and 31, suggesting a mean near $\frac{31 + 15}{2} = 23$, close to the calculated 22.

The range is $31 - 15 = 16$, which suggests a standard deviation of between $\frac{16}{3} \approx 5.3$ and $\frac{16}{6} \approx 2.7$. The calculated value (5.92) is only slightly outside this range, so there is no reason to doubt the calculations.

Exercise 1E

1 The numbers of television licences bought at a particular post office on a sample of five randomly chosen weekdays were 15, 9, 23, 12, 17.

Find: a) the mean ($\bar{x}$), b) the standard deviation (s) of this sample.

2 The numbers of potatoes in a sample of 2 kg bags were 12, 15, 10, 12, 11, 13, 9, 14.

Find: a) the mean ($\bar{x}$), b) an unbiased estimate (s^2) of the population variance.

3 During his entire life, Mr I. Walton, a most unlucky angler, caught just six fish. Their masses, in kg, were 1.35, 0.87, 1.61, 1.24, 0.95, 1.87.

Find: a) the mean (μ), b) the variance (σ^2) of this population.

4 A random sample of seven runner beans have lengths (in cm, to the nearest cm) given as 28, 31, 24, 33, 28, 32, 30. Find the sample standard deviation s.

5 In an experiment, a cupful of cold water is placed in a kettle and the time taken for the water to boil is noted. The experiment was conducted six times giving the following results (in seconds): 125, 134, 118, 143, 128, 131. Find the value of s^2.

6 A random sample has values summarized by:

$$n = 8 \qquad \sum x = 671 \qquad \sum(x - \bar{x})^2 = 4024$$

Find: a) the mean ($\bar{x}$), b) the variance (s^2).

Variance and standard deviation for grouped data

When working with grouped data, the formulae for the estimates of σ^2 and s^2 become:

$$\sigma^2 = \frac{1}{n}\left\{\sum fx^2 - \frac{(\sum fx)^2}{n}\right\} \qquad (1.14)$$

$$s^2 = \frac{1}{n-1}\left\{\sum fx^2 - \frac{(\sum fx)^2}{n}\right\} \qquad (1.15)$$

where class frequency is denoted by f and $n = \sum f$.

The x-values are taken to be the mid-points of the class intervals.

Note that $\sum fx^2 \neq \sum(fx)^2$.

Example 22

Determine an estimate of the variance (σ^2) of the marks obtained by 99 students, summarized in this grouped frequency table.

Mark range	10–19	20–29	30–39	40–49	50–59	60–69	70–79	80–89
Midpoint, x	14.5	24.5	34.5	44.5	54.5	64.5	74.5	84.5
Frequency, f	8	18	25	22	16	6	3	1

Since the mid-points have a range of $(84.5 - 14.5) = 70$, σ would be expected to lie in the interval

$$\left(\frac{70}{6}, \frac{70}{3}\right) \approx (11.7, 23.3)$$

A calculator gives $\sigma = 15.3$ (to 3 sf). This value lies in the interval (11.7, 23.3), suggesting that the calculations are probably correct.

In this case, adding 0.01 (a penny) to all the prices helps. The new prices (in pounds sterling) are:

2, 4, 3, 3, 2, 2.5, 2, 2.5

You can also get rid of the decimal places by doubling the prices. The new prices (in pounds sterling) are:

4, 8, 6, 6, 4, 5, 4, 5

For these new prices, $\sum x = 42$ and $\sum x^2 = 234$. For the new prices $\bar{x} = \frac{42}{8} = 5.25$ and

$$s = \sqrt{\frac{1}{7}\left(234 - \frac{42^2}{8}\right)}$$

$$= \sqrt{\frac{1}{7}(234 - 220.5)}$$

$$= \sqrt{\frac{13.5}{7}} = 1.3887$$

To undo the effects of the linear scaling, it is necessary to first divide by 2 and then subtract a penny. Thus the mean of the original data is:

$$\frac{5.25}{2} - 0.01 = 2.615$$

The standard deviation of the original data is obtained by dividing by 2:

$$\frac{1.389}{2} = 0.694 \quad \text{(to 3 sf)}$$

The sample mean is approximately £2.60 and the standard deviation is approximately 69p.

Remember The standard deviation is unaltered by the addition or the subtraction of a constant from the original data.

S1

Exercise 1F

1 The gap, x mm, in a sample of spark plugs was measured with the following results:

0.81, 0.83, 0.81, 0.81, 0.82, 0.80, 0.81, 0.83,
0.84, 0.81, 0.82, 0.84, 0.80

Use the linear scaling of multiplying by 100 and then subtracting 80 (so that 0.81 becomes 1). Determine the unbiased estimate of the population variance of the scaled values, and hence of the spark plug gaps.

2 Records are kept for 18 days of the midday barometric pressure, in millibars.

1022, 1016, 1032, 1008, 998, 985, 993, 1004, 1009,
1011, 1015, 1020, 1007, 1001, 995, 993, 975, 972

Using your calculator, or otherwise, determine the mean of these readings. Repeat your calculations using an appropriate linear scaling. Verify that the results are the same.

3 To test their ability to perform tasks accurately, a class of chemistry students are asked to put precisely 1 kg of flour into a beaker. The class teacher then chooses six students at random and uses an extremely accurate balance (that records weights in milligrams) to determine the actual amounts of flour. The results are:

1 000 007, 1 000 006, 999 992, 1 000 015, 999 988, 1 000 000

Using a suitable linear scaling, obtain: a) the sample mean, b) the value of s. Give your answers in milligrams, to two decimal places.

1.4 Choice of numerical measures

Advantages and disadvantages of the various measures of location

Advantages

- If a **mode** exists, it is certain to have a value which was actually observed.
- The **median** can be calculated in some cases where the mean or mode cannot. For example, suppose 99 homing pigeons fly from A to B. The median time of flight can be calculated as soon as the 50th pigeon has arrived at B. There is no need to wait for the last exhausted pigeon (which may never arrive)!
- The **mean** is influenced equally by each value in the data. Statistical modelling (such as that in Chapter 4) usually requires knowledge of the mean.

Disadvantages

- The **mode** may not be unique (because two or more values may be equally frequent). It may give little useful information about the data. For example, the modal number of broken eggs in egg boxes is likely to be zero in both an inferior supermarket and a superior supermarket, so it provides no information as to which supermarket is the more careful with its egg boxes.
- In a small sample, the **mean** may be significantly affected by the inclusion of a mistaken observation (for example, a can of soup misreported as having a weight of 4000 grams) or of an unusual observation (for example, the salary of the boss of a factory included with those of the factory workers).
- The **median** is difficult to calculate when there is much data.

The sort function of a spreadsheet may prove useful in determining the median of a large set of data.

In practice, statisticians rarely use the mode. The mean is generally the first choice measure, except where it is known that a small proportion of the values are likely to be in error. In such a case, the median is used.

Advantages and disadvantages of the various measures of spread

Advantages

- The **range** is easy to calculate.

- The **interquartile range** does not involve squares or square roots, and is not affected by extreme values.
- The **standard deviation** is influenced equally by each value in the data. In statistical modelling, it is the standard deviation (or, equivalently, the variance) that plays an important role.

Disadvantages

- The **range** is too dependent on the outlying extreme values.
- Without using a spreadsheet, both the **interquartile range** and the **standard deviation** are difficult to calculate when there are many values.

The standard deviation and its square (the variance) are the only measures of spread that are commonly used in statistical modelling.

Summary

S1

You should know how to ...	Check out
1 Calculate the mean, median and mode of a set of numbers.	**1** Determine the mean, median and mode of each of the following sets of numbers. a) 0 0 0 0 1 1 1 2 2 b) 0 0 1 1 1 2 2 c) 0 1 1 2 3 3 3 3
2 Estimate the mean, median and modal class of a set of grouped data.	**2** Estimate the mean, median and modal class each of the following sets of grouped data. a) Weight: 10– 20– 30– 40–50; Frequency: 8 15 11 6 b) Weight: 0– 20– 30– 50–100; Frequency: 19 25 34 22
3 Determine the range and interquartile range of a set of data.	**3** Determine the range and interquartile range of the following data: 1 7 11 12 12 18 19 22 40 61 77
4 Estimate the interquartile range of a set of grouped data.	**4** Estimate the interquartile range of the following data: x: 0– 20– 30– 50– 100–200; f: 11 19 20 37 13
5 Calculate the variance and standard deviation of a set of data.	**5** Calculate the variance and standard deviation of the following data: 1.4 2.8 4.1 6.6 3.6 9.3 8.8
6 Estimate the variance and standard deviation of a set of grouped data.	**6** Estimate the variance and standard deviation of the following data: x: 0– 30– 40– 50– 100–160; f: 21 19 12 37 31

Revision exercise 1

1 As part of a transport study, a sample of people who commuted regularly from a town in Surrey into London was asked to complete a questionnaire.

a) The first question asked how many of their five most recent journeys into London had been made by car. The replies are summarized below.

Number of journeys by car	Frequency
0	69
1	18
2	12
3	15
4	19
5	65

Illustrate the data using a bar chart or line diagram.

b) The second question asked for an estimate of the time taken on their most recent journey into London. The replies are summarized below.

Time (minutes)	Frequency
35–	12
55–	54
75–	68
95–	41
115–155	23

Calculate estimates of the mean and the standard deviation of these times.

c) A sample of people who commuted regularly from a town in Essex into London was also asked the second question. Their answers had a mean of 86 minutes with a standard deviation of 35 minutes.

Compare, briefly, the journey times of commuters from the two towns.

(*AQA, 2002*)

2 Sally's Safaris is a holiday company which organizes adventurous holidays. The ages, in years, of the customers who booked holidays in the year 2002 are summarized in the table.

Age	Frequency
15–24	35
25–29	29
30–34	20
35–44	27
45–59	30
60–79	28

a) Sally drew the histogram (on page 32) to illustrate the data. Unfortunately, both coordinates of the point marked R have been plotted incorrectly.

State the correct coordinates of the point R.

S1

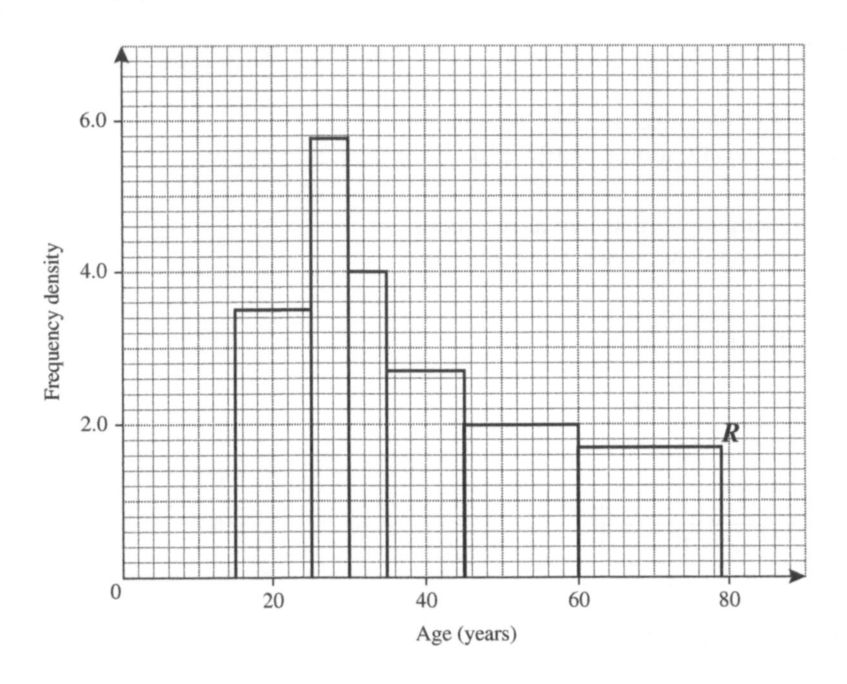

b) Estimate the mean and standard deviation for these data. (*AQA, 2003*)

3 A small firm wishes to introduce an aptitude test for applicants for assembly work. The test consists of a mechanical puzzle. The assembly workers, currently employed, were asked to complete the puzzle. They were timed to the nearest second and the times taken by 35 of them are shown in the table.

Time to complete puzzle (seconds)	Frequency
20–39	6
40–49	8
50–54	7
55–59	5
60–99	9

a) Draw a cumulative frequency diagram of the data and estimate the median and the interquartile range.

b) Calculate estimates of the mean and the standard deviation of the data.

c) In addition to the data in the table, five other assembly workers completed the puzzle, but took so long to do so that their times were not recorded. These times all exceeded 100 seconds. Estimate the median time to complete the puzzle for all 40 assembly workers. (*AQA, 2001*)

4 A company sells two makes of washing machines, Ace and Champion, and provides free after-sales service.

a) For Ace washing machines sold in June 1999, the times, in days, from installing a machine to first being called out to deal with a breakdown are summarized in the table.

Estimate the median and the interquartile range.

Time to first call-out	Frequency
0–	9
100–	19
200–	28
400–	27
800–1200	17

b) For Champion washing machines sold in June 1999, the median time from installing a machine to first being called out to deal with a breakdown was 505 days and the interquartile range was 710 days. Compare, briefly, the reliability of Ace and Champion washing machines.

c) It was later discovered that 28 Ace washing machines sold in June 1999 had been omitted from the table of data. They had been overlooked because the company had not, after 1200 days, been called out to deal with any breakdowns of these 28 machines. Using this additional information:
   i) Modify the estimates you made in part a).
   ii) State how, if at all, your answer to part b) would be changed.

d) Give a reason why the median and the interquartile range were used in preference to the mean and standard deviation of times to first call-out. *(AQA, 2003)*

5 In an aptitude test, 100 apprentices were timed to see how long they took to dismantle, clean and reassemble a particular piece of machinery. The results are shown below.

Time (minutes)	Frequency
5 but less than 10	8
10 but less than 12	12
12 but less than 14	22
14 but less than 15	21
15 but less than 17	18
17 but less than 20	12
20 but less than 25	7

a) Represent these data by a histogram.

b) Showing all your working, estimate:
   i) the sample mean of the times taken,
   ii) the sample variance of the times taken.

c) Draw a cumulative frequency diagram based on these data. Hence, or otherwise, determine the sample median of the time taken.

d) It is required to grade the apprentices, on the basis of their times taken, into three groups containing approximately equal numbers. Estimate the grade limits. *(AQA/JMB, 1987)*

6 a) Data are often presented in graphical form rather than in their raw state.
Give:
   i) **one** reason for using graphical presentation,
   ii) **one** disadvantage of graphical presentation.
Explain briefly the difference **in use** between a *bar diagram* and a *histogram*.

continued

b) Electric fuses, nominally rated at 30 A, are tested by passing a gradually increasing electric current through them and recording the current, x amperes, at which they blow. The results of this test on a sample of 125 such fuses are shown in the table.

Draw a histogram to represent these data.

For this sample calculate:

i) the median current,
ii) the mean current,
iii) the standard deviation of current.

Current (x A)	Number of fuses
$25 \leqslant x < 28$	6
$28 \leqslant x < 29$	12
$29 \leqslant x < 30$	27
$30 \leqslant x < 31$	30
$31 \leqslant x < 32$	18
$32 \leqslant x < 33$	14
$33 \leqslant x < 34$	9
$34 \leqslant x < 35$	4
$35 \leqslant x < 40$	5

(AQA/JMB, 1989)

S1

7 The table summarizes the time, in minutes, taken by each of a random sample of 160 computer science students to complete successfully a particular programming task.

a) Draw a histogram to represent these data, and describe what it suggests about their distribution.

b) Calculate estimates of the mean and the standard deviation of the times.
[You may assume that

$$\sum f_i m_i = 4617.5 \quad \text{and} \quad \sum f_i m_i^2 = 138\,006.75$$

where f_i and m_i are the frequency and mid-point, respectively, of the ith interval.]

Time (minutes)	Number of students
20–	25
25–	14
26–	28
27–	24
28–	24
30–	30
35–	10
40–60	5

(AQA/AEB, 1995)

8 A random sample of 121 thirteen-year-old children completed a questionnaire about the way they spent their time outside school. One of the questions asked them the length of time they had spent watching television on the previous evening.

a) One child gave the answer 11 hours. Explain why this response was excluded from the analysis of results.

The answers given by the other 120 children are summarised in the following table.

Time in hours	Number of children
Less than 1.0	22
At least 1.0 and less than 1.5	12
At least 1.5 and less than 2.0	16
At least 2.0 and less than 2.5	11
At least 2.5 and less than 3.0	16
At least 3.0 and less than 4.0	14
At least 4.0 and less than 5.0	14
At least 5.0	15

b) Draw a histogram to illustrate these results.

c) Calculate estimates of the mean and standard deviation of the lengths of time spent watching television on the previous evening by this sample of 120 children. Take the mid-value of the final class interval to be 6.0.

d) You are given the additional information that seven of the 120 children watched no television at all on the previous evening. State, *with reasons but without further calculation*, how using this information would change the values found in part c).

e) Estimate the proportion of children who had watched television for less than three and a half hours on the previous evening.

(*AQA/NEAB, 1993*)

9 The basic weekly earnings, to the nearest £, of 150 workers in a factory are shown in the following table.

Weekly earnings (£)	100–109	110–129	130–149	150–174	175–204
Number of workers	12	35	62	28	13

a) Calculate estimates of the mean and the standard deviation of this distribution.

The union, negotiating a pay increase for the workers, puts forward two proposals to the management of the factory.

Proposal 1: A 5% basic pay increase.

Proposal 2: A 3% basic pay increase plus a fixed lump sum of £156 per worker **per annum**.

b) For **each** proposal, state new estimates of the mean and the standard deviation of the basic weekly earnings.

c) The management decide to accept one of the above proposals but wish to minimise their wage bill. Which of the proposals should the management accept? Justify your answer.

(*AQA/NEAB, 1994*)

10 In an attempt to devise an aptitude test for applicants seeking work on a factory's assembly line, it was proposed to use a simple construction puzzle. As an initial step in the evaluation of this proposal, the times taken to complete the puzzle by a random sample of 95 assembly line employees were observed with the results in the table.

Time to complete puzzle (seconds)	Number of employees
10–	5
20–	11
30–	16
40–	19
45–	14
50–	12
60–	9
70–	6
80–100	3

continued

a) Draw a cumulative frequency diagram to represent these data. Hence, or otherwise, estimate the median and the interquartile range.

b) Calculate estimates of the mean and the standard deviation of this sample.

It is decided to grade the applicants on the basis of their times taken, as good, average or poor.

c) Method A states that the percentages of applicants in these grades are to be approximately 15%, 70% and 15%, respectively. Estimate the grade limits.

d) Method B grades applicants as:

✦ good, if the time taken is less than (mean − standard deviation),
✦ poor, if the time taken is more than (mean + standard deviation),
✦ average, otherwise.

Compare methods A and B with respect to the percentages in each grade, and comment. *(AQA/JMB, 1990)*

S1

11 At an outpatients' clinic, where all consultations are by appointment, a survey of 500 such appointments revealed that 420 were delayed. The delay times, in minutes, for these 420 delayed appointments are summarized in the table.

Delay x minutes	Number of appointments
$0 < x < 1$	49
$1 \leqslant x < 3$	76
$3 \leqslant x < 5$	60
$5 \leqslant x < 10$	95
$10 \leqslant x < 15$	55
$15 \leqslant x < 20$	25
$20 \leqslant x < 30$	30
$30 \leqslant x < 60$	30

a) Draw a histogram to represent the delay times for these 420 delayed appointments, and describe what it suggests about their distribution.

The report of the survey stated that, when an appointment is delayed, the median delay time is approximately 6.3 minutes, but that 50% of all appointments are delayed for less than 4.5 minutes.

b) Show, by appropriate calculations or otherwise, why **both** of these statements are correct.

c) Estimate the mean and the standard deviation of the delay times for the 420 delayed appointments.

[You may assume that

$$\sum f_i m_i = 4354 \quad \text{and} \quad \sum f_i m_i^2 = 102\,370$$

where f_i and m_i are the frequency and mid-point, respectively, of the ith interval.] *(AQA/NEAB, 1993)*

2 Probability

This chapter will show you how to

- Understand the terminology and notation associated with probability
- Calculate the probabilities of an event or a combination of events
- Solve problems by applying the laws of probability

Before you start

You should know how to ...	Check in
1 List the possible outcomes of an event.	**1** List the possible outcomes for each of the following events. a) A coin is tossed. b) A six-sided die is rolled. c) One of Abdel, Ben, Carl, Dai and Ewan is chosen to be captain of a five-a-side team
2 Calculate a relative frequency.	**2** Calculate the relative frequency for each outcome in the table.

Outcome	1	2	3	4
Frequency	18	32	40	10

S1

2.1 Elementary probability

Relative frequency

Suppose you roll a die and are interested in the outcome 6. To get some idea of how likely the outcome is, you roll the die repeatedly. Here are the outcomes of the first 10 rolls:

2 4 4 1 2   3 2 4 3 1

After 10 rolls, you have had no 6s and you might begin to think that getting a 6 was impossible! However, as you increase the number of rolls, the 6s begin to appear. Here are the outcomes of the next 20 rolls:

4 5 6 4 3   2 3 6 2 4   3 4 2 2 5   4 6 5 3 3

After 30 rolls, you have had three 6s – a **relative frequency** of $\frac{3}{30} = 0.1$.

The relative frequency of a particular outcome is given by:

$$\text{Relative frequency} = \frac{\text{Number of times the outcome occurs}}{\text{Total number of trials}}$$

As you further increase the number of rolls, you would expect the number of 6s to increase but the relative frequency to stabilize.

Relative frequency is the proportion of trials in which an outcome occurs.

So, if all six faces of the die are equally likely, the limiting value of the relative frequency will be $\frac{1}{6}$. You can then say that the **probability** is $\frac{1}{6}$.

When a fair die is rolled, each face is equally likely to appear.

Probability is the name for the limiting value of the relative frequency.

Preliminary definitions

- In a **statistical experiment** or **trial**, there is a set of possible outcomes that can occur. Examples of statistical experiments are the toss of a coin or the roll of a six-sided die.
- An **event** is any outcome, or set of possible outcomes, of the experiment or trial. Simple examples are 'getting a Head', or 'getting an even number'.

Sometimes the experiment may have already taken place, but the outcome may be unknown.

S1

The probability scale

Assigned to an event E, is a number, known as the probability of the event E, which takes a value in the range 0 to 1 (inclusive). The number is denoted by $P(E)$. In addition to satisfying:

$$0 \leqslant P(E) \leqslant 1$$

the value of $P(E)$ is chosen so that:

If E is impossible $\quad P(E) = 0$
If E is certain to occur $\quad P(E) = 1$

Intermediate values of $P(E)$ have natural interpretations:

$P(E) = 0.5 \rightarrow E$ is as likely to occur as not to occur ('evens')
$P(E) = 0.001 \rightarrow E$ is very unlikely
$P(E) = 0.999 \rightarrow E$ is highly likely

Impossible Unlikely Evens Likely Certain
0 $\frac{1}{2}$ 1
P(E)

Probability is measured by a number between 0 and 1, inclusive: 0 corresponds to impossible; 1 corresponds to certain.

Example 1

Suppose you toss an ordinary coin. Define the events A and B to be:

A: 'The coin comes down Heads'
B: 'The coin explodes in a flash of green light'

State the probabilities of these events.

You can reasonably assume that $P(A) = \frac{1}{2}$ and that $P(B) = 0$.

Probability with equally likely outcomes

Suppose that there are N possible outcomes, and that each is *equally likely*. Suppose also that the number of outcomes resulting in the event E is $n(E)$. Then $\mathrm{P}(E)$ is given by:

$$\mathrm{P}(E) = \frac{n(E)}{N} \qquad (2.1)$$

Since $n(E)$ cannot be negative and cannot be greater than N, $0 \leqslant \mathrm{P}(E) \leqslant 1$.

Example 2

A fair die is tossed. The event A is defined as: 'The number obtained is a multiple of 3'. Determine $\mathrm{P}(A)$.

The equally likely outcomes are $\{1, 2, 3, 4, 5, 6\}$, so $N = 6$.

The outcomes corresponding to A are $\{3, 6\}$, so $n(A) = 2$. Thus:

$$\mathrm{P}(A) = \frac{n(A)}{N} = \frac{2}{6} = \frac{1}{3}$$

Example 3

Two fair coins are tossed. The event A is defined as: 'Exactly one Head is obtained'. Determine $\mathrm{P}(A)$.

It is helpful to imagine that the coins are tossed one after the other. The first coin is equally likely to give a Head (H) or a Tail (T). The second coin is also equally likely to give a Head or a Tail. If the first coin is a Head, there are therefore two equally likely sequences: HH and HT.

On the other hand, if the first coin gives a Tail, then the equally likely sequences are TH and TT. The four possible outcomes {HH, HT, TH, TT} are equally likely.

The event A corresponds to the outcomes {HT, TH}. Thus $n(A) = 2$, $N = 4$ and so:

$$\mathrm{P}(A) = \frac{n(A)}{N} = \frac{2}{4} = \frac{1}{2}$$

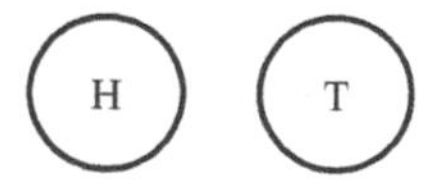

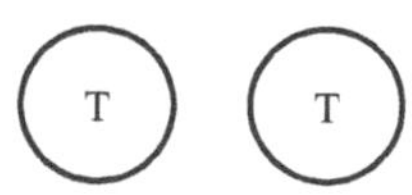

Exercise 2A

1 A fair die, with faces numbered from 1 to 6, is thrown. Find the probabilities of the following events.

a) The score is even.

b) The score is at least 2.

c) The score is at most 2.

d) The score is divisible by 3.

2 A box contains four red balls, six green balls and five yellow balls. A ball is drawn at random.

Find the probabilities of the following events.

a) The ball is green.

b) The ball is red.

c) The ball is not yellow.

3 A nursery school teacher has 14 apples, three bananas and 12 clementines. She randomly distributes the fruit between the 29 children in her class. Amir does not like bananas. Determine the probability that he is given a banana.

4 To raise money for a local charity, there is a raffle in which numbered tickets of two colours (blue and yellow) are sold. One ticket is then drawn at random to determine the winner. I buy five blue tickets. Altogether, 115 blue tickets and 185 yellow tickets are sold.

Calculate the probability that:

a) the winning ticket is blue

b) I have bought the winning ticket.

5 A computer produces a four-digit random number in the range 0000 to 9999 inclusive, in such a way that all such numbers are equally likely.

Work out the probabilities of the following events.

a) The number is at least 1000.

b) The number lies between 1000 and 5000 inclusive.

c) The number is 4321.

d) The number ends in 0.

e) The number begins and ends with 1.

6 A bag contains 30 balls. The balls are numbered 1, 2, 3, …, 30. A ball is drawn at random.

Find the probabilities of the following events which concern the number on the ball.

a) It is divisible by 3.

b) It is not divisible by 3.

c) It is divisible by 4.

d) It is a prime number (2, 3, 5, …).

e) It differs from 10 by less than 5.

f) It differs from 25 by more than 6.

7 I have 14 coins in my purse. There are two 1p coins, three 2p coins, four 5p coins and five 10p coins. I choose a coin at random.

Calculate the probabilities of the following events which concern the chosen coin.

a) It is a 2p coin.

b) It is worth at most 5p.

c) It is worth more than 5p.

d) It is worth less than 3p.

e) It is worth at least 1p.

f) It is worth at least 20p.

2.2 The addition law of probability, and mutually exclusive events

The complementary event, E'

An event E either occurs or it does not. If $n(E)$ is the number of outcomes for which E occurs and N is the total number of possible outcomes, then $N - n(E)$ is the number of outcomes corresponding to the event 'E does not occur'. This is called the **complementary event**, and is denoted by E'. Thus:

$$\begin{aligned} P(E') &= \frac{N - n(E)}{N} \\ &= 1 - \frac{n(E)}{N} = 1 - P(E) \end{aligned}$$

So:

$$P(E') = 1 - P(E) \qquad (2.2)$$

which may be rearranged as:

$$P(E) = 1 - P(E')$$

Using the complementary event often simplifies calculations.

> The complementary event, E', is the event 'E does not occur':
>
> $P(E') = 1 - P(E)$

Example 4

Two fair dice are tossed. Find $P(A)$, where A is the event: 'The total of the numbers shown by the two dice exceeds 3'.

It is helpful to think of the dice as having different colours – say red and blue. There are six equally likely outcomes for the red die. Whichever of these outcomes arises, there will also be six equally likely outcomes for the blue die. In all, therefore, there are 6×6 equally likely outcomes: $N = 36$. You can see this easily on the diagram.

The fact that the dice are coloured does not affect $P(A)$. It simply makes it easier to describe what is happening.

The complementary event, A', is the event 'The total does not exceed 3'. From the diagram, you can see that $n(A') = 3$. The 33 remaining outcomes correspond to the event A.

Now, since all the outcomes are equally likely:

$$P(A') = \frac{n(A')}{N} = \frac{3}{36} = \frac{1}{12}$$

But $P(A) = 1 - P(A')$, so that $P(A) = \frac{11}{12}$.

Red die

Blue die	1	2	3	4	5	6
1	2	3	4	5	6	7
2	3	4	5	6	7	8
3	4	5	6	7	8	9
4	5	6	7	8	9	10
5	6	7	8	9	10	11
6	7	8	9	10	11	12

In this case A' is easier to consider than A because there are fewer outcomes.

S1

Two events

Probability situations often involve two events.

Example 5

Interviews with 18 randomly chosen people revealed that five of the eight women and eight of the ten men preferred drinking coffee to tea. Determine the probability that the first person interviewed was either a woman or someone who preferred coffee to tea.

First, define the events:

W: 'The first person interviewed was a woman.'
C: 'The first person interviewed preferred coffee to tea.'

Summarize the information in a table:

Since the interviewing was done at random, each of the 18 people has a probability of $\frac{1}{18}$ of being the first to be interviewed.

	Preferred coffee	Preferred tea	Total
Women	$\underline{5}$	$\underline{3}$	8
Men	$\underline{8}$	2	10
Total	13	5	18

In the table, the three cells that correspond to the event of interest have been underlined. Totalling these cells, 16 of the 18 people interviewed were either women, or people who preferred coffee to tea. Hence, the required probability is:

$$\frac{16}{18} = \frac{8}{9}$$

Notice that the total of 16 includes the cases where both W and C occur.

Since there are just two classifications, you may represent the situation graphically. The shaded region corresponds to the event of interest.

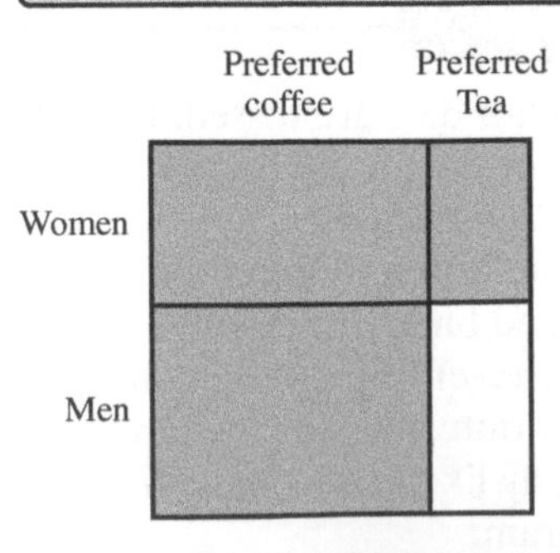

Venn diagrams

A Venn diagram is a simple graphical representation which can often prove helpful in illustrating multiple events. Usually, a rectangle is used to represent all the possible outcomes. Events are illustrated by circles within the rectangle.

The Venn diagrams shown here illustrate the events E and E'.

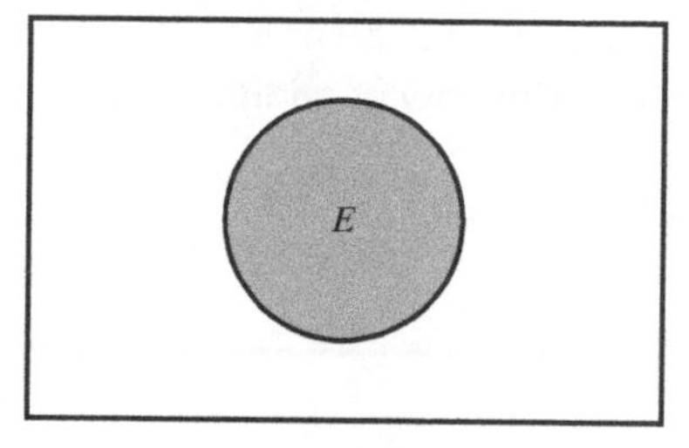

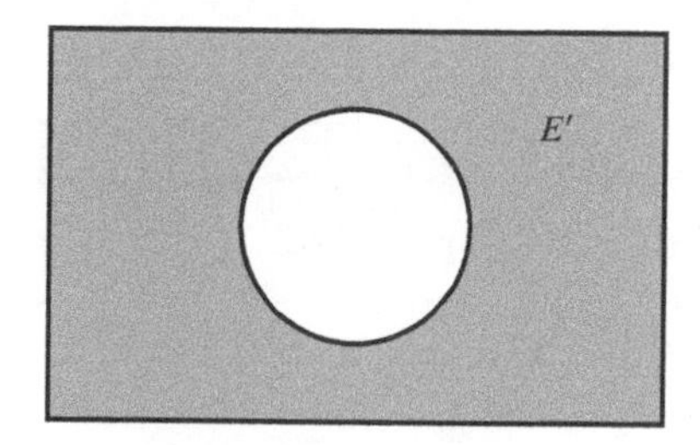

S1

Unions and intersections of events

Suppose A and B are two events associated with a particular statistical experiment. Consider the events expressed in **set notation** by $A \cup B$ and $A \cap B$, which are defined as follows:

$A \cup B$	A **or** B	*'At least one of A and B occurs'*
$A \cap B$	A **and** B	*'Both A and B occur'*

$A \cup B$ includes the possibility that both A and B occur.

$A \cup B$ is called the **union** of A and B, and $A \cap B$ is called the **intersection** of A and B.

The Venn diagram on the left illustrates the union of A and B, and that on the right their intersection.

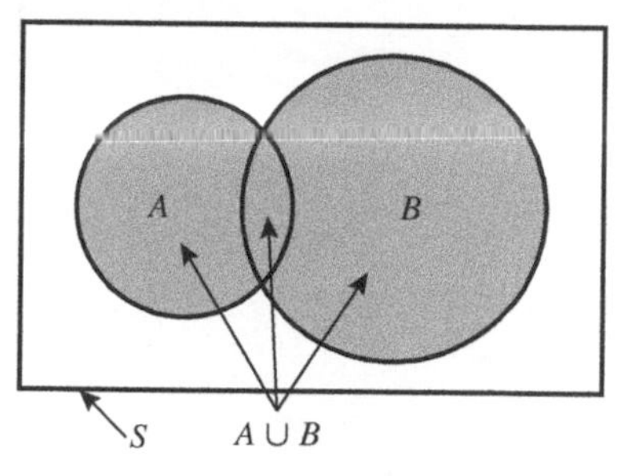

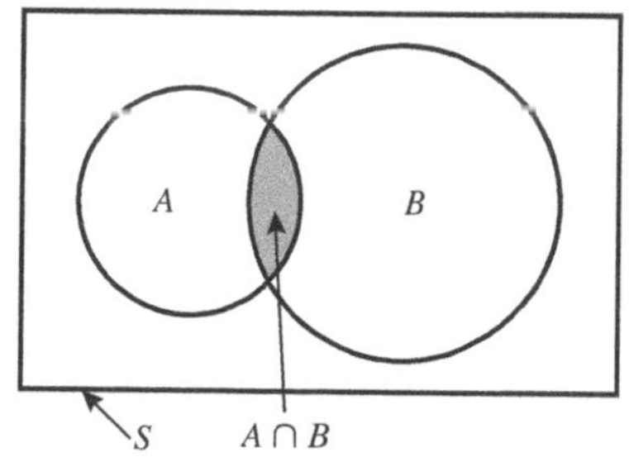

Denote the numbers of outcomes in A, B, $A \cup B$ and $A \cap B$ by $n(A)$, $n(B)$, $n(A \cup B)$ and $n(A \cap B)$ respectively. The entire set of possible outcomes is denoted by S. This is known as the **sample space** and is indicated by the rectangular bounding region. The total number of possible outcomes in S is $N = n(S)$.

With the assumption that all the outcomes are equally likely, the calculation of probabilities is simple. For example:

$$P(A) = \frac{n(A)}{N}$$

The outcomes in $A \cup B$ include all those in A and all those in B but no others. However, if you add together $n(A)$ and $n(B)$, you will overstate the number in $A \cup B$ because you will have counted those in $A \cap B$ twice. Hence:

$$n(A \cup B) = n(A) + n(B) - n(A \cap B)$$

Dividing throughout by N gives:

$$P(A \cup B) = P(A) + P(B) - P(A \cap B) \qquad (2.3)$$

For two events A and B:

$$P(A \text{ or } B) = P(A \cup B) = P(A) + P(B) - P(A \cap B)$$

Equation (2.3) is known as the **addition law** or **addition rule**.

Note that it also holds for cases where the outcomes are not all equally likely.

S1

Example 6

Each month, a mail order firm awards a 'Star Prize' to a randomly chosen shopper. The firm uses the following procedure. It first chooses eight shoppers at random. The names of these eight shoppers are put into a hat. A guest celebrity then draws the name of the lucky winner of the Star Prize from the hat and the other seven shoppers are awarded consolation prizes.

A summary of the locations and genders of the eight lucky shoppers in August is as follows:

	Male	Female
North	1	2
South	1	4

The events A and B are defined by:

A: 'The winner of the Star Prize is male'.
B: 'The winner of the Star Prize lives in the south'.

a) Define, in words, the events $A \cap B$ and $A \cup B$.
b) Determine the probabilities of the events A, B, $A \cap B$ and $A \cup B$.

a) The event $A \cap B$ is the event: 'The winner of the Star Prize is a male living in the south'.
The event $A \cup B$ is the event: 'The winner of the Star Prize is either a male, or lives in the south (or both)'.

b) There are eight shoppers, of whom 2 are male. Each of the eight shoppers is equally likely to be chosen, hence $P(A) = \frac{2}{8} = \frac{1}{4}$.

Five of the eight shoppers come from the south, so $P(B) = \frac{5}{8}$.

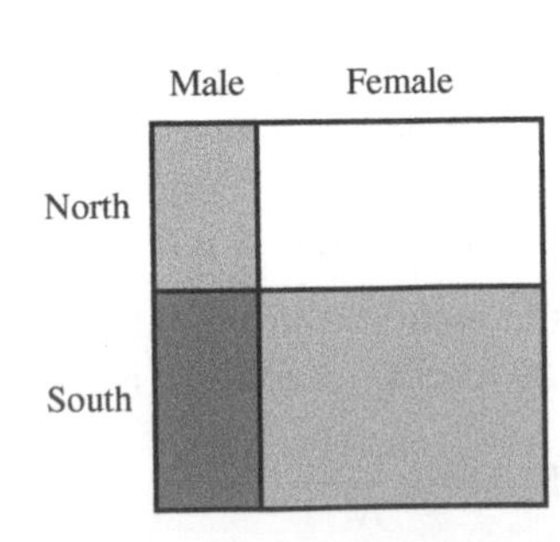

The event $A \cap B$ corresponds to the bottom left region of the diagram. This region corresponds to the single male shopper from the south, so that:

$$P(A \cap B) = \frac{1}{8}$$

The event $A \cup B$ is represented by the entire shaded region. From the table, you can see that this represents six of the eight shoppers, and hence:

$$P(A \cup B) = \frac{3}{4}$$

As a check, apply the addition law:

$$P(A \cup B) = P(A) + P(B) - P(A \cap B) = \frac{2}{8} + \frac{5}{8} - \frac{1}{8} = \frac{6}{8} = \frac{3}{4}$$

as required.

Example 7

The events A and B are such that $P(A) = 0.4$, $P(B') = 0.3$ and $P(A \cap B) = 0.2$.

a) Determine $P(A \cup B)$.

b) Hence determine $P(A' \cap B')$.

a) Since $P(B') = 0.3$:

$$P(B) = 1 - 0.3 = 0.7$$

Applying the addition law:

$$\begin{aligned} P(A \cup B) &= P(A) + P(B) - P(A \cap B) \\ &= 0.4 + 0.7 - 0.2 \\ &= 0.9 \end{aligned}$$

b) $A \cup B$ is the event that at least one of A and B occurs. Its complement is the event that neither A nor B occurs, which means that A does not occur **and** B does not occur. Thus: $(A \cup B)' = A' \cap B'$

Hence:

$$\begin{aligned} P(A' \cap B') &= 1 - P(A \cup B) \\ &= 1 - 0.9 \\ &= 0.1 \end{aligned}$$

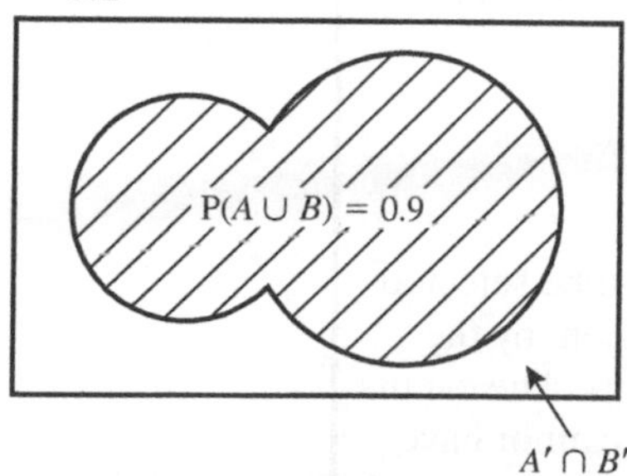

The result

$P(A' \cap B') = 1 - P(A \cup B)$

is always true.

Mutually exclusive events

Events $A, B, \ldots, M$ are said to be **mutually exclusive** when the occurrence of one of them implies that none of the others can have occurred.

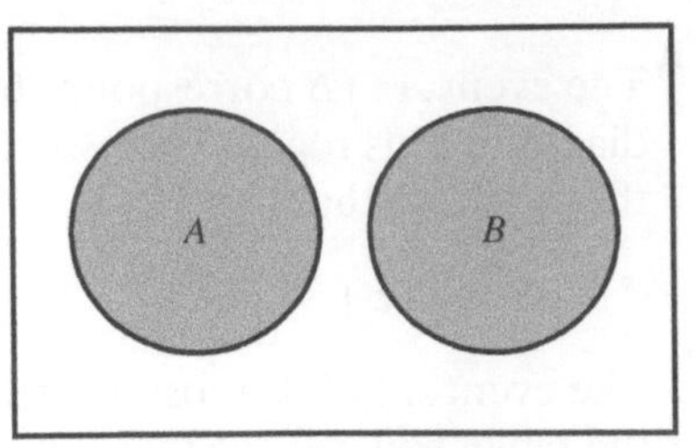

There is no overlap between A and B

Examples of mutually exclusive events are:

a) 'Tossing a head' and 'Tossing a tail', with a coin.

b) 'Throwing an even number' and 'Throwing a 5', with a die.

If A and B are two mutually exclusive events:

$$\mathrm{P}(A \textbf{ and } B \text{ both occur}) = \mathrm{P}(A \cap B) = 0$$

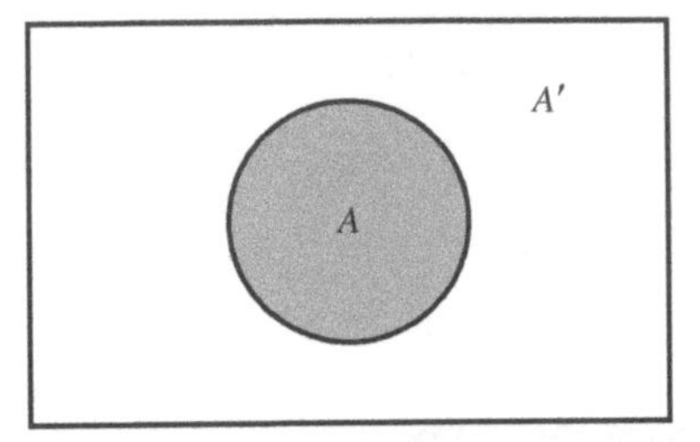

There is no overlap between A and A'

An event A and its complement, A', provide a simple example of mutually exclusive events.

S1

$$\mathrm{P}(A \cap A') = 0$$

The addition law for mutually exclusive events

For the general case of two events A and B, Equation (2.3) states that:

$$\mathrm{P}(A \cup B) = \mathrm{P}(A) + \mathrm{P}(B) - \mathrm{P}(A \cap B)$$

In the special case where A and B are exclusive, this simplifies to:

$$\mathrm{P}(A \cup B) = \mathrm{P}(A) + \mathrm{P}(B) \qquad (2.4)$$

In the case of just two events, the term 'mutually' may be omitted.

since in this case $\mathrm{P}(A \cap B) = 0$. This attractively simple result extends to any number of mutually exclusive events.

When the events $A, B, \ldots, M$ are mutually exclusive:

$$\begin{aligned}\mathrm{P}(A \textbf{ or } B \textbf{ or } \cdots \textbf{ or } M) &= \mathrm{P}(A \cup B \cup \cdots \cup M)\\ &= \mathrm{P}(A) + \mathrm{P}(B) + \cdots + \mathrm{P}(M)\end{aligned}$$

This is the **addition law** for **mutually exclusive** events.

Example 8

An Irish rugby club contains 40 players, of whom seven are called O'Brien, six are called O'Connell, four are called O'Hara, eight are called O'Neill and there are 15 others. The 40 players draw lots to decide who should be captain of the first team. Determine the probability that the captain of the first team:

a) Is called either O'Brien or O'Connell.

b) Is not called either O'Hara or O'Neill.

There are 40 players, each of whom is equally likely to be selected as captain. Denote the event: 'The captain is an O'Brien' by the symbol B, with C, H, and N denoting the similar events. The events B, C, H, and N are mutually exclusive, since a player cannot have two names.

a) Since B and C are exclusive:

$$\mathrm{P}(B \textbf{ or } C) = \mathrm{P}(B) + \mathrm{P}(C) = \frac{7}{40} + \frac{6}{40} = \frac{13}{40}$$

The probability that the captain is called either O'Brien or O'Connell is $\frac{13}{40}$.

b) This question is best answered using the complementary event. As in part a), the probability that the captain is called either O'Hara or O'Neill is:

$$\mathrm{P}(H) + \mathrm{P}(N) = \frac{4}{40} + \frac{8}{40} = \frac{12}{40} = \frac{3}{10}$$

Hence the required probability is $1 - \frac{3}{10} = \frac{7}{10}$.

Exhaustive events

Two events are said to be **exhaustive** when it is certain that at least one of them occurs. For example, when rolling a die, it is certain that at least one of the following events will occur:

Exhaustive events need not be exclusive.

A: 'The number obtained is 1, 2, 3 or 5'
B: 'The number obtained is even'.

When the events A and B are exhaustive:

$$\mathrm{P}(A \textbf{ or } B) = \mathrm{P}(A \cup B) = 1 \qquad (2.5)$$

Note that:

✦ Any event A and its complement, A', are exhaustive. So:

$$\mathrm{P}(A \textbf{ or } A') = \mathrm{P}(A \cup A') = 1$$

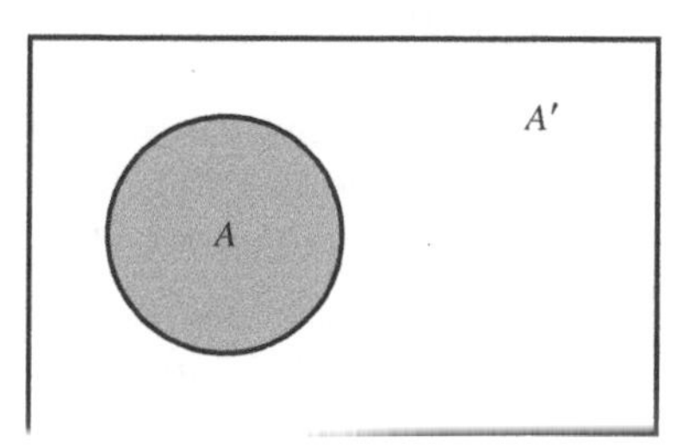

Every outcome in the sample space is either in A or in A'.

✦ The events $A, B, \ldots, M$ are said to be **collectively exhaustive** when it is certain that at least one of them occurs. This condition gives:

$$\mathrm{P}(A \textbf{ or } B \textbf{ or } \ldots \textbf{ or } M) = \mathrm{P}(A \cup B \cup \cdots \cup M) = 1$$

Exercise 2B

1 A survey of 1000 people revealed the voting intentions shown. A person is chosen at random from the sample.

	Women	Men	Total
Con	153	130	283
Lab	220	194	414
LibDem	157	146	303
Total	530	470	1000

Find the probability that the person chosen:

a) intends to vote Conservative
b) is a woman intending to vote Labour
c) is either a woman or intends to vote Conservative
d) is neither a man nor intends to vote LibDem
e) is a man and intends to vote either LibDem or Labour.

2 A man tosses two fair dice. One is numbered 1 to 6 in the usual way. The other is numbered 1, 3, 5, 7, 9, 11. The events A to E are defined as follows.

A: Both dice show odd numbers.
B: The number shown by the normal die is the greater.
C: The total of the two numbers shown is greater than 10.
D: The total is less than or equal to 4.
E: The total is odd.

a) Determine the probability of each event.

b) State:
i) Which pairs of events (if any) are exclusive.
ii) Which pairs of events (if any) are exhaustive.

3 A fair die is thrown. Events A, B, C, D are defined as follows.

S1

A: The score is even.
B: The score is divisible by 3.
C: The score is not more than 2.
D: The score exceeds 3.

a) Verify that $P(A) + P(B) = P(A \cup B) + P(A \cap B)$.

b) Find $P(A')$, $P(B')$, $P(C')$, $P(D')$.

c) Identify two pairs of events that are exclusive, and verify the addition rule in each case.

d) Identify three events that are collectively exhaustive.

e) Find $P(C \cap D)$.

4 Two fair dice, one red and one green, are thrown and the separate scores are observed. The outcome is denoted by (r, g), where r and g are the scores on the red and green dice respectively.

Represent these outcomes on a 6×6 grid, with the r-axis horizontal and the g-axis vertical.

Events A, B, C are defined as follows.

A: The score on the red die exceeds the score on the green die.
B: The total score is six or more.
C: The score on the red die does not exceed 4.

a) Identify on your diagram the sets corresponding to A, B, C.

b) Verify that $P(A) + P(B) = P(A \cup B) + P(A \cap B)$.

c) Verify that $P(A) + P(C) = P(A \cup C) + P(A \cap C)$.

d) Identify a pair of events which are exhaustive.

e) Find $P(A')$, $P(B')$, $P(C')$.

f) Find $P(A' \cup B)$, $P(A \cap B')$, $P(B \cup C)$, $P(B' \cap C')$, $P(B' \cup C')$.

5 A street contains 25 households. There are five households living in bungalows, with the remaining households living in houses. Of the five bungalows, three are occupied by retired people. Three of the houses are occupied by retired people. Eighteen of the households (one living in bungalows and seveneen living in houses) have two or more cars. None of the retired couples has more than one car. A national survey results in one of the households being chosen.

a) Assuming that the household chosen is equally likely to be any of the 25, determine the probabilities of each of the events A, B and C.
   A: The household consists of retired people.
   B: The household lives in a bungalow.
   C: The household has two or more cars.
b) State which pairs of events (if any) are i) exclusive, and ii) exhaustive.

2.3 The multiplication law, conditional probability, and independent events

Probability trees

A **probability tree** is a diagram which shows the outcomes of a sequence of statistical experiments. Each outcome is depicted as a **branch** or branches of the tree, sometimes with its probability written alongside the branch.

Consider this problem.

> A fair coin is tossed three times.
> Determine P(Exactly two Heads are obtained).

Each time the coin is tossed, the number of distinguishable outcomes increases. Denoting a Head by H, and a Tail by T, the outcomes are:

After the first toss	Either H or T
After the second toss	The sequence of outcomes is either HH, HT, TH or TT
After the third toss	The sequence of outcomes is either HHH, HHT, HTH, HTT, THH, THT, TTH or TTT

The same possibilities are represented more simply in a tree diagram.

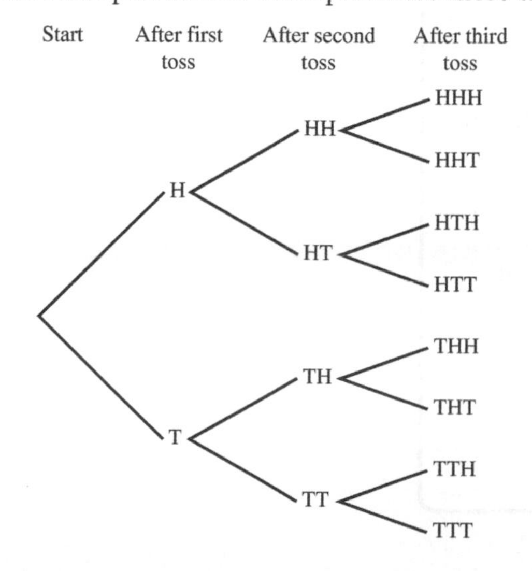

The final column lists the entire set of possible outcomes.

Each of the eight sequences is equally likely to occur. Three sequences include exactly two Heads (HHT, HTH, THH) and so the probability of obtaining exactly two Heads is $\frac{3}{8}$.

The same tree could be constructed if three coins are each tossed once. Although this is a different physical situation, the trees are equivalent in terms of their probability structure.

Physical independence

The coin-tossing scenario set out in the preceding section is an example of a situation in which the separate actions are **physically independent**. That is, the outcome of one action (say, the first toss) can have no possible influence on the outcome of any other action (say, the second toss).

Physical independence gives rise to independent events. You will see later that there is in fact a wider class of events that can be described as independent.

S1 The multiplication law for independent events

If A and B are two independent events:

$$P(A \textbf{ and } B) = P(A \cap B) = P(A) \times P(B) \qquad (2.6)$$

More generally, if $A, B, \ldots, M$ are independent events (for example, the results of separate tosses of a coin) then:

$$P(A \cap B \cap \cdots \cap M) = P(A) \times P(B) \times \cdots \times P(M) \qquad (2.7)$$

When $A, B, \ldots, M$ are independent events, the probability that they all occur is given by:

$$\begin{aligned} P(A \textbf{ and } B \textbf{ and } \ldots \textbf{ and } M) &= P(A \cap B \cap \cdots \cap M) \\ &= P(A) \times P(B) \times \cdots \times P(M) \end{aligned}$$

This is the **multiplication law for independent events.**

Example 9

A bent penny has a probability 0.8 of coming down Heads when it is tossed. The penny is tossed six times. What is the probability that it shows Heads on every occasion?

The six tosses are physically independent. Therefore, applying the multiplication law:

$$\begin{aligned} P(\text{6 Heads}) &= P(\text{Head on first toss } \textbf{and} \text{ Head on second toss } \textbf{and} \ldots \textbf{and} \text{ Head on sixth toss}) \\ &= P(\text{Head on first toss}) \times P(\text{Head on second toss}) \times \cdots \times P(\text{Head on sixth toss}) \\ &= 0.8 \times 0.8 \times \cdots \times 0.8 \\ &= 0.8^6 \\ &= 0.262 \quad (\text{to 3 dp}) \end{aligned}$$

The probability that the bent penny shows Heads on every occasion is 0.262 (to 3 dp).

Example 10

In August, two farmers are making a decision about when to start harvesting. In Kent, Farmer Smith usually harvests early (probability 0.7). In Wales, Farmer Jones usually harvests late (probability 0.6). Assuming that the harvest times can be regarded as being independent of each other, use a probability tree to determine the probability that the two farmers harvest at the same time of the month.

First, construct a probability tree to illustrate the given data:

Farmer Smith		Farmer Jones		Probability
0.7	Early	0.4	Early	0.28
		0.6	Late	0.42
0.3	Late	0.4	Early	0.12
		0.6	Late	0.18
				Total = 1

In a probability tree, proceed as follows:

- ✦ Write the probability alongside the branch of each event.
- ✦ Write the probability of an outcome at the end of its final branch.

The probability of an outcome is found by multiplying together the probabilities of the successive branches, because the events are independent.

Always check that the calculated probabilities for a probability tree add up to 1.

You need to determine the probabilities of both farmers harvesting early and both farmers harvesting late.

$$\text{P(Both farmers harvest early)} = 0.7 \times 0.4 = 0.28$$
$$\text{P(Both farmers harvest late)} = 0.3 \times 0.6 = 0.18$$

Thus, the probability that they harvest at the same time of the month is:

$$0.28 + 0.18 = 0.46$$

The two probabilities (0.18 and 0.28) are added because the two events are exclusive.

Example 11

A computer system consists of a keyboard, a monitor and the computer itself. The three parts are manufactured separately. From past experience, it is known that, on delivery, the probability that the monitor works correctly is 0.99, the probability that the keyboard works correctly is 0.98 and the probability that the computer works correctly is 0.95. Calculate the probabilities of the following events.

a) The entire system works correctly.

b) Exactly two of the components work correctly.

a) Define the events M, K and C as follows:

M: The monitor works correctly.
K: The keyboard works correctly.
C: The computer works correctly.

Since the parts are manufactured separately, the three events are physically independent. Therefore:

$$P(M \cap K \cap C) = P(M) \times P(K) \times P(C) = 0.99 \times 0.98 \times 0.95 = 0.922 \text{ (to 3 dp)}$$

The probability that the entire system works correctly is 0.922 (to 3 dp).

b) The probability tree is as follows.

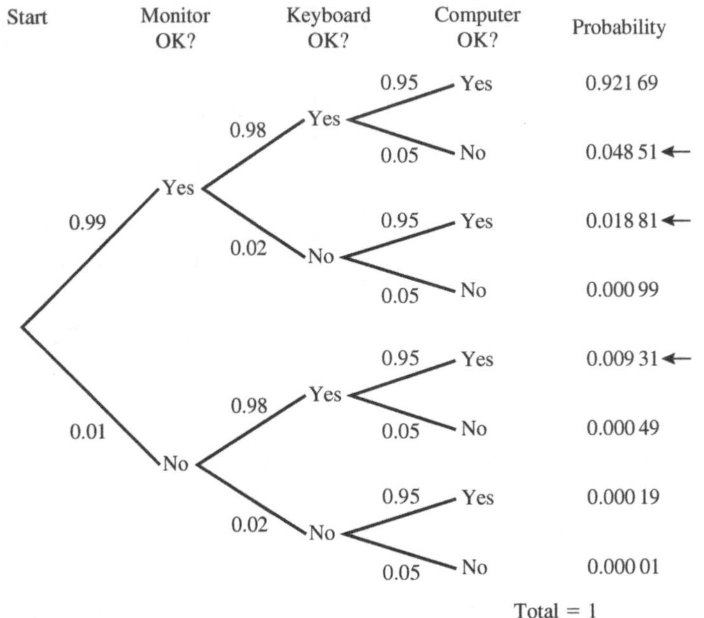

The three situations of interest are identified with arrows.

The required probability is given by:

P(Exactly two components work correctly)
$= 0.048\,51 + 0.018\,81 + 0.009\,31 = 0.077$ (to 3 dp)

Exercise 2C

1 Two fair dice, each having faces numbered 1, 1, 2, 2, 2, 3, are thrown. Draw up a probability tree. Hence find the probabilities of the following events.

a) The total score is 4.

b) The total score is less than 4.

c) The total score exceeds 4.

d) At least one die shows 2.

2 Two fair dice, each having faces numbered 1, 1, 1, 1, 2, 2, are thrown. Construct a probability tree for the scores.

Find the probabilities of the following events.

a) The total score is 2. b) The total score is 3.

c) The total score is 4.

A third identical die is thrown. Add this to your probability tree and hence find the probabilities of the following events.

d) The total score is 4. e) The total score is 5.

3 A man travels to work each day by train for three days. Each day, the probability that the train is late is 0.1.

Find the probability that his train to work is late on at most two occasions.

4 According to a genetic model, when a horse of type A is mated with a horse of type B, each of the young is equally likely to be of type A or type B, independent of the types of the other young. Following such matings, the types of five young horses are determined.

Determine the probability of each of the following events.

a) All five are of type A.

b) There is at least one of each type.

5 The probability that a biased coin comes down Heads is 0.4. It is tossed three times. Find the probability of obtaining:

a) exactly two Heads b) at least two Heads

6 Family A has two girls and one boy. Family B has three girls and one boy. Family C has two girls and two boys. One child is chosen at random from each family.

a) Construct a probability tree.

b) Hence, find the probabilities of the following events.

i) Three girls are chosen.

ii) At least two girls are chosen.

iii) No girls are chosen.

iv) A girl is chosen from family A and the other two children are of opposite sex to each other.

7 A child is allowed a lucky dip from each of three boxes. One box contains 10 chocolates and 15 mints, the second box contains 8 apples and 4 oranges, and the third box contains 7 (plastic) dinosaurs and 3 (plastic) turtles. Events A, B, C are defined as follows:

A: The child gets a chocolate and a dinosaur.

B: The child gets a mint or a turtle (or both).

C: The child gets an apple.

Find each of the following: a) $P(A)$, b) $P(B)$, c) $P(A \cap C)$, d) $P(B \cup C)$, e) $P(A \cap B)$, f) $P(A \cup B)$.

8 A woman travels to work by car. There are three roundabouts on the road. The probability that she is delayed at the first roundabout is 0.3. The corresponding figures for the second and third roundabouts are 0.5 and 0.7 respectively.

Assuming independence, find the probability that:

a) she is only delayed at one roundabout,

b) she is delayed at two or more roundabouts.

9 Two chess grand masters, Xerxes and Yorick, play a tournament of three games. Past experience of games between these two players suggests that the results of successive games are independent of one another and that, for each game:

$$\mathrm{P}(\text{Xerxes wins}) = \tfrac{1}{4}$$

$$\mathrm{P}(\text{Yorick wins}) = \tfrac{1}{5}$$

$$\mathrm{P}(\text{Draw}) = \tfrac{11}{20}$$

Determine the probabilities of each of the following events.

A: Xerxes wins all three games.
B: Exactly two games are drawn.
C: Yorick wins at least one game.
D: Xerxes wins more games than Yorick.

Conditional probability

The probability that is associated with the occurrence of an event is always likely to be influenced by the available information. Suppose, for example, that you see a man lying motionless on the grass in a park and you are interested in the probability of the event 'The man is dead'. In the absence of other information, a reasonable guess might be that the probability is one in a million. However, if you have just heard a shot ring out, and a suspicious looking man with a smoking revolver is standing nearby, then the probability would be rather higher.

> The probability that the event B occurs (or has occurred) given the information that the event A occurs (or has occurred) is denoted by $\mathrm{P}(B|A)$.

$\mathrm{P}(B|A)$ is described as a **conditional probability**, since it refers to the probability that B occurs (or has occurred) *conditional* on the occurrence of A.

The expression "$\mathrm{P}(B|A)$" is read as "the probability of B given A."

Example 12

A statistician has two coins, one of which is fair, the other of which is double-headed. She chooses one coin at random and tosses it. The events A_1, A_2 and B are defined as follows:

A_1: The fair coin is chosen.
A_2: The double-headed coin is chosen.
B: A Head is obtained.

Determine the values of $P(B|A_1)$ and $P(B|A_2)$.

When the fair coin is tossed, the probability of a Head is $\frac{1}{2}$: so $P(B|A_1) = \frac{1}{2}$. When the double-headed coin is tossed, the probability of a Head is 1: so $P(B|A_2) = 1$.

Example 13

An electronic display is equally likely to show any of the numbers 1, …, 8, 9. Determine the probability that it shows a prime number (2, 3, 5 or 7):

a) given no knowledge about the number,
b) given the information that the number is odd.

Let B be the event 'A prime number' and A be the event 'An odd number'.

a) There are nine possible outcomes ($N = 9$), all equally likely. Since there are four outcomes corresponding to the event of interest, $n(B) = 4$. Because the outcomes are all equally likely:

$$P(B) = \frac{n(B)}{N} = \frac{4}{9}$$

$A \cap B$ is the event 'An odd prime number'.
"$B|A$" means "A prime number given that the number is odd."

b) Given that the number is odd, it must be one of the $n(A)$ numbers 1, 3, 5, 7 and 9. Initially, each of these outcomes is equally likely. The knowledge that one of them has occurred does not make their chances of occurrence unequal. Of these five possible outcomes, three (3, 5 and 7) are prime. These are the outcomes corresponding to the event $A \cap B$. Thus:

$$P(B|A) = \frac{n(A \cap B)}{n(A)} = \frac{3}{5}$$

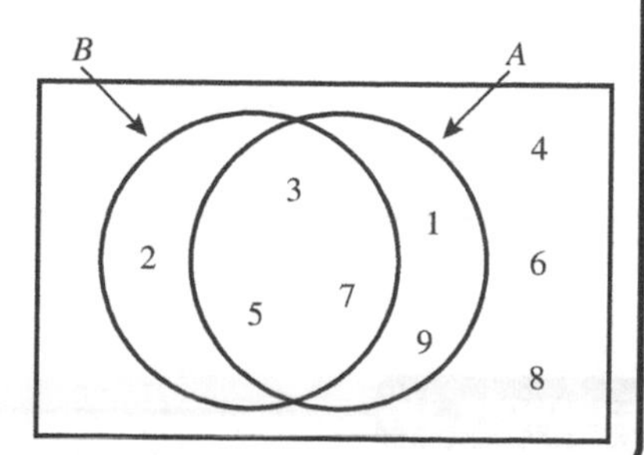

Example 13 illustrates, for a particular case, the result that, for equally likely events:

$$P(B|A) = \frac{n(A \cap B)}{n(A)}$$

Dividing both the numerator and the denominator of the right-hand side by N gives:

$$\mathrm{P}(B \textbf{ given } A) = \mathrm{P}(B|A) = \frac{\mathrm{P}(A \cap B)}{\mathrm{P}(A)} = \frac{\mathrm{P}(A \textbf{ and } B)}{\mathrm{P}(A)} \qquad (2.8)$$

This result is *always true* (provided A is a possible event) and is not confined only to equally likely events.

Thus:

$$\mathrm{P}(A \cap B) = \mathrm{P}(A) \times \mathrm{P}(B|A) \qquad (2.9)$$

Reversing the roles of A and B gives:

$$\mathrm{P}(B \cap A) = \mathrm{P}(B) \times \mathrm{P}(A|B) \qquad (2.10)$$

Since $A \cap B$ and $B \cap A$ are descriptions of the same event, namely, the intersection of A and B:

'A and B' is the same as 'B and A'.

$$\mathrm{P}(A \cap B) = \mathrm{P}(B \cap A) = \mathrm{P}(A) \times \mathrm{P}(B|A) = \mathrm{P}(B) \times \mathrm{P}(A|B) \qquad (2.11)$$

S1

$$\mathrm{P}(A \cap B) = \mathrm{P}(A) \times \mathrm{P}(B|A) = \mathrm{P}(B) \times \mathrm{P}(A|B) = \mathrm{P}(B \cap A)$$

Example 14

Two events, A and B, are such that $\mathrm{P}(A) = 0.7$, $\mathrm{P}(B) = 0.4$, and $\mathrm{P}(A|B) = 0.3$. Determine the probability that neither A nor B occurs.

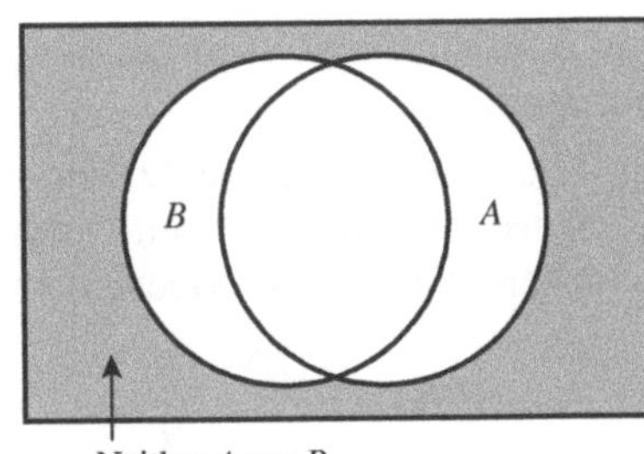

From Equation (2.10):

$$\begin{aligned}\mathrm{P}(B \cap A) &= \mathrm{P}(B) \times \mathrm{P}(A|B) \\ &= 0.4 \times 0.3 = 0.12\end{aligned}$$

From Equation (2.3), you can now obtain $\mathrm{P}(A \cup B)$:

$$\begin{aligned}\mathrm{P}(A \cup B) &= \mathrm{P}(A) + \mathrm{P}(B) - \mathrm{P}(A \cap B) \\ &= 0.7 + 0.4 - 0.12 = 0.98\end{aligned}$$

But, looking at a Venn diagram, you will see that:

$$\mathrm{P}(\textbf{Neither } A \textbf{ nor } B) = 1 - \mathrm{P}(A \cup B)$$

The required probability is therefore $1 - 0.98 = 0.02$.

This result was used in Example 7 (page 45).

Example 15

A person is chosen at random from the population. Let A be the event 'The person is female' and let B be the event 'The person is aged at least 80'. Suppose that $\mathrm{P}(A) = 0.5$, $\mathrm{P}(B) = 0.1$ and $\mathrm{P}(A|B) = 0.7$. Let the event C be defined by $C = A \cap B'$.

a) Describe the event C in words.

b) Determine $\mathrm{P}(A|B')$.

This question is much easier to understand when written in English!

In a certain population, 50% are female, 10% are aged at least 80 and 70% of these aged people are female.

a) The event C is 'A female aged less than 80'.

b) Start by noting that:

$$P(A \cap B') = P(A) - P(A \cap B)$$

which you will see clearly from a Venn diagram.

Now:

$$P(A \cap B) = P(B) \times P(A|B) = 0.1 \times 0.7 = 0.07$$

which gives:

$$P(A|B') = \frac{P(A \cap B')}{P(B')} = \frac{0.5 - 0.07}{1 - 0.1} = \frac{0.43}{0.90} = \frac{43}{90}$$

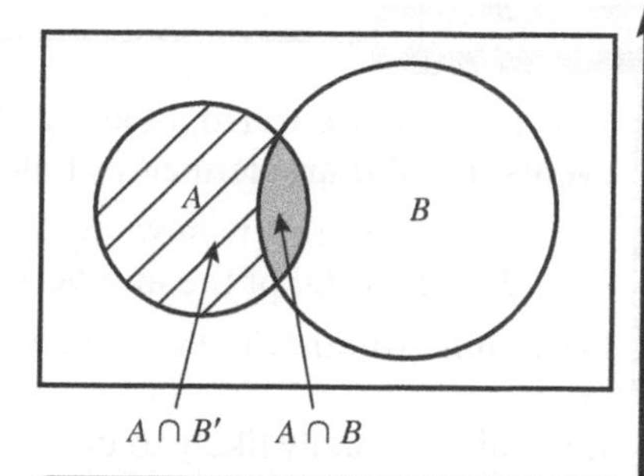

The result

$$P(A \cap B') = P(A) - P(A \cap B)$$

can be rearranged to give the following useful general result:

$$P(A) = P(A \cap B) + P(A \cap B')$$

S1

Independent events

Two events, A and B, are said to be **independent** when knowledge that one occurs, or does not occur, does *not* alter the probability that the other occurs.

Events may be independent without being physically independent (see Example 17, page 58). Physically independent results are always statistically independent.

If A and B are independent events then:

$$P(A|B) = P(A|B') = P(A)$$

A has the same probability whether or not B occurs.

$$P(B|A) = P(B|A') = P(B)$$

B has the same probability whether or not A occurs.

$$P(A \cap B) = P(A) \times P(B)$$

The multiplication law for independent events.

If any of the above equations hold, then all the other equations hold and the events A and B are independent.

Example 16

Two events, A and B, are such that $P(A) = 0.5$, $P(B) = 0.4$, and $P(A|B) = 0.3$.

a) State whether the events are independent.

b) Find $P(A \cap B)$.

a) The events A and B are not independent since $P(A) \neq P(A|B)$.

b) Using Equation (2.10):

$$P(A \cap B) = P(B) \times P(A|B) = 0.4 \times 0.3 = 0.12$$

Example 17

Two fair dice are rolled. One is red and the other is green. The events A and B are defined as follows:

A: The number shown by the red die is odd.
B: The total of the numbers on the two dice is odd.

Determine whether the two events are independent.

Each die is equally likely to display an odd number or an even number. In the table below, therefore, each of the outcomes has a probability of $\frac{1}{4}$.

		Red die	
		Even	Odd
Green die	Even	Even total $P = \frac{1}{4}$	Odd total $P = \frac{1}{4}$
	Odd	Odd total $P = \frac{1}{4}$	Even total $P = \frac{1}{4}$

The total of the probabilities in the second column is $\frac{1}{2}$, so $P(A) = \frac{1}{2}$. The total of the probabilities for the outcomes with odd totals is also $\frac{1}{2}$, so $P(B) = \frac{1}{2}$.

The event 'A **and** B' is the event: 'An odd number is shown by the red die **and** the total of the numbers on the two dice is odd'. This corresponds to the top right cell in the table, for which the probability is $\frac{1}{4}$. Since this equals $\frac{1}{2} \times \frac{1}{2}$, it has been shown that, for the events A and B given in the question:

$$P(A \cap B) = P(A) \times P(B)$$

This is sufficient to prove that the events A and B are independent.

Here A and B are independent events even though they are not physically independent.

Example 18

The table gives information on two aspects of the perches of some tropical lizards for a sample of 207 habitats.

		Perch diameter (cm) $\leqslant 10$	>10	Total
Perch height (m)	>1.5	64	22	86
	$\leqslant 1.5$	86	35	121
Total		150	57	207

Suppose that one of the 207 perches in the sample is chosen at random.

Determine, to three decimal places, the probability that:

a) The diameter is greater than 10 cm.
b) The diameter is greater than 10 cm, given that the height is more than 1.5 m.
c) The height is more than 1.5 m.
d) The height is more than 1.5 m, given that the diameter is greater than 10 cm.

Define the events A and B as follows:

A: The diameter is greater than 10 cm.
B: The height is more than 1.5 m.

You can read the answers directly from the table.

a) $P(A) = \frac{57}{207} = 0.275$ (to 3 dp).
b) $P(A|B) = \frac{22}{86} = 0.256$ (to 3 dp).
c) $P(B) = \frac{86}{207} = 0.415$ (to 3 dp).
d) $P(B|A) = \frac{22}{57} = 0.386$ (to 3 dp).

S1

Conditional probability with more than two events

For any two events A and B, the probability of their both occurring is:

$$P(A \textbf{ and } B) = P(A \cap B) = P(A) \times P(B|A)$$

This is Equation (2.9) on page 56.

The extension to three events is straightforward:

$$\begin{aligned} P(A \textbf{ and } B \textbf{ and } C) &= P(A \cap B \cap C) \\ &= P(A) \times P(B|A) \times P(C|A \cap B) \end{aligned}$$

For the extension to events $A, B, \ldots, M$:

$$\begin{aligned} P(A \textbf{ and } B \textbf{ and } \ldots \textbf{ and } L \textbf{ and } M) &= P(A \cap B \cap \cdots \cap L \cap M) \\ &= P(A) \times P(B|A) \times P(C|A \cap B) \times \cdots \\ &\quad \times P(M|A \cap B \cap \cdots \cap L) \end{aligned}$$

This is the multiplication law for any number of events.

Example 19

The mother of three children (Beryl, Cheryl and Daryl) has a box containing 24 apples, of which 20 are red and four are green. She chooses one apple, at random, for each child. Determine the probabilities of each of the following events.

a) All three apples are red.
b) All three apples are the same colour.
c) Exactly two apples are red.

Let B, C and D denote the events that Beryl, Cheryl and Daryl (respectively) are given red apples.

a) The event 'All three apples are red' is $B \cap C \cap D$, with probability given by:

$$P(B \cap C \cap D) = P(B) \times P(C|B) \times P(D|B \cap C)$$

For $P(B)$: Since there are 24 apples, all equally likely to be chosen, the probability that Beryl is given a red apple is:

$$P(B) = \frac{20}{24}$$

For $P(C|B)$: Cheryl could have been given any apple other than the (red) one given to Beryl. All the remaining apples are equally likely. Since 19 of the remaining 23 apples are red:

$$P(C|B) = \frac{19}{23}$$

For $P(D|B \cap C)$: A similar argument applies. There are 22 apples available, of which 18 are red, and so:

$$P(D|B \cap C) = \frac{18}{22}$$

Thus:

$$\begin{aligned} \text{P(All three apples are red)} &= \frac{20}{24} \times \frac{19}{23} \times \frac{18}{22} \\ &= 0.563\,24\ldots \\ &= 0.563 \quad \text{(to 3 dp)} \end{aligned}$$

b) For all three to be the same colour, they must all be red or they must all be green (the event $B' \cap C' \cap D'$). These two events are mutually exclusive. Using the same argument as before, but for the green apples:

$$\begin{aligned} \text{P(All three apples are green)} &= \frac{4}{24} \times \frac{3}{23} \times \frac{2}{22} \\ &= 0.001\,98\ldots \\ &= 0.002 \quad \text{(to 3 dp)} \end{aligned}$$

Thus, the probability that all three apples are the same colour is:

$$0.563\,24\ldots + 0.001\,98\ldots = 0.565 \quad \text{(to 3 dp)}$$

The probabilities are added because the events are mutually exclusive. This also occurs in part c).

c) It is important to note that the colours of all three apples must be specified. The event 'Exactly two apples are red' is:

$$(B \cap C \cap D') \cup (B \cap C' \cap D) \cup (B' \cap C \cap D)$$

with the three bracketed components corresponding to the cases where Daryl, Cheryl, or Beryl get the green apple. Hence:

$$\begin{aligned} \text{P(Exactly two apples are red)} &= P(B \cap C \cap D') + P(B \cap C' \cap D) \\ &\quad + P(B' \cap C \cap D) \\ &= \left(\frac{20}{24} \times \frac{19}{23} \times \frac{4}{22}\right) \\ &\quad + \left(\frac{20}{24} \times \frac{4}{23} \times \frac{19}{22}\right) \\ &\quad + \left(\frac{4}{24} \times \frac{20}{23} \times \frac{19}{22}\right) \end{aligned}$$

All three of the bracketed terms are equal since each child is equally likely to be the one with the green apple. So:

$$\begin{aligned} \text{P(Exactly two apples are red)} &= 3 \times \left(\frac{20}{24} \times \frac{19}{23} \times \frac{4}{22}\right) \\ &= 0.375\,49\ldots = 0.375 \quad \text{(to 3 dp)} \end{aligned}$$

Alternatively, this problem could be solved using a tree diagram.

Exercise 2D

1 Given that $P(A) = 0.8$, $P(B) = 0.7$, $P(C) = 0.6$, $P(A|B) = 0.8$, $P(C|B) = 0.7$, $P(A \cap C) = 0.48$, determine whether the following conditions apply.

a) A and B are independent.

b) A and C are independent.

c) B and C are independent.

2 It is given that C and D are independent with $P(C|D) = \frac{2}{3}$ and $P(C \cap D) = \frac{1}{3}$.

a) Find $P(C)$.

b) Find $P(D)$.

3 Three fair dice, one red, one green and one blue, are thrown simultaneously. Events R, G, S and T are defined as follows:

R: The score on the red die is 3.
G: The score on the green die is 2.
S: The sum of the scores on the red and the green dice is 4.
T: The total score for the three dice is 5.

Find: a) $P(R \cap G)$, b) $P(S|R)$, c) $P(R|S)$, d) $P(R \cup G)$, e) $P(T)$, f) $P(S|T)$.

S1

Summary

You should know how to ...	Check out
1 Calculate a probability when the possible outcomes are equally likely.	**1** A fair twelve-sided die has faces labelled 1, 2, ..., 12. Determine the probability that, when rolled, it comes to rest on a face that is a multiple of 4.
2 Define the 'complementary event' for a given event.	**2** Define the complementary event to the event 'When a die is rolled, the face showing is a multiple of 3'.
3 Draw a Venn diagram to illustrate unions and intersections of events.	**3** A, B and C are events. Draw Venn diagrams to illustrate: a) $A \cup B$, b) $A \cap B \cap C$.
4 Determine probabilities associated with mutually exclusive events, and with exhaustive events.	**4** a) A fair six-sided die is rolled. Determine the probability that the number obtained is either even, or a multiple of 3 (or both). b) With A' as the complement of the event A, write down the probabilities of: i) $A \cup A'$, ii) $A \cap A'$. c) Events A and B are both mutually exclusive and exhaustive. Given that $P(A) = 0.2$, determine $P(B)$.

5 Use the addition law.	**5** a) Events A and B are such that $P(A) = 0.7$, $P(B) = 0.4$ and $P(A \cap B) = 0.2$. Determine $P(A \cup B)$. b) Events A and B are exclusive, with $P(A) = 0.2$ and $P(B) = 0.3$. Determine: i) $P(A \cup B)$, ii) $P(A \cap B)$.
6 Use the multiplication law.	**6** Events A and B are independent. Each has probability $\frac{1}{4}$. Determine the probability that both occur.
7 Calculate a conditional probability.	**7** A fair coin is tossed. If the coin shows a Head, then a score of 4 is obtained. If the coin shows a Tail, then the score is equally likely to be 4, 5 or 6. Given that the score obtained is 4, determine the probability that the coin shows a Head.

Revision exercise 2

1 At a station, the probability that the first train in the morning is late is 0.4. Thereafter, the probability of a train being late is 0.6 if the previous train was late and 0.2 if the previous train was on time.

Find the probability that on a particular morning:

a) the first three trains are all late;

b) the first three trains are all on time;

c) exactly one of the first three trains is late. *(AQA, 2001)*

2 Shahid, Tracy and Dwight are friends who all have birthdays during January. Assuming that each friend's birthday is equally likely to be on any one of the 31 days of January, find the probability that:

a) Shahid's birthday is on January 3rd;

b) both Shahid's and Tracy's birthdays are on January 3rd;

c) all three friends' birthdays are on the same day;

d) all three friends' birthdays are on different days. *(AQA, 2002)*

3 At a university, 60% of students are studying arts subjects and the rest are studying science subjects. Of the arts students, 55% are female, and of the science students, 35% are female.

a) Find the probability that a student, selected at random:
  i) is female and studying an arts subject;
  ii) is male and studying a science subject;
  iii) is male;
  iv) is studying science, given that the student is male.

b) Of all the female students, one third of those studying a science subject and one half of those studying an arts subject live in a hall of residence. Find the probability that a female student, who lives in a hall of residence, is studying a science subject. (*AQA, 2003*)

4 Amy, Bruce and Carmen take part in an archery competition. The final test of the competition involves these three archers trying to hit the target centre.

The independent probabilities that Amy, Bruce and Carmen hit the target centre are 0.2, 0.3 and 0.6 respectively.

Find the probability that the target centre will be hit by:

a) Bruce only;

b) Carmen only;

c) exactly one of the three archers;

d) Bruce, given that exactly one of the three archers hits the target centre. (*AQA, 2002*)

S1

5 A rugby club has three categories of membership: adult, social and junior. The number of members in each category, classified by gender, is shown in the table.

	Adult	Social	Junior
Female	25	35	40
Male	95	25	80

One member is chosen, at random, to cut the ribbon at the opening of the new clubhouse.

a) Find the probability that:
i) a female member is chosen;
ii) a junior member is chosen;
iii) a junior member is chosen, given that a female member is chosen.

b) V denotes the event that a female member is chosen.
W denotes the event that an adult member is chosen.
X denotes the event that a junior member is chosen.

For the events V, W and X:
i) Write down two which are mutually exclusive.
ii) Find two which are neither mutually exclusive nor independent. Justify your answer. (*AQA, 2003*)

6 Keith, Yasmin and Suzie are friends who often go to a jazz club on a Friday night. The probability that Keith goes to the club on a particular Friday is 0.7 and is independent of whether or not Yasmin and Suzie go.

The probability that Yasmin goes to the club is 0.8 if Keith goes and 0.6 if Keith does not go.

The probability that Suzie goes to the club:

is 0.9 if both Keith and Yasmin go;
is 0.65 if Keith goes but Yasmin does not;
is 0.55 if Yasmin goes but Keith does not;
is 0.4 if neither Keith nor Yasmin go.

continued

By drawing a tree diagram, or otherwise, find the probability that on a particular Friday:

a) all three friends go to the club;

b) Keith goes to the club but Yasmin and Suzie do not;

c) Yasmin and Suzie go to the club but Keith does not;

d) Suzie goes to the club. *(AQA, 2003)*

7 Denzel and Cherie are friends who often go to the cinema together. On such visits there is a probability of 0.4 that Denzel will buy popcorn. The probability that Cherie will buy popcorn is 0.7 if Denzel buys popcorn and 0.35 if he does not.

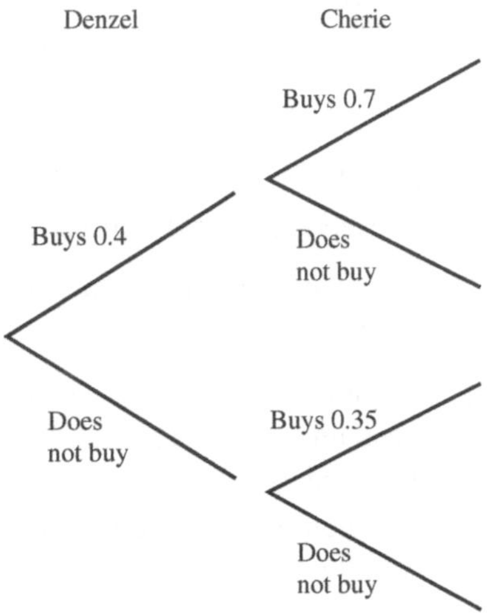

Denzel
Cherie
Buys 0.7
Buys 0.4
Does not buy
Does not buy
Buys 0.35
Does not buy

a) When Denzel and Cherie visit the cinema together:

   i) find the probability that both buy popcorn;

   ii) show that the probability that neither buys popcorn is 0.39;

   iii) find the probability that exactly one of them buys popcorn.

b) Sohaib sometimes joins Denzel and Cherie on their cinema visits. On these occasions, the probability that Sohaib buys popcorn is 0.55 if both Denzel and Cherie buy popcorn and 0.25 if exactly one of Denzel and Cherie buys popcorn.

   Find the probability that when Denzel, Cherie and Sohaib visit the cinema together:

   i) all three buy popcorn;

   ii) Cherie and Sohaib buy popcorn but Denzel does not. *(AQA, 2003)*

8 Transport inspectors carry out roadside safety tests on lorries.

a) The probability of a randomly selected lorry failing the test is 0.25. A transport inspector chooses two lorries at random. Find the probability that:

   i) both will fail the test;

   ii) exactly one will pass the test.

b) Of 12 lorries parked outside a transport café, four would fail if tested.

   i) An inspector chooses two of these twelve lorries at random. Find the probability that both will pass the test.

   ii) An inspector chooses three of these lorries at random. Find the probability that two will pass the test and one will fail the test.

   iii) An inspector chooses four of these lorries at random. Find the probability that at least one will fail the test. *(AQA, 2003)*

9 The senior driving examiner at a test centre decides to collect some data about the candidates who are taking a driving test for the first time. The candidates are asked how many driving lessons they had before they took the test. The results are given in the table below.

Number of lessons	Gender	
	Male	Female
20 or fewer	35	47
between 21 and 50	87	75
more than 50	8	21

A candidate is selected at random.

M is the event 'The candidate is male'.
T is the event 'The candidate had 20 or fewer lessons'.
S is the event 'The candidate had more than 50 lessons'.
M' is the event 'Not M'.
S' is the event 'Not S'.

Find: a) $P(M \cap S)$; b) $P(T)$; c) $P(M|T)$; d) $P(M' \cap T)$; e) $P(M'|S')$. *(AQA, 2003)*

10 A blood test for determining the type of hepatitis from which a patient is suffering involves testing for the Australian antigen. A 'positive' result to this test indicates that a patient has hepatitis C.

Unfortunately, this test is not completely reliable.

If an individual has hepatitis C, there is a probability of 0.8 that the test will give a 'positive' result. If a patient does **not** have hepatitis C, there is a probability of 0.1 that the test will give a 'positive' result.

It is known that 18% of patients suffering from hepatitis have type C.

Find the probability that a person chosen at random from all hepatitis sufferers:

a) has type C and gives a 'positive' result to the test;

b) gives a 'positive' result to the test;

c) does not have hepatitis C, given that the test has given a 'positive' result. *(AQA, 2002)*

S1

3 The binomial distribution

This chapter will show you how to

- ✦ Recognise a discrete random variable
- ✦ Recognise a binomial probability situation
- ✦ Calculate binomial probabilities
- ✦ Determine the mean and variance of a binomial distribution

Before you start

You should know how to ...	Check in
1 Apply the descriptions 'mutually exclusive' and 'exhaustive' to events.	**1** Two fair six-sided dice are rolled. One die is red and the other is blue. The events A, B, C and D are defined as follows. A: The red die shows a larger number than the blue die B: The sum of the two numbers shown is greater than 8. C: The two dice show the same number. D: The sum of the two numbers shown is less than 9. a) Determine which pairs of events (if any) are mutually exclusive. b) Determine which pairs of events (if any) are exhaustive.
2 Use a probability tree to determine the probabilities of possible outcomes.	**2** In a fleet of buses, 70% are red. Of the bus drivers, 60% are male. Assuming that the colour of a bus is independent of whether the driver is male or female, construct a probability tree showing the possible outcomes and their probabilities.
3 Substitute into a formula involving powers and calculate the resulting value.	**3** Determine the value of y, when: a) $y = 0.3^4$ b) $y = 0.2^2 \times 0.8^4$ c) $y = p^3(1 - p)^2$ with $p = 0.4$
4 Determine the ranges of values specified by one or more inequalities.	**4** X takes the values 0, 1, 2, …, 8. Determine which values are identified by each of the following. a) $X > 6$ b) $X \leqslant 2$ c) $3 < X < 6$ d) $X \geqslant 4$ and $X < 8$

3.1 Discrete random variables

Before the meaning of the term 'binomial distribution' is defined, three basic statistical terms must be introduced.

- A **variable** is a characteristic measured or observed when an experiment or trial is carried out or an observation is made.
- When the value of a variable may be subject to random variation, the variable is described as being a **random variable**.
- A random variable is described as being a **discrete random variable** when (in theory) a list can be made of its possible values.

Here are some examples.

Discrete random variable	Possible values
The amount (in £) won in a lottery which has prizes of 50p, £5 and £50	0, 0.5, 5, 50
The net gain (in £) from buying a 25p ticket in the above lottery	−0.25, 0.25, 4.75, 49.75
The number of rainy days in May	0, 1, …, 31
The number of tosses of a fair coin until a head is obtained	1, 2, 3, … (no limit)

In each case, the possible outcomes can be written down as a list of numerical values.

Notation

Random variables are normally denoted by italic capital letters, such as X, Y and Z. Observed values, however, are usually denoted by italic lower-case letters, such as x, y and z.

This leads to a statement such as:

$$P(X = x) = \frac{1}{4}$$

which should be read as:

'The probability that the random variable X takes the value x is $\frac{1}{4}$.'

In cases where the definition of X is clear from the context, the simpler $p(x)$ may be used. The previous statement then becomes:

$$p(x) = \frac{1}{4}$$

This statement can be linked to the probability of an event by defining the event A as: 'The random variable X takes the particular value x'. So:

$$P(A) = \frac{1}{4}$$

Probability distributions

Suppose a biased die, with faces numbered 1 to 6, is rolled. Define the random variable X as: 'The number showing on the top of the die'. Two things are known:

- The observed value of X must be 1, 2, 3, 4, 5, or 6.
- On a given roll, the random variable X can only take *one* of those values.

These two things correspond to statements that the six outcomes are both collectively exhaustive and mutually exclusive. Hence:

$$p(1) + p(2) + \cdots + p(6) = 1$$

Exhaustive and mutually exclusive events are explained in Chapter 2, pages 46–47.

Generalizing, for a discrete random variable X which can take only the distinct values $x_1, x_2, \ldots, x_n$:

S1

$$\sum p(x_i) = p(x_1) + p(x_2) + \cdots + p(x_n) = 1 \qquad (3.1)$$

To further simplify the notation, sometimes $p(x_i)$ is written as p_i, so that:

$$\sum p_i = 1$$

The sizes of $p_1, p_2, \ldots, p_n$, show how the total probability is *distributed* amongst the possible values of X. This is analogous to a frequency distribution, and the values of $p_1, p_2, \ldots, p_n$, together with the values $x_1, x_2, \ldots, x_n$ to which they refer, are said to define a **probability distribution.**

A probability distribution is often displayed as a table of the possible values and their probabilities.

Example 1

Tabulate the probability distribution of the number of Heads obtained when a fair coin is tossed twice.

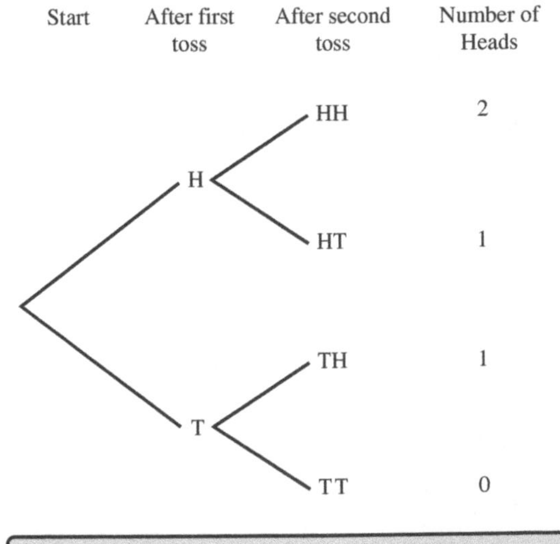

Let the random variable X be the number of Heads obtained. The possible values of X are 0, 1 and 2. The simplest way of finding the required probabilities is to use a probability tree.

Since the coin is fair and the tosses are independent, each of the four outcomes is equally likely and therefore has a probability of $\frac{1}{4}$.

The required table is therefore:

Number of Heads, x	0	1	2	All other values
$P(X = x)$	$\frac{1}{4}$	$\frac{2}{4} = \frac{1}{2}$	$\frac{1}{4}$	0

The last column in this table is a statement (usually omitted) that no values other than 0, 1 or 2 are possible. (This follows since the probabilities must sum to 1.)

The probability function

For many situations you do not need to make a list of all the probabilities, because some simple all-embracing formula (sometimes called the **probability function**) can be found.

Example 2

Obtain a formula for the probability distribution of the random variable X defined as: 'The result of rolling a fair die'.

Each of the six possible values for X has a probability of $\frac{1}{6}$. So:

$$P(X = x) = \begin{cases} \frac{1}{6} & (x = 1, 2, \ldots, 6) \\ 0 & \text{otherwise} \end{cases}$$

Illustrating probability distributions

As always in Statistics, it is a good idea to draw pictures whenever possible. Since a discrete random variable can only take discrete values, a bar chart is appropriate, with the y-axis measuring probability.

Example 3

The random variable X is defined as: 'The sum of the numbers shown by two fair dice'. Tabulate the probability distribution of X and represent it on an appropriate diagram.

Draw up a table to show the 36 possible outcomes, all of which (since the dice are fair and the tosses are independent) are equally likely. The entries are the values of X.

Second die \ First die	1	2	3	4	5	6
1	2	3	4	5	6	7
2	3	4	5	6	7	8
3	4	5	6	7	8	9
4	5	6	7	8	9	10
5	6	7	8	9	10	11
6	7	8	9	10	11	12

By inspection of the table, you can see that there is just one outcome leading to the event $X = 2$. So:

$$p(2) = \frac{1}{36}$$

The most likely value for X is 7, which has a probability of $\frac{6}{36} = \frac{1}{6}$.

The full distribution is tabulated below, and the diagram is as shown.

x	2	3	4	5	6	7	8	9	10	11	12
$\mathrm{p}(x)$	$\frac{1}{36}$	$\frac{2}{36}$	$\frac{3}{36}$	$\frac{4}{36}$	$\frac{5}{36}$	$\frac{6}{36}$	$\frac{5}{36}$	$\frac{4}{36}$	$\frac{3}{36}$	$\frac{2}{36}$	$\frac{1}{36}$

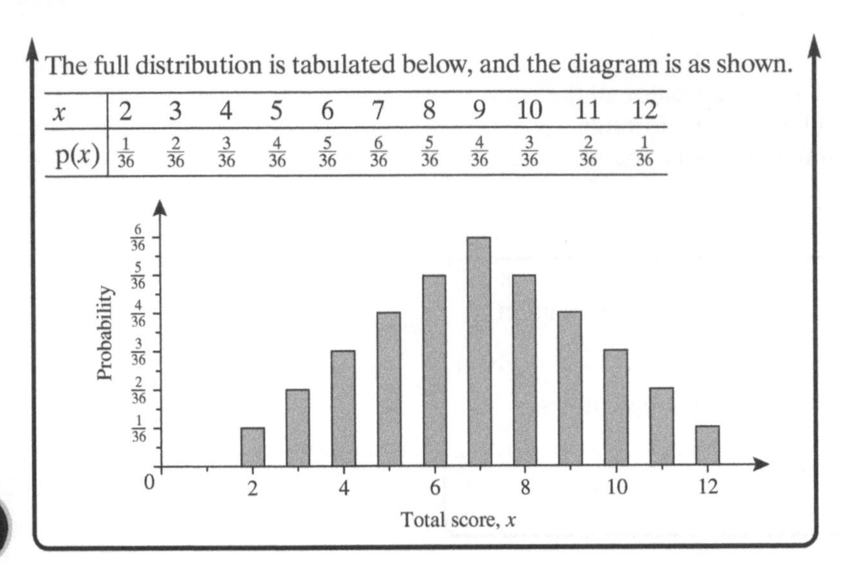

Exercise 3A

For the following questions, find, in each case, the set of possible values of the random variable X, and draw up a table showing $\mathrm{p}(x)$ for each value of x.

1 A box contains three red marbles and five green marbles. Two marbles are taken at random *without* replacement. The random variable X is the number of green marbles obtained.

2 A box contains three red marbles and five green marbles. Two marbles are taken at random *with* replacement. The random variable X is the number of green marbles obtained.

3 A fair coin, having the number one marked on one face and the number two marked on the other, is tossed at the same time as a fair die. The random variable X is the sum of the scores on the coin and the die.

4 In a raffle, 20 tickets are sold and there are two prizes. One ticket number is drawn at random and the corresponding ticket earns a £10 prize. A second, different, ticket number is drawn at random, and the corresponding ticket earns a £3 prize. The prize earned by a particular one of the original 20 tickets is £X.

5 A fair die is thrown. The random variable X is the reciprocal of the score.

> Note for Question 5:
> If the score is 2, $X = \frac{1}{2}$.

6 Two fair dice, one red and the other green, are thrown. The random variable X is the score on the red die minus the score on the green die.

7 Two fair dice, one red and the other green, are thrown. The random variable X is the positive difference in the scores.

> Note for Question 7:
> X is the modulus of the random variable in Question 6.

8 Packets of 'Hidden Gold' cornflakes are sold for £1.20 each. One in twenty of the packets contains a £1 coin. A shopper buys two packets. The random variable X is the net cost of the two packets (in £).

3.2 Conditions for application of a binomial distribution

Here are some examples of binomial random variables.

Binomial random variable	Possible values
1 The number of Heads obtained when a single fair coin is tossed once	0, 1
2 The number of Heads obtained when a biased coin is tossed once	0, 1
3 The number of Heads obtained when a biased coin is tossed five times	0, 1, 2, 3, 4, 5
4 The number of matches that will break when struck, in a matchbox containing 50 matches, assuming that breakages occur independently, and that each match has the same probability of breaking	0, 1, 2, …, 50
5 The number of males on a 12-person jury, assuming that the probability of each jury member being male is the same, independent of the gender of all other jury members	0, 1, 2, …, 12
6 The number of coconuts won in three attempts at a coconut shy, assuming that the probability of a success is the same at each attempt, and that the attempts are independent of one another	0, 1, 2, 3

These examples have certain common themes.

A binomial random variable is such that:

- ✦ There is a fixed number, n, of independent trials.
- ✦ Each trial results in one of two outcomes: success or failure.
- ✦ The probability of success, p, is the same for each trial.

Possible definitions of trial and success for the examples are given in the table below.

Example	Trial	Success
1–3	The toss of a coin	The coin showing Heads
4	The striking of a match	The match breaking
5	The gender of a jury member	The jury member being male
6	An attempt at a coconut shy	The coconut being won

A tree diagram can prove helpful for these types of situation.

Example 4

Determine the probability of getting two Heads in three tosses of a bent coin which has P(Head) $= \frac{1}{5}$.

The tree of possible outcomes is shown below.

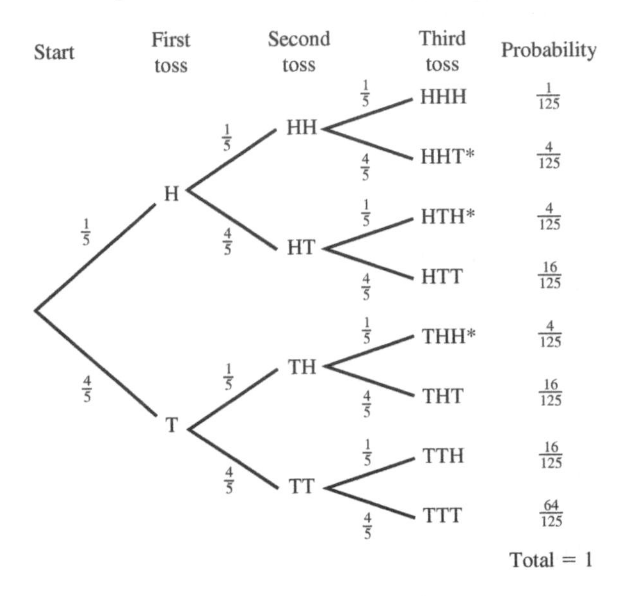

There are three outcomes (indicated by *) that lead to the event 'Exactly two Heads'. Each sequence has probability $\frac{4}{125}$. Hence, the probability of obtaining exactly two Heads is $\frac{12}{125}$.

Exercise 3B

In the following questions, the outcomes of trials are assumed to be independent of one another.

1 Give possible definitions of the trials and successes for each of the following binomial situations. In each case, give the range of possible values for the binomial random variable.

a) The number of cracked eggs in a box of six eggs.

b) The number of black socks in a drawer containing twelve socks.

c) The number of households that have a widescreen television, in a street of 25 households.

d) The number of trees in a wood that show signs of attack by a virus. There are n trees in the wood.

e) The number of airline passengers who do not take up their seat on a cheap flight. Tickets were sold to m passengers.

S1

2 A cube has the letter A on four faces and the letter B on the remaining two faces. It is thrown three times.

Draw an appropriate tree diagram and find the probability that the number of As obtained is: a) 0, b) 1, c) 2, d) 3.

Find also the probability that the number of Bs obtained is: e) 0, f) 1, g) 2, h) 3.

3 Suppose that 10% of cars are coloured silver. Determine the probability that only one of the next three cars to pass my house is coloured silver.

4 A coin is tossed at the start of each cricket match in a series of four Test matches. One captain tosses and the other calls 'Heads' or 'Tails', at random.

Find the probability that the toss is called correctly:
a) exactly once, b) exactly twice.

Suppose the caller always calls 'Heads'. Does this alter the probabilities? Give a reason for your answer.

5 A woman is trying to light a bonfire. She has only four matches left in her matchbox.

Given that 10% of matches break when struck, determine the probabilities of the following events.

a) All four matches will break when struck.

b) At least one match will not break when struck.

[Assume that all four matches are struck in each case.]

6 Every thousandth visitor to an exhibition is given a voucher for £50.

Assuming that 65% of the visitors to the exhibition are female, find the probability that, out of the first five to be given a voucher, exactly three are female.

S1

3.3 Calculation of binomial probabilities using the formula

Use of a tree diagram is only feasible when the number of trials, n, is small. Otherwise a formula is needed.

Look back at Example 4. There are three possible sequences leading to the desired outcome, and each sequence has the same probability. The answer is in effect:

$$\begin{aligned}\text{P(Exactly 2 Heads)} &= \text{(Number of sequences)} \times \{\text{P(Head)}\}^2 \times \{\text{P(Tail)}\}^1 \\ &= 3 \times \left(\frac{1}{5}\right)^2 \times \left(\frac{4}{5}\right)^1 \\ &= \frac{12}{125}\end{aligned}$$

There are three sequences, each involving two Heads and one Tail.

This approach works every time.

Example 5

Suppose a rich gambler has a biased coin for which the probability of a Head is 0.55. He tosses the coin eight times. Assuming that the outcomes of the tosses are independent of one another, determine the probability that he obtains six Heads.

Using the previous method:

$$\begin{aligned}&\text{P(6 Heads in 8 tosses)}\\&\quad = (\text{Number of sequences}) \times \{\text{P(Head)}\}^6 \times \{\text{P(Tail)}\}^2\\&\quad = (\text{Number of sequences}) \times (0.55)^6 \times (0.45)^2\end{aligned}$$

In this case, the number of sequences leading to the desired result happens to be 28. So:

$$\begin{aligned}\text{P(6 Heads in 8 tosses)} &= 28 \times (0.55)^6 \times (0.45)^2\\ &= 0.157 \ \text{(to 3 dp)}\end{aligned}$$

You could list all 28 sequences:

H H H H H H T T
H H H H H T H T
H H H H T H H T
⋮ ⋮
T T H H H H H H

S1

For the general case of n independent trials, the question is: 'How many sequences in a probability tree lead to exactly x successes?'.

Because this type of question occurs frequently, you need to know the special notation used to handle it.

The number of different (unordered) sets of x objects, selected from a collection of n objects, is denoted by $\binom{n}{x}$, where:

$$\binom{n}{x} = \frac{n!}{x!(n-x)!}$$

for $x = 0, 1, \ldots, n$.

For example, $\binom{8}{6}$ represents the number of different sets of six objects chosen from eight objects.

The quantities $n!$ and $x!$ are called **factorial n** and **factorial x**.

For a positive integer k, $k!$ is defined by:

$k! = k \text{ factorial} = k \times (k-1) \times (k-2) \times \ldots \times 3 \times 2 \times 1$

Factorial zero, $0!$, is arbitrarily defined to be 1.

For example, $6!$ is given by:

$6 \times 5 \times 4 \times 3 \times 2 \times 1 = 720$

Note: $\binom{n}{0} = \binom{n}{n} = 1$

Since $n! = n \times (n-1) \times \cdots \times 1$, it would appear that calculating $\binom{n}{x}$ may involve the manipulation of very large numbers. Fortunately, this is not the case because of the possibility of cancelling terms in the numerator and the denominator. For example, suppose you wish to calculate $\binom{50}{4}$. Most calculators cannot work out $50!$, because it is a very large number. However, you can calculate $\binom{50}{4}$ by writing:

$$\binom{50}{4} = \frac{50!}{4! \times 46!}$$

$$= \frac{50 \times 49 \times 48 \times 47 \times \cancel{46!}}{(4 \times 3 \times 2 \times 1) \times \cancel{46!}}$$

$$= \frac{50 \times 49 \times \overset{2}{\cancel{48}} \times 47}{\cancel{4} \times \cancel{3} \times \cancel{2} \times \cancel{1}}$$

$$= 230\,300$$

A similar simplification always works. Thus:

$$\binom{20}{5} = \frac{20 \times 19 \times 18 \times 17 \times 16}{5 \times 4 \times 3 \times 2 \times 1}$$

If your calculator can determine $\binom{n}{x}$, you can confirm that this value is correct.

Alternative notations to $\binom{n}{x}$ are ${}^nC_x$ and C^n_x.

S1

Example 6

A marksman fires ten times at a target. Assuming that the outcomes of the shots are independent of one another, and that each shot has a probability of 0.96 of hitting the target centre, determine the probability that exactly nine shots hit the target centre.

In this problem, each shot is either a 'success' (hitting the centre) or a 'failure'.

Let X be the number of shots that hit the centre. So, you need to find $P(X = 9)$.

The number of sequences leading to exactly nine centre hits is $\binom{10}{9}$, where:

$$\binom{10}{9} = \frac{10!}{9! \times 1!} = \frac{10 \times 9!}{9!} = 10$$

Thus:

$$P(X = 9) = 10(0.96)^9(0.04)^1$$
$$= 0.277 \text{ (to 3 dp)}$$

What would have happened in Example 6 if the marksman's probability of hitting the centre had been 0.92, instead of 0.96? To find out, replace 0.96 by 0.92 and replace 0.04 by 0.08, to get:

$$P(X = 9) = 10(0.92)^9(0.08)^1$$
$$= 0.378 \text{ (to 3 dp)}$$

If the marksman's probability of hitting the centre had been p, you would have:

$$P(X = 9) = \binom{10}{9} p^9(1 - p)^1$$

This leads to an important general result.

The probability of obtaining exactly x successes in n independent trials, when, for each trial, the probability of a success is p, is given by:

$$P(X=x) = \binom{n}{x} p^x (1-p)^{n-x}$$

for $x = 0, 1, \ldots, n$.

For other values of x, $P(X=x) = 0$.

The quantity $1-p$ is sometimes written as q, in which case:

$$P(X=x) = \binom{n}{x} p^x q^{n-x}$$

This result provides the definition of the **binomial distribution**.

S1

Calculator practice

Many calculators provide values for $\binom{n}{x}$, and some provide the values of binomial probabilities. (You should learn which keys to press.)

Example 7

According to a motoring magazine, Japanese cars account for 5% of the cars on the road in England. Whilst held up in a traffic jam, I occupy my time in examining the cars racing past on the other side of the road. Assuming that the magazine is correct, determine the probability that, of the first 50 cars that pass me, exactly four are Japanese.

For a second solution to this question, see Example 9, page 79.

Each car is either Japanese (a 'success') or not Japanese. Assuming that the traffic jam is not immediately outside a car manufacturing plant, the 50 cars can be assumed to be a random sample of the cars on the road. The number of trials, n, is 50, since 50 cars are examined. The probability of a 'success', p, is 0.05 and the value of x is 4. Hence, the required probability is:

Note that four successes means that the rest are failures. Thus, both $(0.05)^4$ and $(0.95)^{46}$ must appear.

$$\binom{50}{4}(0.05)^4(0.95)^{46} = \frac{50 \times 49 \times 48 \times 47}{4 \times 3 \times 2 \times 1}(0.05)^4(0.95)^{46}$$

$$= 0.136 \quad \text{(to 3 dp)}$$

So, there is a probability of about 14% that exactly four of the next 50 cars are Japanese.

Example 8

In a competition, a contestant is asked ten questions. The contestant wins a prize if eight or more questions are answered correctly. To help the contestant, four possible answers (one of which is correct) for each question, are suggested by the quizmaster. One contestant, Ivor Noidea, answers each question by choosing one of the four possible answers at random, so that his probability of giving a correct answer is $\frac{1}{4}$. What is the probability that Ivor wins a prize?

Each question is either answered correctly (a 'success') or is not. For each question, p, the probability of success, is $\frac{1}{4}$. There are 10 $(=n)$ questions. Answers are independent of one another. This is, therefore, a binomial situation. Let X be the number of questions answered correctly. The required probability is $P(X \geqslant 8)$, which is:

$$P(X=8) + P(X=9) + P(X=10)$$

$$= \binom{10}{8}\left(\frac{1}{4}\right)^8\left(\frac{3}{4}\right)^2 + \binom{10}{9}\left(\frac{1}{4}\right)^9\left(\frac{3}{4}\right)^1 + \binom{10}{10}\left(\frac{1}{4}\right)^{10}\left(\frac{3}{4}\right)^0$$

$$= \left(\frac{10 \times 9}{2 \times 1} \times \frac{9}{4^{10}}\right) + \left(\frac{10}{1} \times \frac{3}{4^{10}}\right) + \left(1 \times \frac{1}{4^{10}}\right)$$

$$= \frac{1}{4^{10}} \times (405 + 30 + 1) = 0.0004 \text{ (to 4 dp)}$$

With less than one chance in 2000, Ivor is unlikely to win a prize.

S1

Exercise 3C

1 The number of successes in n independent trials is X. The probability of a success in each trial is p.

a) Given that $n = 10, p = \frac{1}{4}$, find $P(X = 3)$.

b) Given that $n = 8, p = \frac{3}{4}$, find $P(X = 6)$.

c) Given that $n = 12, p = \frac{1}{3}$, find $P(X \leqslant 3)$.

d) Given that $n = 11, p = \frac{4}{5}$, find $P(X \geqslant 9)$.

e) Given that $n = 7, p = \frac{1}{2}$, find $P(3 \leqslant X \leqslant 5)$.

2 Five per cent of bluebells (confusingly) have white flowers. The remainder have blue flowers.

Determine the probability that a random sample of ten bluebell plants includes exactly one with white flowers.

3 In a telephone poll, 22% of the respondents believed in astrology and 78% did not.

Assuming that the same proportions apply to the whole population, find the probability that, in a random sample of 10 people, less than 20% believe in astrology.

Comment on the validity of the extrapolation from the poll to the population.

4 There are 15 students in a class. Assuming that each student is equally likely to have been born on any day of the week, find the probability that three or fewer were born on a Monday.

Find also the probability that four or more were born on a Tuesday.

5 Two parents each have the gene for cystic fibrosis. For each of their children, the probability of developing cystic fibrosis is $\frac{1}{4}$.

If there are four children, all of different ages, find the probability that exactly two develop cystic fibrosis.

6 When the Romans punished rebellious legions, they lined up the men and executed every tenth man.

Six brothers stood in random places in the line. Find the probability that: a) none was executed; b) four or more escaped execution.

7 A large box contains a mixture of three different types of bolt, in equal numbers. Another box contains the nuts for the bolts. Each nut only fits a bolt of the same type. A nut and a bolt are chosen at random and checked to see if they match (that is, they are of the same type). The process is repeated 12 times.

Find the probability that more than four matches are obtained.

8 Driving to work, Priscilla has to negotiate three sets of traffic lights. She has observed that each of these shows green for 0.45 of the time, red for 0.45 of the time, and amber (or red and amber) for the remaining time.

Assuming that the colours of the traffic lights are independent of one another and of the time at which Priscilla reaches them, determine the probability that exactly two of the lights require her (a law-abiding citizen) to stop (by showing either amber, red, or red and amber).

9 The characters in a film are classified as being either 'Good', 'Bad', or 'Ugly'. The proportions in these classes are, respectively, 0.4, 0.4, and 0.2. Seven of the characters have red hair.

Assuming that class and hair colour are independent, determine the probability that exactly two of the red haired characters are 'Ugly'.

'Successes' and 'failures'

It does not matter which of the two possible outcomes you think of as being a 'success' – the calculations will be the same.

Example 9

In Example 7 (page 76), where the probability was required of observing four Japanese cars in a random sample of 50 cars, a 'success' was defined to be 'a Japanese car'. Suppose instead a 'success' is defined to be 'a *non*-Japanese car'. Thus n is 50 as before, but the probability of a 'success', p, is now 0.95 and the value of x, the required number of 'successes', is now 46. The required probability is:

$$P(X = 46) = \binom{50}{46}(0.95)^{46}(0.05)^4$$
$$= 0.136 \text{ (to 3 dp)}$$

which is the value obtained previously.

$$\binom{50}{46} = \binom{50}{4}$$

In fact, it is always true that:

$$\binom{n}{x} = \binom{n}{n-x}$$

S1

Notation

Instead of writing:

> 'The random variable X has a binomial distribution. There are n independent trials. The probability of a 'success' is p for each trial',

it is easier to use the following notation:

$$X \sim B(n, p)$$

in which the symbol '$\sim$' means 'has distribution' and 'B' means 'binomial'.

The quantities n and p are called the **parameters** of the distribution. Their values are required in order to specify the distribution completely. These values must satisfy the obvious requirements that n is a positive integer and $0 \leqslant p \leqslant 1$.

The shape of the distribution

The shape of the binomial distribution depends upon the value of p. When $p = \frac{1}{2}$, this means that a 'success' is just as likely as a 'failure'. So, for example, the probability of obtaining two 'successes' (and hence $n - 2$ 'failures') is equal to the probability of obtaining two 'failures' (and hence $n - 2$ 'successes'). When $p = \frac{1}{2}$, the binomial distribution is symmetric. For other values of p, the distribution is asymmetric (skewed), with a mode (the value for which the probability is a maximum) near np.

Example 10

The random variable X has a binomial distribution with $n = 5$ and $p = 0.94$. Determine $P(X > 2)$.

Now:

$$P(X > 2) = P(3, 4, \text{or } 5 \text{ 'successes'}) = P(2, 1, \text{or } 0 \text{ 'failures'})$$

Since P('success') = 0.94, P('failure') = 0.06.

Write Y to denote the number of 'failures'. Thus $Y \sim B(5, 0.06)$ and $P(Y \leqslant 2) = 0.9980$ (from Table 1). Hence, $P(X > 2) = 0.998$ (to 3 dp).

S1

Example 11

Example 8 (page 77) asked for the probability of Ivor Noidea winning a prize on a quiz show. There were ten questions, and Ivor's answers were independent of one another with each having a probability of $\frac{1}{4}$ being correct. Use Table 1 (Appendices, pages 213–218) to verify the accuracy of the answer.

Let X denote the number of correct answers. $P(X \geqslant 8)$ is required, with $X \sim B(10, 0.25)$. The table gives the values of $P(X \leqslant x)$, for various x, so:

$$P(X \geqslant 8) = 1 - P(X \leqslant 7) = 1 - 0.9996 = 0.0004 \quad \text{(to 4 dp)}$$

It is easy to confuse $P(X < x)$ with $P(X \leqslant x)$. So, questions should always be read very carefully.

Example 12

A gardener plants 20 hyacinth bulbs. For each bulb, independently of the other bulbs, the probability that it produces two flower heads is 0.7. Use Table 1 (Appendices, pages 213–218) to determine the probability that between 10 and 16 (inclusive) of the bulbs produce two flower heads.

Since the table refers to binomial distributions with $p \leqslant 0.50$, the question must be restated in terms of bulbs that do *not* produce two flower heads.

Let X be the number of bulbs not producing two flower heads. If 16 produce two flower heads, then 4 do not. If 10 produce two flower heads, then 10 do not.

$P(4 \leqslant X \leqslant 10)$ is required, with $X \sim B(20, 0.3)$. So:

$$P(4 \leqslant X \leqslant 10) = P(X \leqslant 10) - (X \leqslant 3) = 0.9829 - 0.1071 = 0.8758$$

The probability that between 10 and 16 (inclusive) of the bulbs produce two flower heads is 0.876 (to 3 dp).

Inevitably, the tables do not provide for *every* combination of n and p. When a value is required that cannot be obtained directly from the tables, it should be calculated from the formula defining the binomial distribution.

Exercise 3D

1 Given that $X \sim B(8, 0.3)$, find: a) $P(X \leqslant 4)$, b) $P(X > 6)$.

2 Given that $X \sim B(10, 0.4)$, find: a) $P(X \geqslant 7)$, b) $P(X = 6)$, c) $P(X < 5)$.

3 Given that $X \sim B(15, 0.7)$, find: a) $P(X \geqslant 9)$, b) $P(X \leqslant 11)$.

4 Given that $X \sim B(12, 0.6)$, find $P(5 \leqslant X \leqslant 8)$.

5 When serving at tennis, the probability that Harriet Hitter gets the first service in court is 30%. If the first service is a fault (that is, does not go in court), there is a second service and the probability that the second service goes in court is 90%.
   a) Find the probability that out of 15 first services more than 10 go in court.
   b) Show that the probability of a double fault (that is, neither service goes in court) is 0.07.
   c) Find the probability that out of 15 (combined) serves, at least four are double faults.

6 University student Joe Sleepwell often misses 9 o'clock lectures through oversleeping. The probability that he oversleeps is 0.6.
   Find the probability that, in a ten-week term, with two 9 o'clock lectures each week, he misses more than half of them.

S1

3.5 The mean, variance and standard deviation of a binomial distribution

The mean of a binomial distribution with parameters n and p is np.

The corresponding variance is $np(1-p)$.

> A random variable having a $B(n, p)$ distribution has a mean of np and a variance of $np(1-p)$.

Imagine that you conduct 100 independent trials in which the probability of a success is $\frac{1}{4}$. You would expect to see a total of about 25 successes because about $\frac{1}{4}$ of the trials will be successful. For the general case, you would expect to see np successes.

The standard deviation of the distribution is therefore $\sqrt{np(1-p)}$.

Example 13

It is claimed that a random variable X can be modelled by a binomial distribution with parameters $n = 20$ and $p = 0.1$. To back up the claim, a random sample of 100 observations are taken on X, and these are found to have mean $\bar{x} = 2.4$ and variance $s^2 = 17.2$. Does the claim seem reasonable?

Since $n = 20$ and $p = 0.1$, you would expect the sample to have a mean near $np = 2$ and a variance near $np(1-p) = 1.8$. The observed mean of 2.4 is a little high, but this might be due to chance. However, the variance is nearly ten times the value to be expected. The claim does not seem reasonable.

If n is not too small, and p is not close to 0 or 1, then on about 95% of occasions, the observed value of a random variable X having a $B(n, p)$ distribution will lie in the range:

Mean $\pm$ 2 $\times$ standard deviation

That is, in the range:

$np \pm 2\sqrt{np(1-p)}$.

Example 14

A very lazy candidate has done no revision for his multiple-choice statistics examination and guesses the answer to each of the 40 questions. Given that each question offers four alternative answers, only one of which is correct, determine a likely range for the number of correct answers which the candidate obtained.

The probability, p, that the candidate guesses the correct answer to a question is $\frac{1}{4}$. The situation is binomial, since, for each question, the candidate is either correct or not correct. Thus $X \sim B(40, \frac{1}{4})$. This binomial distribution has mean $np = 10$ and standard deviation:

$$\sqrt{np(1-p)} = \sqrt{7.5} = 2.74 \quad \text{(to 3 sf)}$$

Hence, a likely range for the number of correct answers that the lazy candidate obtains is from $(10 - 2 \times 2.74)$ to $(10 + 2 \times 2.74)$, which is approximately a range from 4 to 16.

Here, greater accuracy in the range would not be appropriate.

S1

Exercise 3E

1 Determine the mean and the variance of a binomial random variable X for which $n = 50$ and $p = 0.3$.

2 Two boys are throwing skimmers. The probability that a skimmer thrown by Alec will hop five times (a success!) is 0.2, whereas for Bill the probability is 0.1. Both boys throw 10 skimmers.

a) Determine the mean and the variance of the number of successes obtained by Alec.

b) Determine the mean and the standard deviation of the number of successes obtained by Bill.

3 A die is thrown 10 times. Let X be the number of sixes obtained.

a) Find the mean and the variance of the distribution of X.

b) Determine the probability that X takes a value less than the mean of the distribution, giving your answer correct to 3 dp.

4 Mrs Li, who always makes the same journey to work, finds that she is delayed at a level-crossing once in five journeys, on average.

a) Using a binomial model, find the mean number of her journeys that are delayed at the level crossing in a month when she makes 25 journeys to work.

b) Find also the probability that she is delayed on fewer than four occasions.

5 Published articles in medical journals indicate that, on average, 35 out of 100 patients having a lumbar puncture will suffer SSH (severe spinal headache). Twelve patients are given a lumbar puncture.

a) Using a binomial model, find the mean number of patients who will suffer SSH, and also find the standard deviation.

b) Find the probability that four or more of the twelve patients will suffer SSH.

6 The random variable X has a binomial distribution with a mean of 12 and a variance of 2.4. Find $P(X \geqslant 14)$.

7 It is given that $Y \sim B(10, p)$ and that the variance of Y is 2.1.

a) Find the possible values of p.

b) For each value of p, find $P(Y = 4)$, giving your answer to 3 dp.

8 The random variable X is such that $X \sim B(n, p)$. It is known that when the variance of the distribution of X is divided by the mean of the distribution, the answer is 0.3.

Given that the mean is equal to 10.5, determine the values of n and p.

9 The random variable X is such that $X \sim B(n, 0.5)$.

Determine the smallest value of n for which the ratio of the standard deviation of the distribution of X to the mean of the distribution is less than 1 to 10.

Summary

You should know how to ...	Check out
1 Identify a binomial situation and the values of n and p.	1 For each of the following situations, decide whether it can be binomial. If it can be, then state any requirements and, where possible, determine the values of n and p. a) The number of dented cans in a four-can pack of baked beans. b) The number of cars passing your house between 08:00 and 08:30. c) One quarter of the inhabitants of a Welsh village have the surname Jones. Ten inhabitants, randomly selected, are given a prize. The variable of interest is the number of prize-winners with the surname Jones.

2 Perform calculations using factorials.	**2** Without using a calculator, determine the value of the following: a) $\frac{5!}{5}$ b) $\frac{6!}{5!}$ c) $\frac{6!}{4! \times 2!}$ d) $\frac{n!}{x! \times (n-x)!}$, with $n = 6$ and $x = 5$
3 Determine a binomial probability using the formula.	**3** a) Given that X has a binomial distribution, with $n = 6$ and $p = 0.4$, determine the probability that X is equal to 4. b) Given that $X \sim \mathrm{B}(10, 0.2)$, determine $\mathrm{P}(X = 3)$.
4 Determine a binomial probability using tables.	**4** a) Given that $X \sim \mathrm{B}(10, 0.2)$, determine $\mathrm{P}(X \leqslant 3)$. b) Given that $X \sim \mathrm{B}(15, 0.4)$, determine $\mathrm{P}(8 < X \leqslant 12)$. c) Given that $X \sim \mathrm{B}(50, 0.25)$, determine $\mathrm{P}(X \geqslant 13)$.
5 Determine the mean variance and standard deviation.	**5** a) Given that $X \sim \mathrm{B}(12, 0.1)$, determine the mean and variance of X. b) Given that $X \sim \mathrm{B}(20, 0.8)$, determine the mean and standard deviation of X.

S1

Revision exercise 3

1 A gardener plants beetroot seeds. The probability of a seed not germinating is 0.35, independently for each seed.

Find the probability that, in a row of 40 seeds, the number not germinating is: a) nine or fewer; b) seven or more; c) equal to the number germinating. *(AQA, 2003)*

2 Jeremy sells a magazine which is produced in order to raise money for homeless people. The probability of making a sale is, independently, 0.09 for each person he approaches. Given that he approaches 40 people, find the probability that he will make: a) two or fewer sales; b) exactly four sales; c) more than five sales. *(AQA, 2002)*

3 a) The probability that Azher, who always walks to work, arrives late on any day is 0.11.

Assuming independence, calculate the probability that, during a period of 20 working days, he is late on exactly four days.

b) The probability that Brenda, who always cycles to work, arrives late on any day is 0.15.

Assuming independence, find the probability that, during a period of 50 working days, she is late on at most 10 days. *(AQA, 2003)*

4 A specialist bicycle shop builds made-to-measure bicycle frames. The shop has 40 orders for frames. Past experience shows that the probability of a customer, who has ordered a frame, failing to complete the purchase is 0.04 and is independent for each customer.

a) Find the probability that, of the 40 orders, the number of purchases not completed is: i) four or fewer; ii) exactly two.

b) Find the probability that the purchase is completed for all 40 orders.

(AQA, 2002)

5 The probability that at least one computer is available at any time in an Internet cafe is 0.75.

a) Mr World makes 16 visits to the cafe. Assuming independence, calculate the probability that, on entry, at least one computer is available on exactly 10 occasions.

b) Miss Wyde makes 30 visits to the cafe. Assuming independence, determine the probability that, on entry, at least one computer is available on 20 or more occasions.

(AQA, 2002)

6 Paper clips are produced in a variety of colours.

The proportion of red paper clips produced is 0.20. Determine the probability that, in a random sample of 50 coloured paper clips, the number of red clips is:

a) fewer than 10;

b) at least 8 but at most 12.

(AQA, 2003)

7 a) For each random variable defined below, state whether or not a binomial distribution is a suitable model. If you think a binomial distribution is a suitable model, give appropriate values for the parameters. If you think a binomial distribution is **not** suitable, give **one** reason why it is not.

A: The number of red beads in a random selection of 10 beads chosen, without replacement, from a jar containing 15 red beads and 25 blue beads.

B: The number of red beads in a selection of 10 beads, chosen at random, from a bin filled with a large number of beads of which 82 per cent are **not** red.

C: The number of red beads when one bead is chosen at random from each of 10 different jars filled with a random selection of beads.

b) A company, which produces fine crystal goblets, knows from experience that 17 per cent of goblets have cosmetic flaws and so must be classified as seconds.

i) Calculate the probability that, among six randomly selected goblets, at most two must be classified as seconds.

continued

Of those goblets classified as seconds, 80 per cent can be sold at halfprice.

ii) Determine the probability that, among 40 randomly selected goblets classified as seconds, fewer than 30 can be sold at halfprice.

iii) A random sample of 1000 goblets is chosen from all those produced. Specify completely the distribution of the number of goblets in the sample that can be sold at halfprice.

(*AQA, 2001*)

8 Siballi is a student who travels to and from university by bus. He believes that the probability of having to wait more than six minutes to catch a bus is 0.4 and is independent of the time of day and direction of travel.

a) Assuming that Siballi's beliefs are correct, find the probability that, during a particular week when he catches 10 buses, the number of times he has to wait more than six minutes is:
i) three or fewer; ii) more than four.

b) Assuming that Siballi's beliefs are correct, calculate values for the mean and the standard deviation of the number of times he has to wait more than six minutes to catch a bus in a week when he catches 10 buses.

c) During a thirteen week period, the numbers of times (out of 10) he had to wait more than six minutes to catch a bus were as follows:

4 8 8 9 3 2 2 7 0 1 5 2 0

i) Calculate the mean and the standard deviation of these data.

ii) State, giving reasons, whether your answers to part c) i) support Siballi's beliefs that the probability of having to wait more than six minutes to catch a bus is 0.4 and is independent of the time of day and direction of travel.

(*AQA, 2002*)

9 Toothbrushes have bristles that are firm, medium or sensitive. The proportions of toothbrushes with these bristles are 0.12, 0.53 and 0.35 respectively.

A random sample of 50 toothbrushes is selected.

a) Calculate the probability that the sample contains exactly 6 toothbrushes with **firm** bristles.

b) Determine the probability that the sample contains at most 20 toothbrushes with **sensitive** bristles.

c) State values for the mean and the variance of the number of toothbrushes with **medium** bristles.

(*AQA, 2002*)

10 The proportions of people with blood groups O, A, B and AB in a particular population are in the ratio 48 : 35 : 12 : 5, respectively.

a) Determine the probability that a random sample of 20 people from the population contains:
   i) exactly 10 with blood group O;
   ii) at most 2 with blood group AB;
   iii) at least 8 with blood group A.

b) A random sample of 400 people is selected from the population and the number, R, with blood group B is recorded.

   State values for the mean and the standard deviation of R. *(AQA, 2003)*

4 The normal distribution

This chapter will show you how to

- ✦ Recognise a continuous random variable
- ✦ Recognise a normal distribution
- ✦ Calculate probabilities associated with a normal distribution
- ✦ Find the mean and the variance of a normal distribution

Before you start

You should know how to ...	Check in
1 Draw and interpret a histogram.	**1** a) The lengths (in mins) of the telephone calls made by Jean in March are summarised below.

Length (mins)	0–	10–	20–	30–40
Number of calls	52	25	11	4

Represent these data using a histogram. Which class has the greatest relative frequency density?

b) The weights (in grams) of 100 pebbles are summarised in the table below.

Weight (g)	0–	100–	200–	300–500
Number of pebbles	20	32	12	36

Represent these data using a histogram. Remember to scale to take account of the different class widths. Which class has the greatest relative frequency density?

You should know how to ...	Check in
2 Relate a relative frequency to a probability.	**2** A quality controller inspects randomly chosen boxes of eggs. After inspecting 800 boxes the inspector has found 736 that contained no cracked eggs. In 5 boxes all the eggs are cracked. Estimate the probability that a randomly chosen box of eggs: a) contains no cracked eggs, b) contains no uncracked eggs.
3 Solve a pair of simultaneous equations.	**3** Solve:

a) $2x + 5y = 24$
   $x + y = 6$

b) $3x + 7y = 5$
   $5x - 4y = 24$

c) $10 - x = 2y$
   $4 - x = -y$

d) $3.98 - \mu = 1.96\sigma$
   $2.48 - \mu = -1.04\sigma$

e) $5 - \mu = -3.0902\sigma$
   $33 - \mu = 2.5758\sigma$

4.1 Continuous random variables

Chapter 3 focused on discrete random variables, quantities whose values may be unpredictable but for which a list of the possible numerical values can be made.

Continuous random variables differ in that no such list can be made, though the range of values can be described. For a continuous random variable, the number of possible values is infinite. Here are some examples.

Continuous random variable	Possible values
Height of a randomly chosen 18-year old male student	1.7 m to 2.3 m
True weight of a 1 kg bag of sugar	990 g to 1010 g
Time between successive earthquakes of magnitude > 7 on the Richter scale	Any length of time

All the above are **measurements** of **physical quantities**. This contrasts with the random variables of Chapter 3, which were mostly concerned with counts.

With continuous random variables, the number of values is limited only by the inefficiency of the instruments making the measurements. For a continuous random variable, the probability of any particular exact value is zero. Instead, probabilities are associated with ranges of values.

> Measurements of quantities such as length, time and weight yield continuous random variables.

Exercise 4A

1 Which of the following experiments give rise to a discrete random variable? Which give rise to a continuous random variable? (You are not asked to find any probabilities.)

a) A book is chosen at random from a shelf with 50 books and the number of pages noted.

b) A pupil is chosen at random from a particular class and the pupil's height is recorded.

c) The number of cars passing a given point on the road, between 0800 and 0900 tomorrow.

d) The time, after 0900 tomorrow, at which the telephone first rings in the local town hall.

e) A point is chosen at random in the x–y plane and its distance from the origin is recorded.

Displaying data on continuous random variables

The appropriate method for displaying data on a continuous variable is a **histogram**, in which the areas of the sections represent frequencies, and the heights represent relative frequency densities.

As an illustration, consider some data concerning the geyser known as 'Old Faithful', which is situated in Yellowstone National Park in Wyoming, USA. This geyser is a great tourist attraction because of the regularity of its eruptions of steam. In August 1985, the geyser was watched continuously for a fortnight, with the times between its eruptions being recorded to the nearest minute. The first 50 times are shown below.

S1

80	71	57	80	75	77	60	86	77	56
81	50	89	54	90	73	60	83	65	82
84	54	85	58	79	57	88	68	76	78
74	85	75	65	76	58	91	50	87	48
93	54	86	53	78	52	83	60	87	49

To create a histogram, first collect the data into classes. An easy choice is to collect the data into the ranges 40–49, 50–59, ... Because the data have been rounded to the nearest minute, the class boundaries are at 39.5, 49.5, ...

The histogram based on relative frequency densities looks like this.

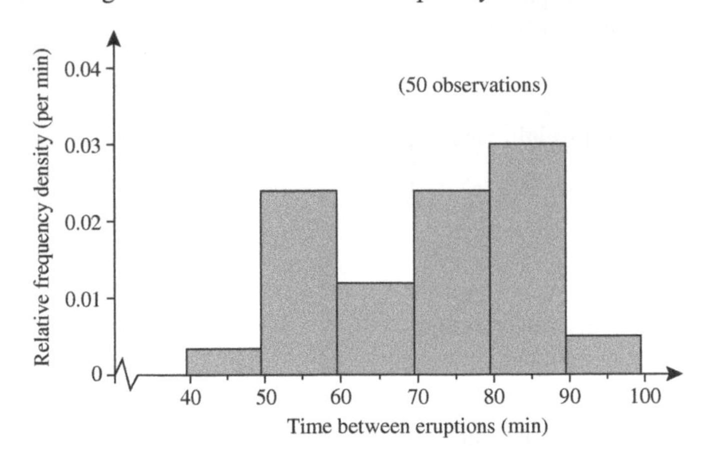

There are just two observations in the 39.5–49.5 class, so the relative frequency for that class is $\frac{2}{50} = 0.04$. Since the class is 10 minutes wide, on a per minute basis this is a relative frequency density of $\frac{0.04}{10} = 0.004$ per minute.

At present, the histogram has a fairly chunky appearance. By increasing the sample size to 100 observations, more detail is gained by using narrower classes. So, the next histogram uses a class width of 5 minutes.

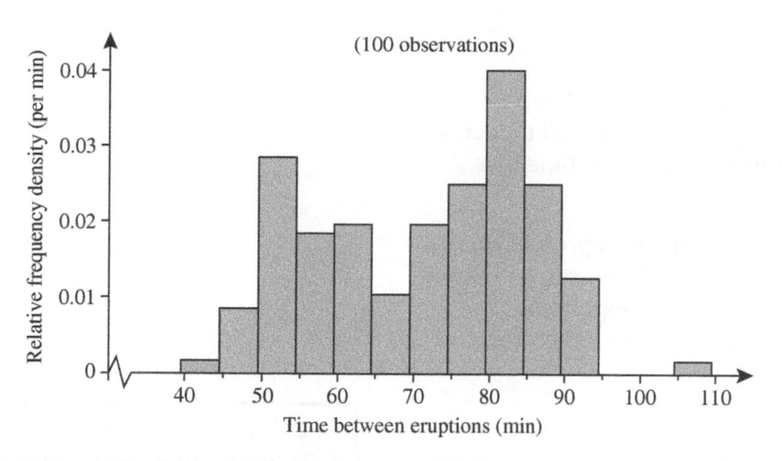

Because **relative frequency density** is being plotted, the area of the histogram remains the same, no matter how many observations are taken.

A further 150 observations have been added for the final histogram, raising the total to 250. A class width of 2 minutes has been introduced.

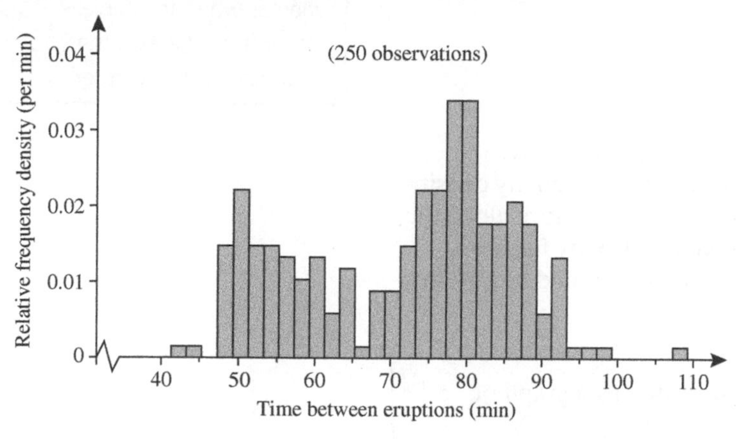

As the amount of data is increased, so also is the precision with which the outline of the histogram can be observed. With a very large sample (assuming 'Old Faithful' was still working faithfully!), a diagram might be obtained which would be outlined by a smooth curve, something like that shown below.

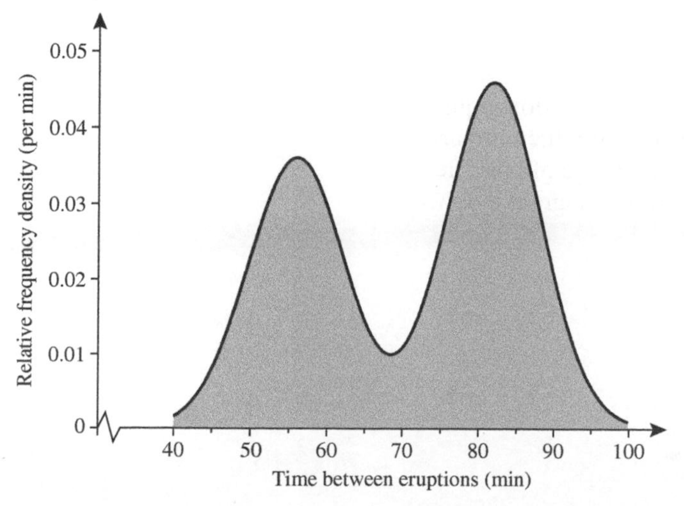

It is clear that 'Old Faithful' behaves in a rather odd fashion. The periods between eruptions are either short (around 50–60 minutes) or long (around 75–90 minutes), with durations of around 66 minutes being rather unusual. The time distribution is thus bimodal. That is, it has two modes.

S1

The probability density function, f

The data from 'Old Faithful' suggests a general result. For a continuous random variable, as the sample size is allowed to increase (with correspondingly narrower class intervals), the outline of a histogram will usually converge on a smooth curve.

The areas of the individual sections of a histogram represent relative frequencies. It is known that, as the sample size increases, so sample relative frequencies approach the corresponding population probabilities. The area of any section under the curve therefore represents a probability.

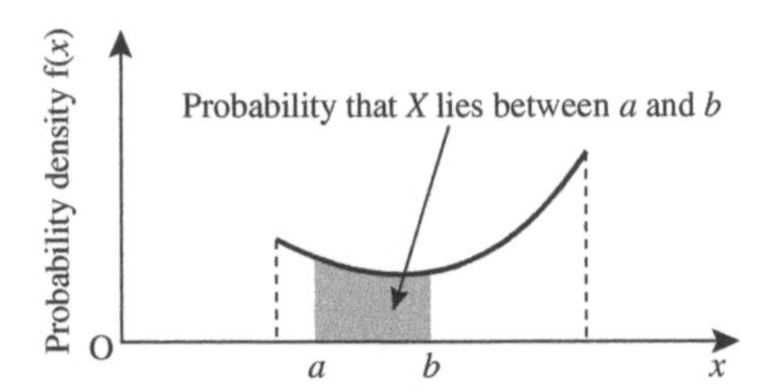

When the curve is close to the x-axis, the probability associated with a unit range of x is small, whereas when the curve is distant from the axis, the probability is much larger.

The height of the curve, being the limiting value of a relative frequency density, represents probability density. Probability density is the rate at which probability is accumulated as you move along the x-axis. The curve is the graph of the **probability density function**, usually shortened to **pdf**. The function is usually denoted by f, so that the curve is a plot of $f(x)$ against x.

> Continuous distributions are usually illustrated by a graph of probability density against value.

Properties of a pdf

- Since probabilities cannot be negative, the graph of f cannot dip below the x-axis. Hence for all x:

$$f(x) \geqslant 0 \qquad (4.1)$$

- The total of a set of relative frequencies is, by definition, equal to 1. The same is true for probabilities. Therefore, the total area between the graph of f and the x-axis, for the range of possible values of X represents a probability of 1. In the diagram below, X can only take values between c and d.

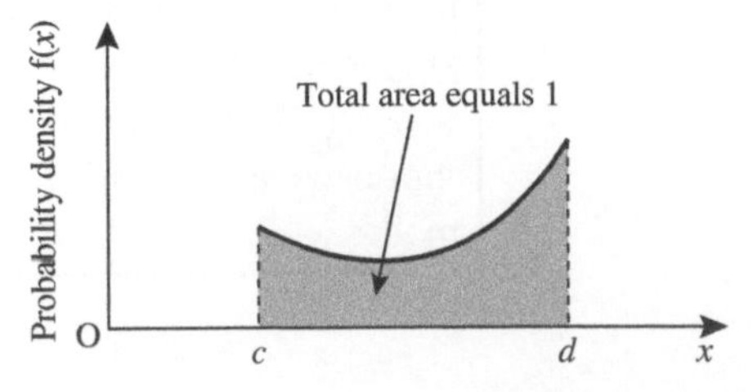

Here are some other features of a pdf.

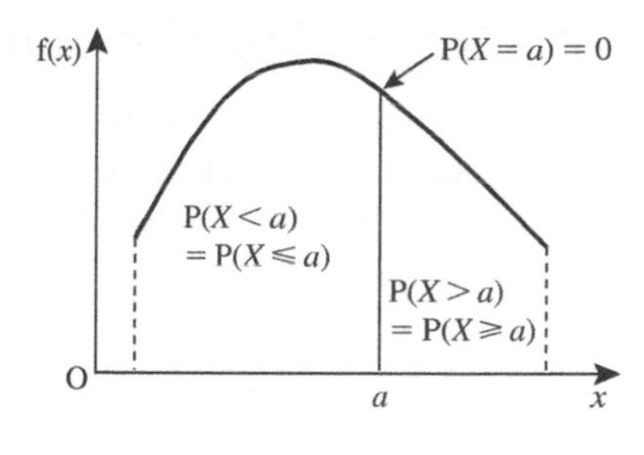

- For a continuous random variable, X:

$$P(X = a) = 0$$

for *any* particular value of a.

It follows that:

$$P(X < a) = P(X \leqslant a) \quad \text{and} \quad P(X > a) = P(X \geqslant a)$$

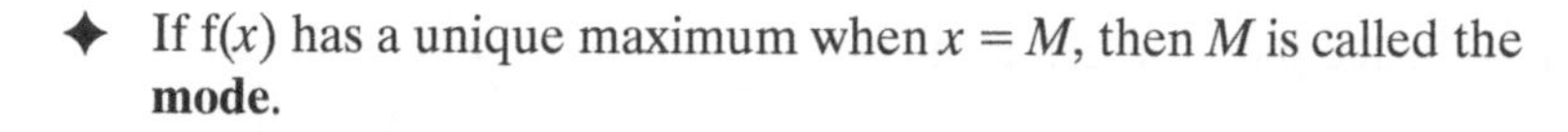

- If $f(x)$ has a unique maximum when $x = M$, then M is called the **mode**.

Often the mode can be located by examination of a sketch of the graph of f.

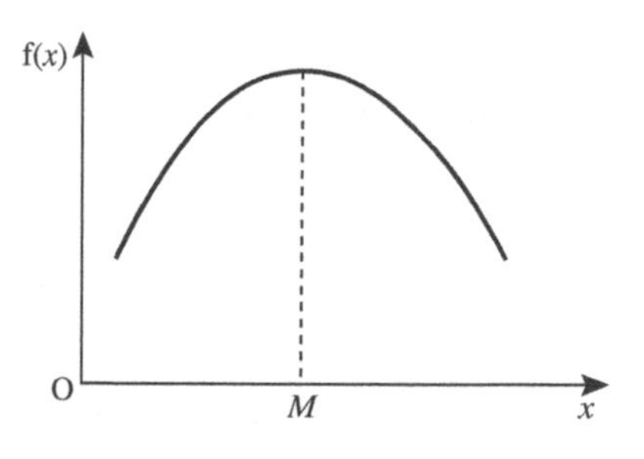

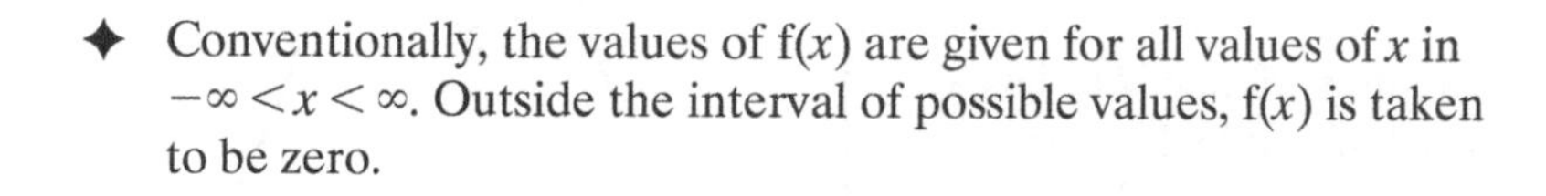

- Conventionally, the values of $f(x)$ are given for all values of x in $-\infty < x < \infty$. Outside the interval of possible values, $f(x)$ is taken to be zero.

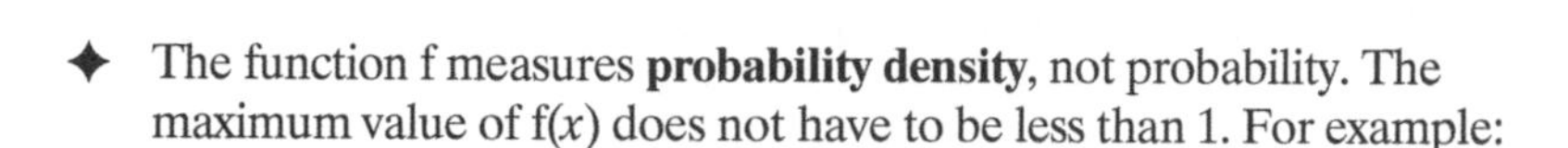

- The function f measures **probability density**, not probability. The maximum value of $f(x)$ does not have to be less than 1. For example:

$$f(x) = \begin{cases} 2 & 0 < x < \frac{1}{2} \\ 0 & \text{otherwise} \end{cases}$$

defines a proper probability density function.

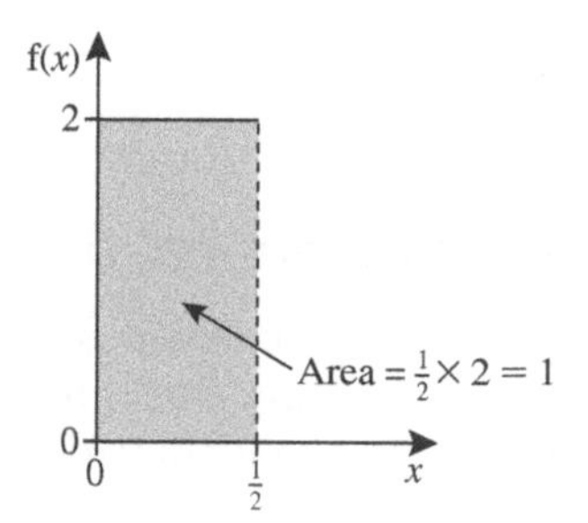

- Probability functions never take a negative value.

Cumulative distribution function

The cumulative distribution function, F, is defined by:

$$F(x) = P(X \leqslant x) = P(X < x) \qquad (4.2)$$

> The cumulative distribution function is also called simply the **distribution function**.

Thus, $F(x)$ is equal to the value of the area between the graph of $f(x)$ and the x-axis for the interval $(-\infty, x)$.

Since $F(x)$ is a probability:

$$0 \leqslant F(x) \leqslant 1$$

Since probabilities are *never* negative, $F(x)$ cannot decrease as x increases.

4.2 Properties of normal distributions

The normal distribution is the most frequently used continuous distribution. It describes a situation in which very large values are rather rare, very small values are rather rare, but middling values are rather common.

Here are some examples:

- Heights and weights of adult males.
- Times taken by students to run 100 m.
- The precise volume of lager in each so-called pint of lager at the local public house.

S1

> The graph of the pdf of a normal distribution is bell-shaped and symmetrical.
>
> A normal distribution whose mean is μ and variance is σ^2 has a range from $-\infty$ to ∞. The distribution is denoted by $N(\mu, \sigma^2)$.
>
> For a $N(\mu, \sigma^2)$ distribution, μ is the mean, median and mode.

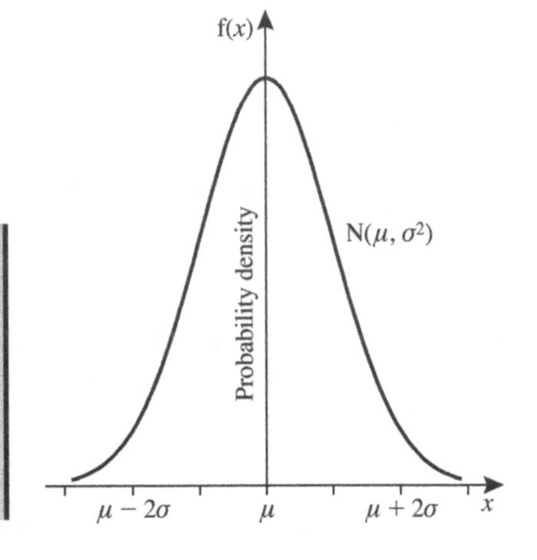

The standard normal distribution

All normal distributions can be related to a single basic distribution, the **standard normal distribution**, which has a mean of 0 and a variance of 1. The random variable with this distribution is denoted by Z. Hence:

$$Z \sim N(0, 1)$$

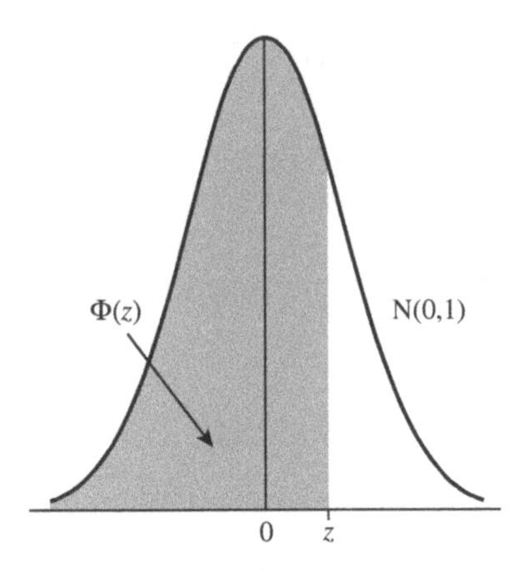

The distribution function of the standard normal random variable is usually denoted by Φ. Thus, from Equation (4.2):

$$\Phi(z) = P(Z \leqslant z) = P(Z < z)$$

Clearly $\Phi(-\infty) = 0$ and $\Phi(\infty) = 1$. However, for practical purposes, you can take $\Phi(-4) = 0$ and $\Phi(4) = 1$.

Φ, pronounced 'phi', is a Greek capital letter.

> The standard normal distribution has mean $\mu = 0$ and variance $\sigma^2 = 1$.

Properties of a general normal distribution

The variance of a normal distribution describes how spread out it is about its mean. Changes in the values of μ and σ can be regarded simply as changes of location and scale. The fundamental shape is unaltered, though its appearance will vary, as exemplified by the next diagram.

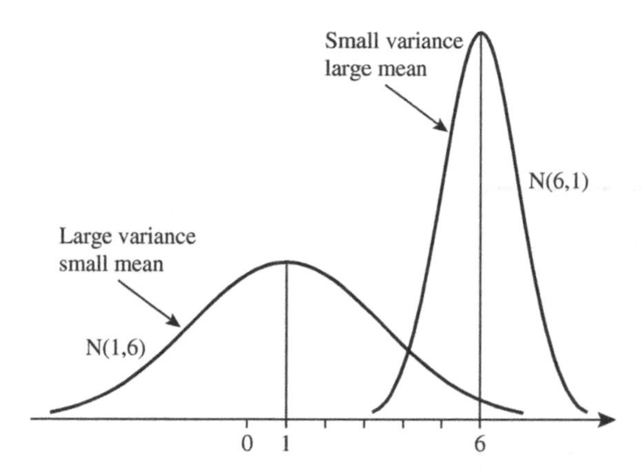

S1

4.3 Calculation of probabilities

Calculation for the standard normal distribution

There is no simple formula for calculating probabilities for normal random variables. Instead, a table of values such as that in the Appendices (page 219) is used. The entries in this table are the values of $p = \Phi(z)$ for $z \geqslant 0$.

The table on page 219 is Table 3 in the AQA examinations booklet.

Here is a greatly abbreviated version of the table.

z	$p = \Phi(z)$	z	$p = \Phi(z)$	z	$p = \Phi(z)$
0.0	0.500 00	1.0	0.841 34	2.0	0.977 25
0.2	0.579 26	1.2	0.884 93	2.2	0.986 10
0.4	0.655 42	1.4	0.919 24	2.4	0.991 80
0.6	0.725 75	1.6	0.945 20	2.6	0.995 34
0.8	0.788 14	1.8	0.964 07	2.8	0.997 44

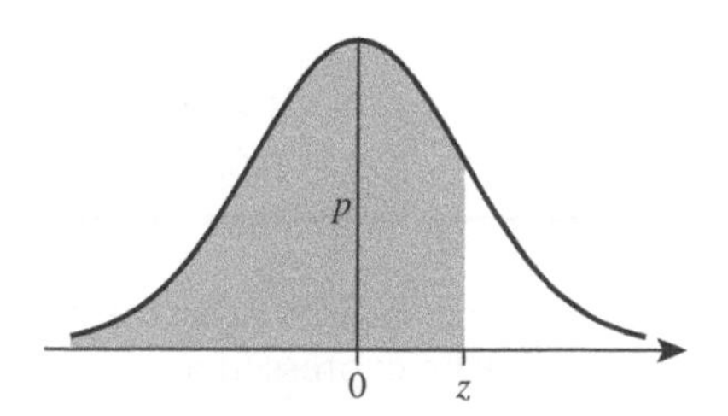

The first entry in the table, $\Phi(0.0) = 0.500\,00$, is one you can easily work out! Since all normal distributions are symmetric about their mean, values are equally likely to be greater or less than the mean.

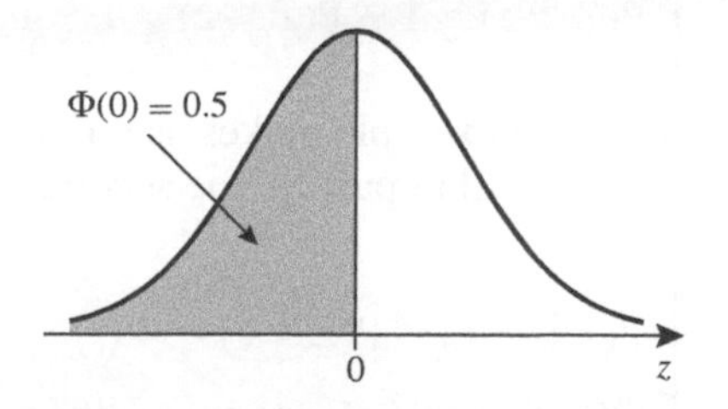

Probabilities corresponding to negative values of z can be obtained by using the symmetry of the distribution. So:

$$\Phi(-z) = 1 - \Phi(z) \qquad (4.3)$$

N(0,1) N(0,1)

$-z$ z

$\Phi(-z)$ $1 - \Phi(z)$

Here are some examples of the application of the table.

Example 1

S1

$P(Z \leqslant 1.0) = 0.841\,34$ $P(Z < 2.0) = 0.977\,25$

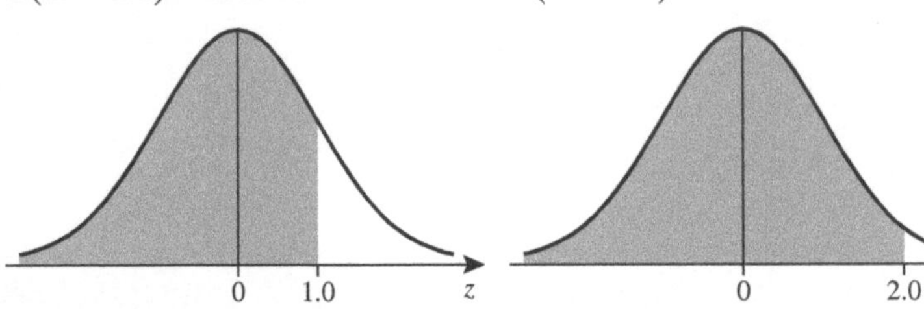

Example 2

Use the tables of the normal distribution function to find $P(Z > 1.6)$.

The total probability is 1. Hence:

$$P(Z > 1.6) = 1 - P(Z \leqslant 1.6) = 1 - \Phi(1.6)$$

Since $\Phi(1.6) = 0.945\,20$:

$$P(Z > 1.6) = 1 - 0.945\,20 = 0.054\,80$$

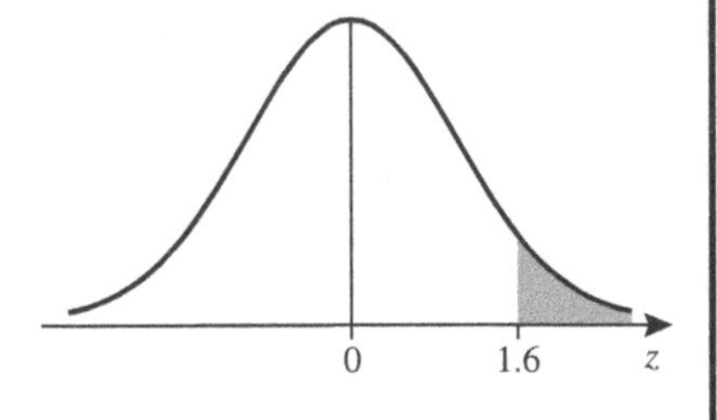

The previous example illustrates the use of the complementary event, which may be expressed as:

$$P(Z > z) = 1 - P(Z \leqslant z) = 1 - \Phi(z)$$

The next example makes use of the following two expressions. The first is used in part a), the second in part b).

$$P(Z > -z) = P(Z \leqslant z) = \Phi(z)$$

$$\Phi(-z) = P(Z < -z) = 1 - P(Z \leqslant z) = 1 - \Phi(z)$$

Example 3

Find: a) $P(Z > -0.6)$, b) $P(Z < -1.4)$.

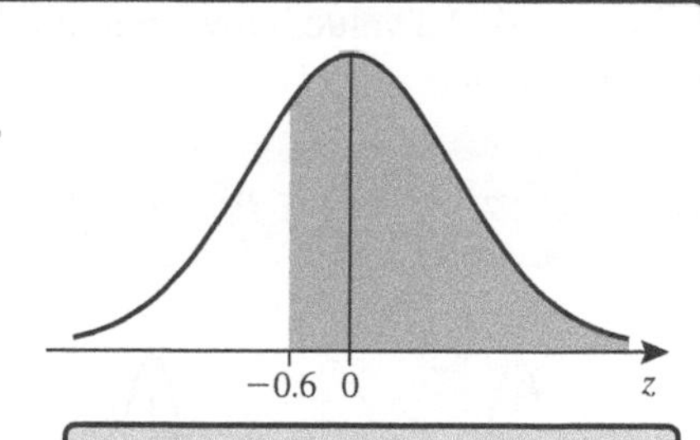

a) Because the standard normal distribution is symmetric about 0, $P(Z > -0.6)$ is equal to $P(Z < 0.6)$. Because Z is a continuous random variable:

$$P(Z < 0.6) = P(Z \leqslant 0.6)$$

Hence, the required probability is $\Phi(0.6) = 0.725\,75$.

Remember *Always* make a quick sketch to elucidate any problems.

b) First, by symmetry:

$$P(Z < -1.4) = P(Z > 1.4)$$

Then, using the complementary event:

$$P(Z > 1.4) = 1 - P(Z \leqslant 1.4) = 1 - \Phi(1.4)$$

Thus:

$$P(Z < -1.4) = 1 - 0.919\,24$$
$$= 0.080\,76$$

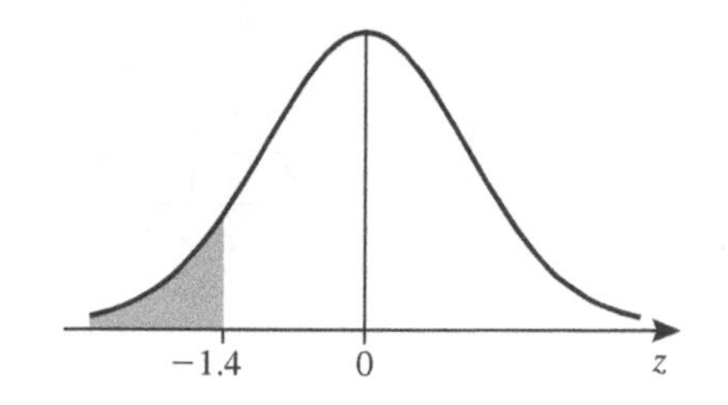

Example 4

The random variable Z has a standard normal distribution. Determine the probability that the value of Z is either greater than 1.2 or less than −1.2.

Using the symmetry of the distribution, the two shaded areas in the diagram are equal. Thus, since:

$$P(Z \leqslant -1.2) = P(Z \geqslant 1.2)$$

the required probability is $2P(Z \geqslant 1.2)$, which is:

$$2\{1 - \Phi(1.2)\} = 2(1 - 0.884\,93)$$
$$= 2 \times 0.115\,07 = 0.230\,14$$
$$= 0.230 \quad \text{(to 3 sf)}$$

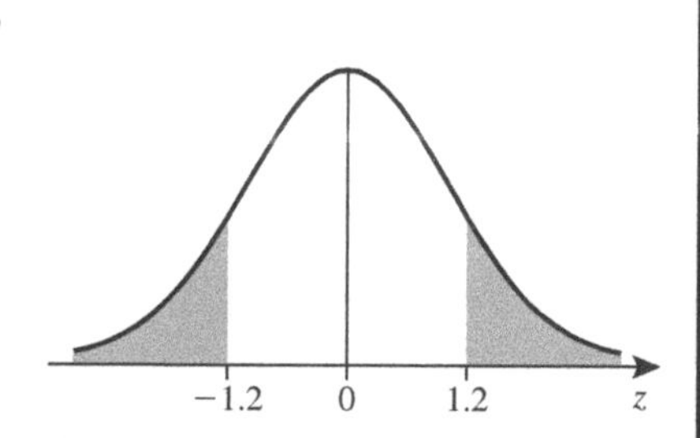

An alternative approach is as follows.

$$P(Z > 1.2 \text{ or } Z < -1.2) = P(Z > 1.2) + P(Z < -1.2)$$
$$= \{1 - P(Z < 1.2)\} + P(Z < -1.2)$$
$$= \{1 - \Phi(1.2)\} + \{1 - \Phi(1.2)\}$$
$$= 2\{1 - \Phi(1.2)\}$$

as in the first approach.

For problems which involve finding the probability that Z takes (or does not take) a value between a and b, the important result is the following (for $a < b$):

$$P(a < Z < b) = P(Z < b) - P(Z < a) = \Phi(b) - \Phi(a)$$

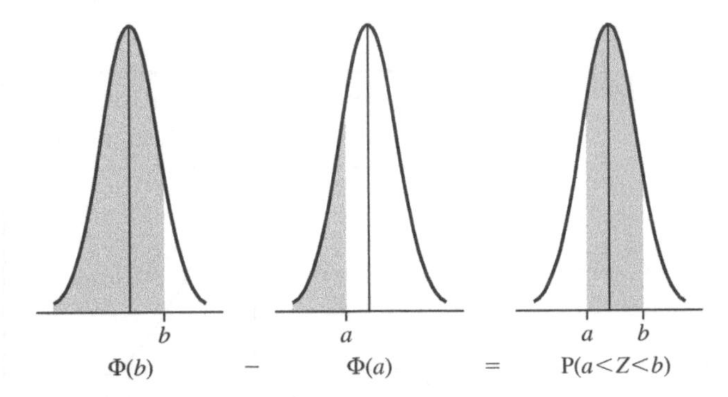

S1

Example 5

The random variable Z has a standard normal distribution. Determine the probability that Z takes a value:
a) between 1.0 and 2.0
b) between −1.0 and 2.0

a) Applying the above key result:

$$\begin{aligned} P(1.0 < Z < 2.0) &= P(Z < 2.0) - P(Z < 1.0) \\ &= \Phi(2.0) - \Phi(1.0) \\ &= 0.977\,25 - 0.841\,34 \\ &= 0.135\,91 = 0.136 \text{ (to 3 sf)} \end{aligned}$$

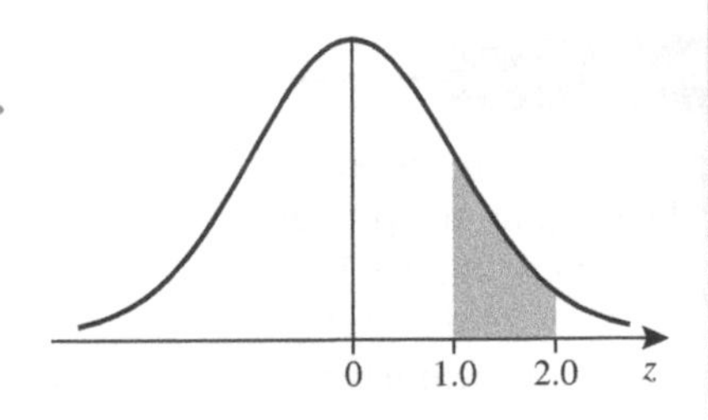

b) As in part a):

$$\begin{aligned} P(-1.0 < Z < 2.0) &= P(Z \leqslant 2.0) - P(Z \leqslant -1.0) \\ &= \Phi(2) - P(Z \leqslant -1.0) \end{aligned}$$

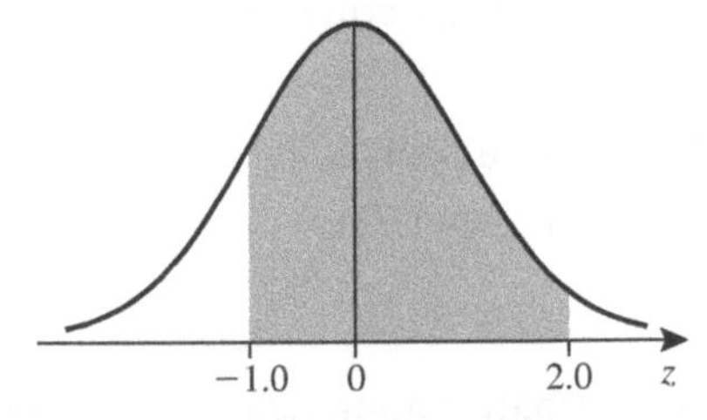

Using symmetry and the complementary event:

$$\begin{aligned} P(Z \leqslant -1.0) &= P(Z \geqslant 1.0) \\ &= 1 - P(Z \leqslant 1.0) \\ &= 1 - \Phi(1.0) \end{aligned}$$

and so:

$$\begin{aligned} P(-1.0 < Z < 2.0) &= \Phi(2.0) - \{1 - \Phi(1.0)\} \\ &= 0.977\,25 - (1 - 0.841\,34) \\ &= 0.977\,25 - 1 + 0.841\,34 \\ &= 0.818\,59 = 0.819 \text{ (to 3 sf)} \end{aligned}$$

Probabilities are given to five decimal places, because that is what is given in Table 3. It is good to work accurately, but, when reporting your final answers, you should usually round them to three significant figures, unless requested to do otherwise.

Sometimes the probability is given and the task is to identify the value to which that probability corresponds. Example 6 illustrates how to do this in three different cases.

Example 6

The random variable Z has a standard normal distribution.

a) Determine the value of z, for which $P(Z \leqslant z) = 0.995\,34$.

b) Determine the value of a for which $P(Z > a) = 0.274\,25$.

c) Determine the value of b for which $P(-b \leqslant Z < b) = 0.576\,28$.

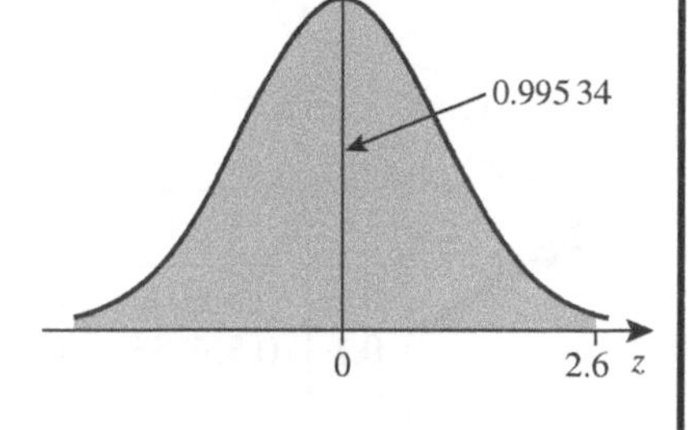

a) From Table 3 (page 219), you will find that $\Phi(2.60) = 0.995\,34$. Hence $z = 2.60$.

b) Since $P(Z > a)$ is less than 0.5, a must lie in the upper tail. So, a must be positive.

Since $P(Z > a) = 0.274\,25$:

$$P(Z \leqslant a) = 1 - 0.274\,25 = 0.725\,75$$

Scanning through Table 3, you will see that $P(Z < 0.6) = 0.725\,75$. Hence, $a = 0.6$.

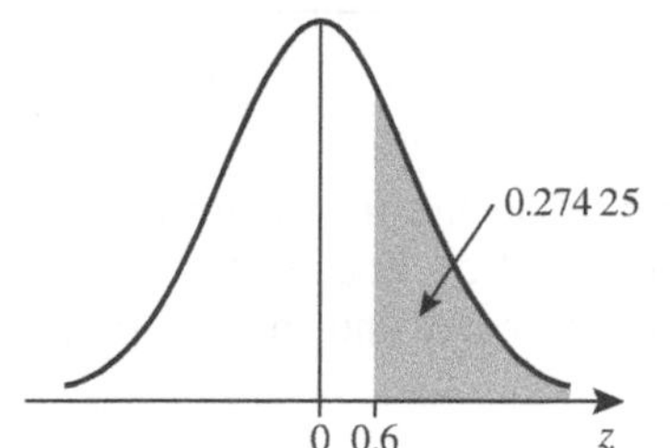

c) Since $P(-b \leqslant Z < b) = 2P(0 < Z < b)$, because of the symmetry about 0:

$$P(0 < Z < b) = \frac{0.576\,28}{2} = 0.288\,14$$

Since $P(Z < 0) = 0.5$, it follows that:

$$\Phi(b) = 0.5 + 0.288\,14 = 0.788\,14$$

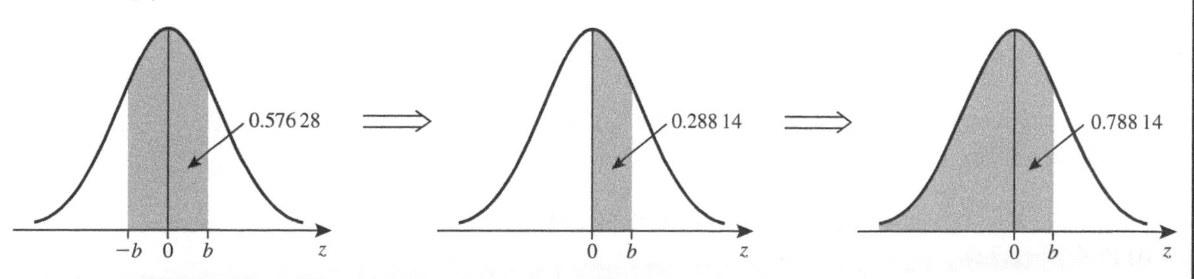

Table 3 shows that $\Phi(0.8) = 0.788\,14$. Hence $b = 0.8$.

S1

A more detailed look at the tables

There is a lot more detail in the tables than has so far been shown. This section from Table 3 shows you how to find $P(Z \leqslant 0.12)$.

1 Locate the value of 0.1 in the z stub.

2 Locate next the column headed 0.02.

z	0.00	0.01	0.02	0.03	0.04
0.0	0.500 00	0.503 99	0.507 98	0.511 97	0.515 95
0.1	0.539 83	0.543 80	0.547 76	0.551 72	0.555 67
⋮	⋮	⋮	⋮	⋮	⋮

3 The cell at the intersection of the 0.1 row and the 0.02 column is the required cell, giving $P(Z \leqslant 0.12) = 0.547\,76$.

The tables are for positive values of z, and give left-hand tail probabilities: $P(Z \leqslant z) = \Phi(z)$. For other situations, you will need to use symmetry and the complementary event as before.

Exercise 4B

In these questions, the random variable Z has a standard normal distribution, with a mean of zero and a variance of 1. Use Table 3 to answer the questions, giving the probabilities to 5 dp.

1 Find: a) $P(Z < 1.2)$, b) $P(Z > 1.8)$, c) $P(Z < -1.4)$, d) $P(Z < -0.8)$.

2 Find: a) $P(2.2 < Z < 2.8)$, b) $P(-1.2 < Z < 0.4)$, c) $P(-1.8 < Z < -0.2)$.

3 Find $P(-1.6 \leqslant Z < 1.6)$.

4 Find: a) $P(Z < 0.93)$, b) $P(Z > 1.26)$, c) $P(Z < -1.41)$, d) $P(Z > -0.52)$.

5 Find: a) $P(Z > 3.21)$, b) $P(Z < 3.62)$, c) $P(Z < -2.84)$, d) $P(Z > -2.72)$.

6 Find z such that:

a) $P(Z < z) = 0.919\,24$ b) $P(Z < z) = 0.344\,58$

c) $P(Z > z) = 0.884\,93$ d) $P(Z > z) = 0.004\,66$

e) $P(1 < Z < z) = 0.129\,94$ f) $P(z < Z < -0.8) = 0.175\,93$

7 Find z such that $P(-z \leqslant Z < z) = 0.451\,50$

Calculator practice

Many calculators have special routines for the standard normal distribution. Typical functions are:

$$P(z) = P(Z \leqslant z) = \Phi(z)$$
$$Q(z) = P(0 \leqslant Z < z) = \Phi(z) - 0.5$$
$$R(z) = P(Z > z) = 1 - \Phi(z)$$

If your calculator has these or similar facilities, you should learn how to use them. Practise using the calculator to answer the questions in Exercise 4B and the preceding examples.

S1

Probabilities for other normal distributions

Remember A normal distribution with a mean of μ and a variance of σ^2 is denoted by $N(\mu, \sigma^2)$

Suppose you want to find $P(X < 10)$, where the random variable X has a normal distribution with a mean of 8 and a variance of 4. So, you have:

$$X \sim N(8, 4)$$

The printed tables are for the standard normal distribution, $N(0, 1)$, not $N(8, 4)$. Hence, you need to translate your problem into an equivalent problem about the standard normal random variable, Z.

The trick is to use linear scaling of the type adopted in Section 1.3 (pages 26–28). For the general case, where $X \sim N(\mu, \sigma^2)$, the procedure is as follows. First, subtract μ to reduce the mean to zero. Next, divide by σ to give a variance of 1. The linear scaling is:

$$Z = \frac{X - \mu}{\sigma}$$

This is often referred to as **standardizing**, since it results in a variable Z with the standard normal distribution.

In this case, since $X \sim N(8, 4)$, $\mu = 8$ and $\sigma = \sqrt{4} = 2$.

Hence:

$$P(X < 10) = P\left(\frac{X - 8}{2} < \frac{10 - 8}{2}\right)$$
$$= P(Z < 1.00) = \Phi(1.00) = 0.841\,34$$

So: $P(X < 10) = 0.841$ (to 3 sf).

The link between the normal distribution for X and the standard normal distribution for Z can be conveniently summarized by showing two scales on the horizontal axis.

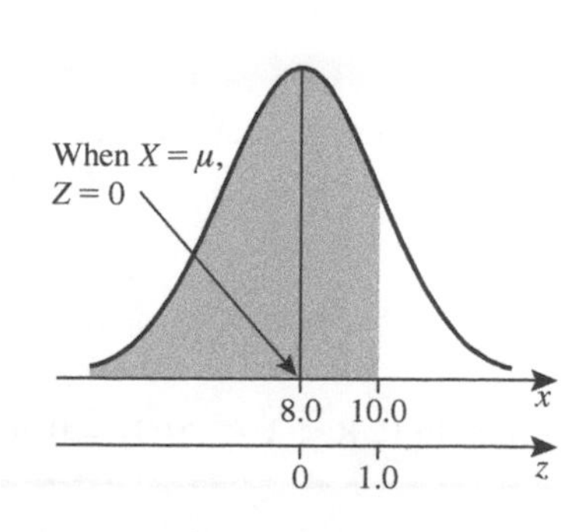

When $X \sim N(\mu, \sigma^2)$, X is **standardized** by writing:

$$Z = \frac{X - \mu}{\sigma}$$

so that $Z \sim N(0, 1)$

Be careful: Standardize using division by σ and not σ^2.

S1

Example 7

The random variable $X \sim N(3.4, 0.09)$. Determine $P(X < 3.1)$.

A quick sketch shows that you should expect a probability appreciably less than 0.5.

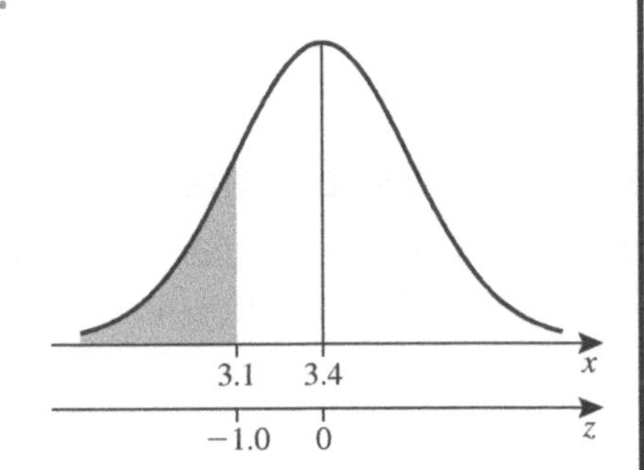

Now $x = 3.1$ corresponds to:

$$z = \frac{3.1 - 3.4}{\sqrt{0.09}} = -1.0$$

which gives:

$$\begin{aligned} P(X < 3.1) &= P(Z < -1.0) \\ &= 1 - \Phi(1.0) \\ &= 1 - 0.841\,34 \\ &= 0.158\,66 \end{aligned}$$

Hence, $P(X < 3.1) = 0.159$ (to 3 sf).

Example 8

The random variable $X \sim N(21, 16)$. Determine $P(17.8 < X < 29.0)$.

A quick sketch shows that the probability is likely to be more than 0.5, and that both negative and positive values of z are involved.

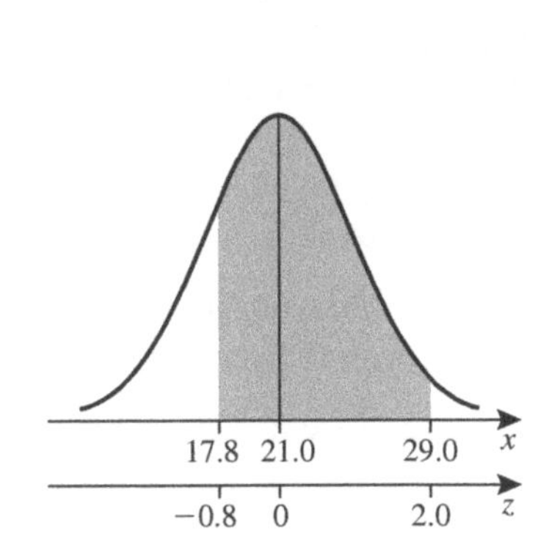

Now $x = 29$ corresponds to:

$$z = \frac{29 - 21}{\sqrt{16}} = 2.0$$

and $x = 17.8$ corresponds to:

$$z = \frac{17.8 - 21}{\sqrt{16}} = -0.8$$

so:

$$\begin{aligned} P(17.8 < X < 29.0) &= P(-0.8 < Z < 2.0) \\ &= \Phi(2.0) - \Phi(-0.8) \\ &= \Phi(2.0) - \{1 - \Phi(0.8)\} \\ &= 0.977\,25 - (1 - 0.788\,14) \\ &= 0.977\,25 - 1 + 0.788\,14 \\ &= 0.765\,39 \end{aligned}$$

Hence, $P(17.8 < X < 29.0) = 0.765$ (to 3 sf).

Example 9

The random variable $X \sim N(50, 36)$. Determine the probability that the difference between X and its mean is greater than 5.

Since the mean is 50, the event of interest occurs when $X > 55$, or when $X < 45$.

$$\begin{aligned} P(X > 55) + P(X < 45) &= 2P(X > 55) \\ &= 2\{1 - P(X \leqslant 55)\} \\ &= 2\left\{1 - P\left(Z \leqslant \frac{55 - 50}{\sqrt{36}}\right)\right\} \\ &= 2\left\{1 - P\left(Z \leqslant \frac{5}{6}\right)\right\} \end{aligned}$$

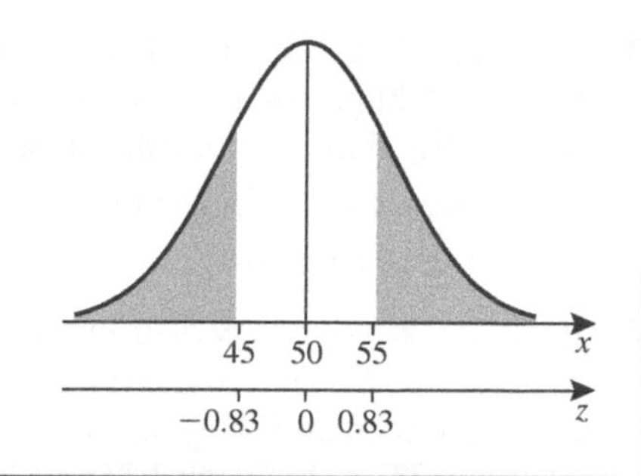

As an approximation, round $\frac{5}{6}$ to two decimal places (0.83), to match the z values in Table 3.

Since:

$$P(Z \leqslant 0.83) = \Phi(0.83) = 0.796\,73$$

the required probability is given by:

$$2(1 - 0.796\,73) = 0.406\,54 = 0.407 \quad \text{(to 3 sf)}$$

A more accurate answer would be obtained by linear interpolation in the tables. This gives a final answer of 0.404 66 = 0.405 to 3 sf.
The difference is slight and this extra accuracy is not expected in your answers (though, of course, it is not wrong).

When $X \sim N(\mu, \sigma^2)$, and $Z = \dfrac{X - \mu}{\sigma}$:

$$P(X \leqslant x) = P\left(Z \leqslant \frac{x - \mu}{\sigma}\right) = \Phi\left(\frac{x - \mu}{\sigma}\right)$$

Exercise 4C

Give your answers to Questions 1–7 correct to three decimal places.

1 Given that $X \sim N(12, 9)$, find: a) $P(X > 15)$, b) $P(X < 16.8)$, c) $P(X < 8.31)$, d) $P(X > 9.39)$.

2 Given that $X \sim N(50, 100)$, find:

a) $P(36 < X < 62)$ b) $P(40 < X < 50)$
c) $P(55.8 < X < 72.3)$ d) $P(38 < X < 42)$

3 Given that $X \sim N(1.6, 4)$, find:

a) $P(X > 0)$ b) $P(X < -1.8)$
c) $P(-2 < X < 2)$ d) $P(0 < X < 2)$

4 Given that $X \sim N(-4, 25)$, find:

a) $P(X > 0)$ b) $P(-5.2 < X < -2.3)$
c) $P(-2 < X < 1)$ d) $P(X > 1 \text{ or } X < -1)$

5 Given that $Y \sim N(3.7, 2.4)$, find:

a) $P(Y > 4)$ b) $P(Y < 4.5)$
c) $P(3.1 < Y < 4.2)$ d) $P(2.8 < Y < 3.5)$

6 Given that $X \sim N(23, 12)$, find:

a) $P(X < 25)$ b) $P(20 < X < 25)$

c) $P(X > 27)$ d) $P(23 < X < 30)$

7 The weight of a small loaf of bread is normally distributed with a mean of 500 grams and a standard deviation of 20 grams. Find the probability that a randomly chosen loaf has a weight:

a) not exceeding 475 grams b) not less than 495 grams

c) at most 510 grams d) at least 515 grams.

8 IQ scores are normally distributed with a mean of 100 and a standard deviation of 15. Determine the proportion (as a percentage, to 1 dp) of people with an IQ: a) below 118, b) above 112, c) below 94, d) above 73, e) between 100 and 112, f) between 73 and 118, g) between 73 and 94.

S1

9 Chicken eggs have a mean weight of 60 grams and a standard deviation of 15 grams. The distribution of their weights may be taken to be normal. Eggs of less than 45 grams are classed as 'small'. The remainder are classed as either 'standard' or 'large'. It is desired that these two classifications should occur with approximately equal frequency. Suggest the weight (to the nearest gram) at which the division between standard and large eggs should be made.

Tables of percentage points

Table 4 in the AQA statistical tables (and in the Appendices, page 220) gives the value of z such that $p = \Phi(z) = P(Z \leqslant z)$, for a range of values of p.

Here are two extracts from Table 4, to illustrate how to find values of z.

Table 3 allows you to find p, given z.

In contrast, Table 4 allows you to find z, given p.

To find the value of z for which $P(Z \leqslant z) = 0.54$, first locate the value 0.5 in the p stub. ⟹ Next, locate the column headed 0.04. ⟹ The cell at the intersection of the 0.5 row and the 0.04 column is the required cell, giving: $p(z = 0.1004) = 0.54$

p	**0.00**	**0.01**	**0.02**	**0.03**	**0.04**	**0.05**	**0.06**	**0.07**	**0.08**	**0.09**	p
0.5	0.0000	0.0251	0.0502	0.0753	0.1004	0.1257	0.1510	0.1764	0.2019	0.2275	**0.5**
0.6	0.2533	0.2793	0.3055	0.3319	0.3585	0.3853	0.4125	0.4399	0.4677	0.4958	**0.6**
⋮	⋮	⋮	⋮	⋮	⋮	⋮	⋮	⋮	⋮	⋮	⋮

p	**0.000**	**0.001**	**0.002**	**0.003**	**0.004**	**0.005**	**0.006**	**0.007**	**0.008**	**0.009**	p
0.95	1.6449	1.6546	1.6646	1.6747	1.6849	1.6954	1.7060	1.7169	1.7279	1.7392	**0.95**
0.96	1.7507	1.7624	1.7744	1.7866	1.7991	1.8119	1.8250	1.8384	1.8522	1.8663	**0.96**
⋮	⋮	⋮	⋮	⋮	⋮	⋮	⋮	⋮	⋮	⋮	⋮

To find the value of z for which $P(Z \leqslant z) = 0.962$, first locate the value 0.96 in the p stub. ⟹ Next, locate the column headed 0.002. ⟹ The cell at the intersection of the 0.96 row and the 0.002 column gives $z = 1.7744$.

Tables 3 and 4 yield the following three important results for a normal distribution $X \sim \mathrm{N}(\mu, \sigma^2)$.

- Almost all the distribution (about 99.7%) of X is in the interval $\mu - 3\sigma, \mu + 3\sigma$.
- About 95% of the distribution is in the interval $\mu - 2\sigma, \mu + 2\sigma$.
- About two-thirds of the distribution is in the interval $\mu - \sigma$, $\mu + \sigma$.

Although the section (and the table) is headed 'Percentage points', the table actually concerns probabilities. The value of the variable corresponding to a cumulative probability of, say, 0.60 may be described as the 60th **percentile**.

When $p < 0.5$, you can find the (negative) value of z for which $\Phi(z) = p$ by using the symmetry of the distribution (see Example 10).

Example 10

Find the value a which is such that $\mathrm{P}(Z \leqslant a) = 0.37$.

Since $\mathrm{P}(Z \leqslant a) < 0.5$, it follows that a is negative. Suppose $a = -b$.

This diagram shows a and the corresponding shaded area.

This diagram is a mirror image of the diagram on its left-hand side, with $b = -a$.

Here, it is the complementary probability (0.63) that has been shaded.

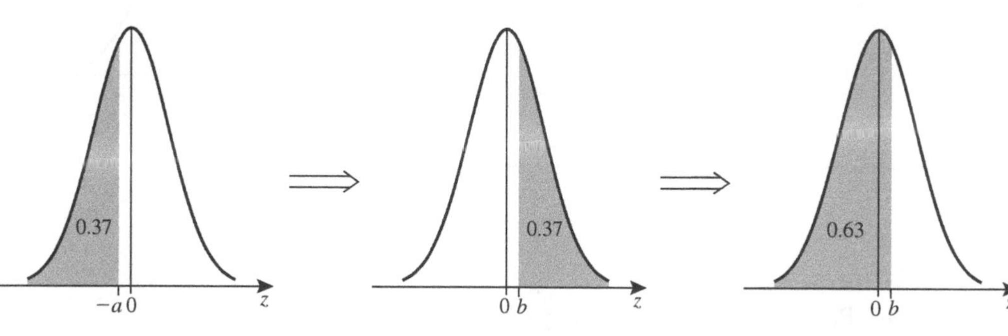

The entry in Table 4, for row 0.6, column 0.03, is 0.3319. So, $b = 0.3319$ and hence $a = -0.3319 = -0.332$ (to 3 sf).

This answer can be checked using Table 3. From that table, you will find (row 0.3, column 0.03) that $\mathrm{P}(Z \leqslant 0.33) = 0.629\,30$. Thus, $\mathrm{P}(Z > 0.33) = 0.370\,70$. By symmetry, therefore, $\mathrm{P}(Z \leqslant -0.33)$ does indeed equal 0.37 to 2 dp.

Example 11

The random variable $Z \sim N(0, 1)$. Determine the value of a which is such that $P(-a < Z < a) = 0.38$.

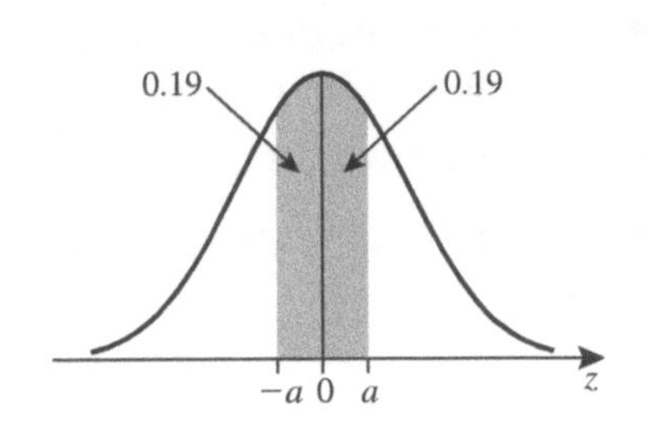

A normal distribution is symmetric about its mean. If a is such that $P(-a < Z < a) = 0.38$, then half the probability lies above the mean and half below.

Hence, $P(0 < Z < a) = 0.19$. But since $P(Z < 0) = 0.5$:

$$P(Z < a) = 0.19 + 0.5 = 0.69$$

From Table 4 you will find that the required value for a is 0.4958, or 0.496 (to 3 sf).

S1

Example 12

The random variable $X \sim N(19, 49)$. Determine the value of the 90th percentile of X, giving your answer to one decimal place.

Some calculators have a function that reports the value of z, for a given value of $\Phi(z)$ (which may be called P(z)). You should check whether your calculator has this facility. If it has, practise using it on the previous examples.

Denote the 90th percentile by a. Thus a is such that $P(X \leqslant a) = 0.90$.

From Table 4, you will find that $\Phi(1.2816) = 0.90$.

Since $\mu = 19$ and $\sigma = \sqrt{49} = 7$:

$$P(X \leqslant a) = P\left(Z \leqslant \frac{a - 19}{7}\right) = \Phi\left(\frac{a - 19}{7}\right) = 0.90$$

which gives:

$$\frac{a - 19}{7} = 1.2816$$

Therefore:

$$a = 19 + 7 \times 1.2816$$
$$= 27.9712$$

Hence, to 1 dp, $a = 28.0$.

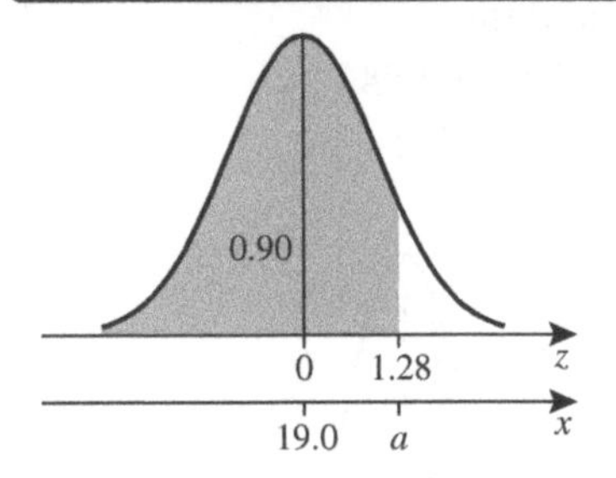

Exercise 4D

1 Given that $Z \sim N(0, 1)$, find a such that:

a) $P(Z < a) = 0.97$ b) $P(Z > a) = 0.05$ c) $P(Z < a) = 0.001$

d) $P(Z > a) = 0.99$ e) $P(Z > a) = 0.003$ f) $P(Z < a) = 0.993$

Give your answers to three decimal places.

2 Given that $X \sim N(20, 25)$, find a such that:

a) $P(X < a) = 0.97$ b) $P(X > a) = 0.05$ c) $P(X < a) = 0.004$

d) $P(X > a) = 0.99$ e) $P(X > a) = 0.002$ f) $P(X < a) = 0.995$

Give your answers to three significant figures.

3 Oranges have weights that are normally distributed with a mean of 90 grams and a standard deviation of 5 grams. Determine, in grams to 1 dp, the weight that is exceeded by 1% of oranges.

4 Bananas have lengths that are normally distributed with a mean of 22 cm and a standard deviation of 1.5 cm. Determine, in cm to 1 dp, the length exceeded by 96% of bananas.

5 Bags of flour have a nominal weight of 1 kilogram. It is known that their weights are normally distributed with a standard deviation of 2 grams. According to law, no more than 3% of the bags may be underweight. Determine, to the nearest gram, the minimum legal mean for the distribution of weights.

6 The weight, M grams, of a randomly chosen tin of baked beans is such that $M \sim \mathrm{N}(420, 100)$.

Find, to one decimal place: a) the 20th percentile, b) the 90th percentile.

4.4 Mean, variance and standard deviation of a normal distribution

For a random variable with a normal distribution:

- Knowledge of the mean and one tail probability enables you to calculate the standard deviation.
- Knowledge of the standard deviation and one tail probability enables you to calculate the mean.
- Knowledge of two tail probabilities enables you to calculate the mean and the standard deviation.

Example 13

The bricks in a large pile have weights which are normally distributed, with a standard deviation of 2 grams. Only 5% of the bricks have weights over 500 grams. Determine: a) the mean weight of the bricks, b) the weight exceeded by 95% of the bricks, c) the weight exceeded by 1% of the bricks. Give each answer in grams to 1 dp.

This is an example of a case where you have one tail probability and the standard deviation.

Let X grams denote the weight of a brick, and μ grams denote the mean weight of the bricks. Start with a sketch of the situation.

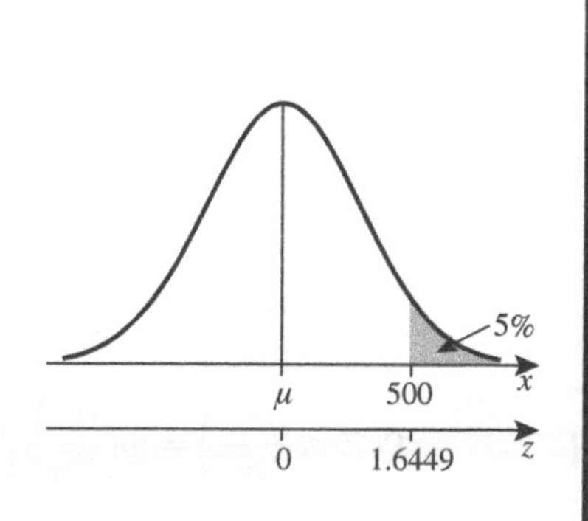

a) It is given that $\mathrm{P}(X > 500) = 5\% = 0.05$. Hence:

$$\mathrm{P}(X \leqslant 500) = 0.95$$

$$\mathrm{P}\left(Z \leqslant \frac{500 - \mu}{2}\right) = 0.95$$

From Table 4, $\mathrm{P}(Z \leqslant 1.6449) = 0.95$. Thus:

$$\frac{500 - \mu}{2} = 1.6449$$

$$500 - \mu = 3.2898$$

$$\mu = 500 - 3.2898 = 496.7102$$

The mean weight of the bricks is 496.7 grams (to 1 dp).

b) By symmetry, the weight exceeded by 95% of the bricks is:

$$\mu - 3.2898 = 496.7102 - 3.2898$$
$$= 493.4204$$

The weight exceeded by 95% of the bricks is 493.4 grams (to 1 dp).

c) Using the value of μ from part a), $X \sim \text{N}(496.7102, 2^2)$. You now require the value of x such that $\text{P}(X > x) = 0.01$. Hence:

$$\text{P}(X \leqslant x) = 0.99$$
$$\text{P}\left(Z \leqslant \frac{x - 496.7102}{2}\right) = 0.99$$

From Table 4, $\text{P}(Z \leqslant 2.3263) = 0.99$. Thus:

$$\frac{x - 496.7102}{2} = 2.3263$$
$$x - 496.7102 = 4.6526$$
$$x = 501.3628$$

The weight exceeded by 1% of the bricks is 501.4 grams (to 1 dp).

Although the question asks for answers to one decimal place, you should use the accuracy of the values given in the tables throughout the working.

S1

Example 14

A machine is supposed to cut up branches into logs which are each 2 metres long. However, the machine is an old one, and while the logs which it produces do have an *average* length of 2 metres, 10% of the logs which it produces are less than 1.95 metres long. Assuming that the machine produces a large number of logs, and that their lengths are normally distributed, find: a) the standard deviation of the distribution of lengths, b) the proportion of the logs that are longer than 2.10 metres.

Let X be the random variable corresponding to the length, in metres, of a log. Denote its standard deviation by σ. So:

$$X \sim \text{N}(2.00, \sigma^2)$$

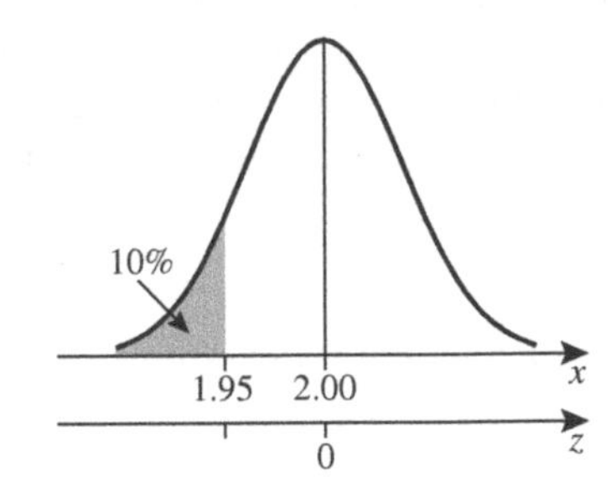

a) Since $\text{P}(X < 1.95) = 10\% = 0.10$:

$$\text{P}\left(Z \leqslant \frac{1.95 - 2.00}{\sigma}\right) = \text{P}\left(Z \leqslant -\frac{0.05}{\sigma}\right) = 0.10$$

By symmetry:

$$\text{P}\left(Z > \frac{0.05}{\sigma}\right) = 0.10$$

so:

$$\text{P}\left(Z \leqslant \frac{0.05}{\sigma}\right) = \Phi\left(\frac{0.05}{\sigma}\right) = 0.90$$

But, from Table 4, $\Phi(1.2816) = 0.90$. Hence:

$$\frac{0.05}{\sigma} = 1.2816$$

and so:

$$\sigma = \frac{0.05}{1.2816} = 0.03901$$

The standard deviation is 0.0390 metres (to 3 sf).

b) Using the value of σ, $X \sim \mathrm{N}(2.00, 0.03901^2)$. Thus:

$$\mathrm{P}(X > 2.10) = \mathrm{P}\left(Z > 2.10 - \frac{2.00}{0.03901}\right)$$
$$= \mathrm{P}(Z > 2.563)$$
$$= 1 - \Phi(2.563)$$

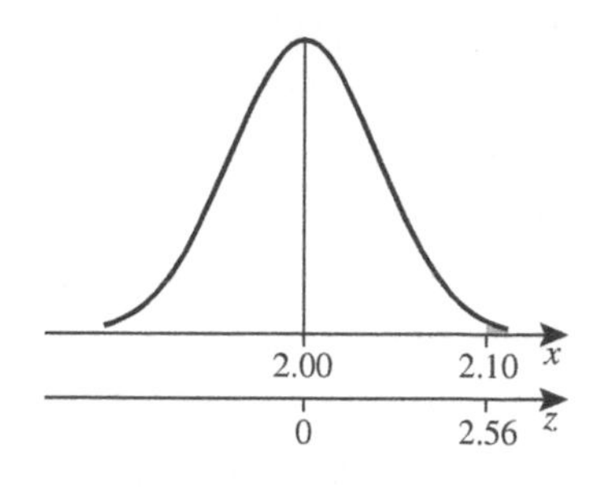

From Table 3, $\Phi(2.56) = 0.994\,77$. Hence, the required probability is:

$$1 - 0.994\,77 = 0.005\,23$$

Thus, just over 0.5% (1 in 200) of the logs have lengths greater than 2.10 metres.

Example 15

The random variable X has a normal distribution. It is known that $\mathrm{P}(X > 9) = 0.92$ and that $\mathrm{P}(X \leqslant 11) = 0.76$.

a) Determine the mean and the standard deviation of X, giving your answers to two decimal places.

b) Determine $\mathrm{P}(X > 10)$, to two decimal places.

a) Denote the unknown mean and the unknown standard deviation by μ and σ, respectively. Start by standardizing:

$$\mathrm{P}(X > 9) = \mathrm{P}\left(Z > \frac{9 - \mu}{\sigma}\right) = 0.92$$

Similarly:

$$\mathrm{P}(X \leqslant 11) = \mathrm{P}\left(Z \leqslant \frac{11 - \mu}{\sigma}\right) = 0.76$$

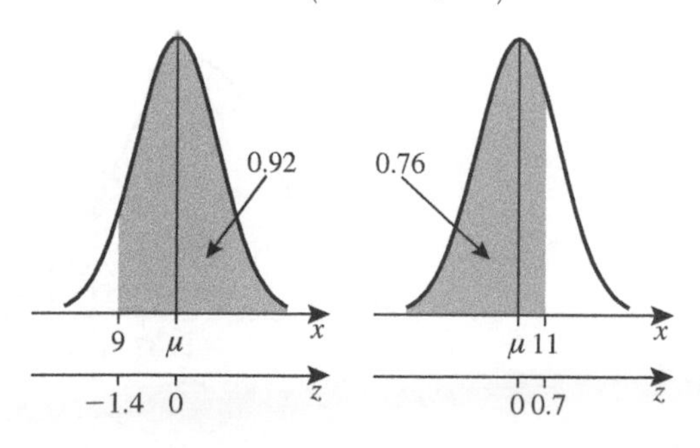

From Table 4, $\mathrm{P}(Z \leqslant 1.4051) = 0.92$, so $\mathrm{P}(Z > -1.4051) = 0.92$. Also, $\mathrm{P}(Z \leqslant 0.7063) = 0.76$, leading to the simultaneous equations:

$$\frac{9 - \mu}{\sigma} = -1.4051$$

$$\frac{11 - \mu}{\sigma} = 0.7063$$

Multiplying through by σ gives:

$$9 - \mu = -1.4051\sigma \quad [1]$$
$$11 - \mu = 0.7063\sigma \quad [2]$$

Subtracting [1] from [2] gives:

$$2 = (0.7063 + 1.4051)\sigma$$

from which $\sigma = 0.947\,24$. Substitution of this value for σ in [1] gives:

$$9 - \mu = -1.4051 \times 0.947\,24 = -1.330\,97$$

Rearranging:

$$\mu = 9 + 1.330\,97 = 10.330\,97$$

Hence, the mean is 10.33 (to 2 dp) and the standard deviation is 0.95 (to 2 dp).

S1

b) To find $P(X > 10)$, first find the corresponding value of z:

$$z = \frac{10 - 10.330\,97}{0.947\,24} = -0.349\,40$$

This must be rounded to two decimal places in order to use Table 3. Hence:

$$P(X > 10) = 1 - \Phi(-0.35)$$
$$= 1 - \{1 - \Phi(0.35)\} = 0.636\,83$$

Thus $P(X > 10)$ is 0.64 (to 2 dp).

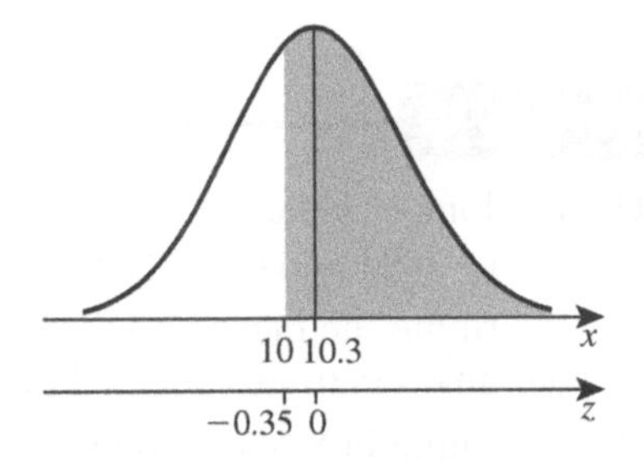

Example 16

The random variable Y has a normal distribution with a mean of μ and a variance of σ^2. Given that, in a large sample, 10% of the values of Y exceed 17.24 and 25% of the values of Y exceed 14.37, find the values of μ and σ.

Begin by writing the given information in terms of left-hand tail probabilities, and standardizing:

$$P(Y \leqslant 17.24) = P\left(Z \leqslant \frac{17.24 - \mu}{\sigma}\right)$$
$$= 1 - 0.10 = 0.90$$
$$P(Y \leqslant 14.37) = P\left(Z \leqslant \frac{14.37 - \mu}{\sigma}\right)$$
$$= 1 - 0.25 = 0.75$$

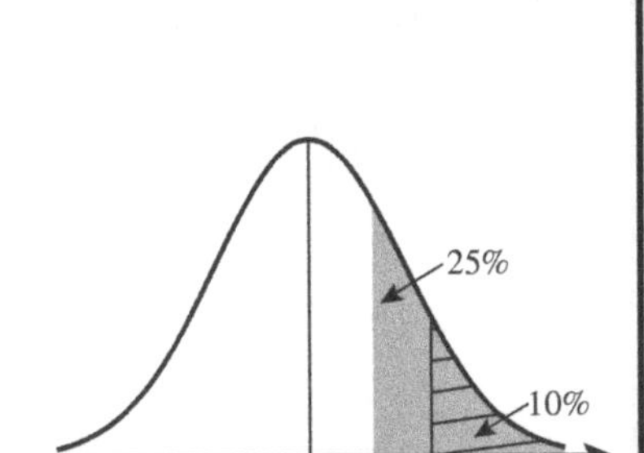

From Table 4, $\Phi(1.2816) = 0.90$ and $\Phi(0.6745) = 0.75$. These give the simultaneous equations:

$$\frac{17.24 - \mu}{\sigma} = 1.2816 \quad [1]$$
$$\frac{14.37 - \mu}{\sigma} = 0.6745 \quad [2]$$

Multiplying each equation by σ and subtracting [2] from [1] give:

$$17.24 - 14.37 = (1.2816 - 0.6745)\sigma$$

which gives $\sigma = 4.7274$. Substitution in [1] gives:

$$17.24 - \mu = 1.2816 \times 4.7274 = 6.0586$$

Rearranging:

$$\mu = 17.24 - 6.0586 = 11.1814$$

The values of μ and σ are, respectively, 11.18 and 4.73 (to 2 dp).

Exercise 4E

Give your answers to Questions 1 to 4 to three significant figures.

1 Given that $X \sim N(\mu, 2.5)$ and that $P(X > 3.5) = 0.970$, find μ.

2 Given that $X \sim N(\mu, 0.5)$ and that $P(X < -1.2) = 0.050$, find μ.

3 Given that $X \sim N(32.4, \sigma^2)$ and that $P(X > 45.2) = 0.300$, find σ.

4 Given that $X \sim N(-7.21, \sigma^2)$ and that $P(X < 0) = 0.900$, find σ.

5 Given that $X \sim N(\mu, \sigma^2)$, that $P(X > 0) = 0.800$, and that $P(X < 5) = 0.700$, find μ and σ.

6 The lengths of time spent each night by Ulrika in watching TV are observations from a normal distribution, with a mean of 190 minutes and a standard deviation of 27 minutes. Determine, to the nearest minute, the length of time spent watching which Ulrika only exceeds on one night in 200 on average.

7 The quantity of milk in a bottle is normally distributed with a mean of 1000 ml. Find the standard deviation given that the probability that there is less than 995 ml in a randomly chosen bottle is 5%. What can you say about the standard deviation if the probability is to be less than 5%?

8 A variety of hollyhock grows to great heights. Assuming a normal distribution of heights, find the mean and standard deviation, given that the 30th and 70th percentiles are 1.83 m and 2.31 m respectively.

9 Due to manufacturing variations, the length of string in a randomly chosen ball of string can be modelled by a normal distribution. Find the mean and the standard deviation, given that 95% of balls of string have lengths exceeding 495 m, and that 99% have lengths exceeding 490 m. Give your answers in metres to two decimal places.

10 The length of a brass cylinder has a normal distribution with a mean of μ and a variance of σ^2, both being unknown. A large sample reveals that 10% of the cylinders are longer than 3.68 cm and that 3% are shorter than 3.52 cm. Find the values of μ and σ^2.

Summary

You should know how to ...	Check out
1 Sketch a normal distribution and illustrate the probability of a normal random variable taking a value in a given interval.	**1** a) Z has a normal distribution with mean 0 and variance 1. Sketch the distribution and indicate on your sketch the region corresponding to $P(Z > 1)$. b) X has a normal distribution with mean 10 and variance 9. Sketch the distribution and indicate on your sketch the region corresponding to $P(7 < X \leqslant 16)$.
2 Use tables to calculate the probability of a specified range of values for a standard normal random variable.	**2** Z has a normal distribution with mean 0 and variance 1. Determine: a) $P(Z < 2)$ b) $P(-1.2 \leqslant Z < 1.2)$ c) $P(Z < -0.24)$ d) $P(Z > -1.43)$
3 Use tables to calculate the probability of a specified range of values for a general normal random variable.	**3** X has a normal distribution with mean 10 and variance 9. Determine: a) $P(X < 13)$, b) $P(7 \leqslant X < 16)$, c) $P(X > 8.5)$.
4 Use the table of percentage points of a standard normal random variable.	**4** a) Given that Z has a normal distribution with mean 0 and variance 1, determine the value of z which is such that $P(Z \leqslant z) = 0.68$. b) Given that X has a normal distribution with mean 10 and variance 9, determine the value of x for which $P(X > x) = 0.28$.
5 Determine the mean and variance of a normal distribution, by using the table of percentage points of a standard normal distribution, and solving simultaneous equations.	**5** Given that X has a normal distribution with $P(X > 4) = 0.42$, and $P(X \leqslant 8) = 0.88$, determine the mean and variance of X.

S1

Revision exercise 4

1 The lengths of components produced by a particular machine may be modelled by a normal distribution with mean 901.0 mm and standard deviation 2.0 mm. Find the probability that the length of a randomly selected component will be less than 902.5 mm. *(AQA, 2002)*

2 The weights of bags of red gravel may be modelled by a normal distribution with mean 25.8 kg and standard deviation 0.5 kg.

a) Determine the probability that a randomly selected bag of red gravel will weigh:

i) less than 25 kg;

ii) between 25.5 kg and 26.5 kg.

b) Determine, to two decimal places, the weight exceeded by 75% of bags. *(AQA, 2003)*

3 The weight of a particular variety of orange is normally distributed with a mean of 155 grams and a standard deviation of 10 grams.

a) Determine the proportion of oranges with weights between 145 grams and 165 grams.

b) Determine the weight exceeded by 67 per cent of the oranges. *(AQA, 1999)*

4 The weights of hens' eggs are normally distributed with a mean of 65 grams and a standard deviation of 10 grams.

Eggs whose weights are less than 56.5 grams are classified as small.

a) Calculate the proportion of eggs classified as small.

Those eggs which are not classified as small are classified as medium or large in equal proportion.

b) Calculate, to one decimal place, the weight above which eggs are classified as large. *(AQA, 1999)*

5 The content, in milligrams, of vitamin C in a litre carton of cranberry juice can be modelled by a normal distribution with a mean of 32 and a standard deviation of 2.

a) Determine the probability that, for a carton chosen at random, the vitamin C content is less than 30 mg.

b) Find, to the nearest milligram, the value of the mean required to ensure that the **percentage** of cartons with a vitamin C content of less than 30 mg is 2.5. *(AQA, 2002)*

6 The number of miles that Anita's motorbike will travel on one gallon of petrol may be modelled by a normal distribution with mean 135 and standard deviation 12.

a) Given that Anita starts a journey with one gallon of petrol in her motorbike's tank, find the probability that, without refuelling, she can travel:
   i) more than 111 miles;
   ii) between 141 and 150 miles.

b) Find the longest journey that Anita can undertake, if she is to have a probability of at least 0.9 of completing it on one gallon of petrol. *(AQA, 2002)*

7 A teacher travels from home to work by car each weekday by one of two routes, X or Y.

a) For route X, her journey times are normally distributed with a mean of 30.4 minutes and a standard deviation of 3.6 minutes.
   i) Calculate the probability that her journey time on a particular day takes between 25 minutes and 35 minutes.
   ii) Determine the 80th percentile of her journey times.

continued

b) For route Y, her journey times are normally distributed with a mean of 33.0 minutes, and 30 per cent of journeys take between 33 minutes and 35 minutes.
Determine, to one decimal place, the standard deviation of these journey times.

c) The teacher is required to arrive at work no later than 8.45 am. On a day when she leaves home at 8.10 am, determine which of routes X or Y she should use. *(AQA, 2000)*

8 Geraint, a smallholder, grows tomatoes to sell at a local market. The weights of these tomatoes may be modelled by a normal distribution with mean 90 grams and standard deviation 15 grams.

a) Geraint classifies tomatoes weighing less than 78 grams as small, those weighing more than 105 grams as large, and the rest as medium.
Find the proportion of Geraint's tomatoes classified as medium.

b) Geraint decides to classify his largest 3% of tomatoes as extra large.
   i) Find the smallest possible weight of one of Geraint's extra large tomatoes.
   ii) Find the median weight of Geraint's extra large tomatoes.

c) Kathleen also takes tomatoes to the market for sale and classifies those weighing less than 78 grams as small and those weighing more than 105 grams as large.
Of her tomatoes, 20% are classified as small and 26% are classified as large.
Assuming the weights of her tomatoes may be modelled by a normal distribution, find the mean and standard deviation. *(AQA, 2003)*

S1

9 A steel rolling mill has two machines, A and B, for cutting steel bars. For each machine the length of a cut bar can be modelled by a normal distribution.

a) Bars cut by machine A have a mean length of 1212 mm and a standard deviation of 5 mm.
   i) Determine the probability that the length of a randomly chosen bar is greater than 1205 mm.
   ii) Calculate the length exceeded, on average, by one bar in five hundred.

Bars with lengths less than 1200 mm are rejected as too short, and bars with lengths greater than 1225 mm are rejected as too long.

b) Of the bars cut by machine B, 1.5 per cent are rejected as too short and 1.9 per cent are rejected as too long. Calculate, to one decimal place, the mean and standard deviation of the lengths of the bars cut by this machine. *(AQA, 2002)*

10 Alan is a member of an athletics club. In long jump competitions, his jumps are normally distributed with a mean of 7.6 m and a standard deviation of 0.16 m.

a) Calculate the probability of him jumping
   i) more than 8.0 m,
   ii) between 7.50 m and 7.75 m.

b) Determine the distance exceeded by 75% of his jumps.

Brian also belongs to the athletics club. In long jump competitions, his jumps are normally distributed with a mean of 7.45 m and 95.2% of them exceeded 7.0 m.

c) Calculate, correct to two decimal places, the standard deviation of Brian's jumps.

The athletics club has to select either Alan or Brian to be its long jump competitor at a major athletics meeting. In order to qualify for the final rounds of jumps at the meeting, it is necessary to achieve a jump of at least 8.0 m in the preliminary rounds.

d) State, with justification, which of the two athletes should be selected *(AQA/NEAB, 1997)*

11 The time taken from entering a self-service canteen at lunchtime to completing the purchase of food may be modelled by a normal distribution with mean 245 seconds and standard deviation 40 seconds.

a) Find the probability that it will take Sheila between 200 and 300 seconds from entering the canteen to completing her purchase of food.

b) Sheila agrees to purchase her food prior to meeting Kofi in the canteen at 1.00 pm. Find how many seconds before 1.00 pm she should enter the canteen in order to have a probability of 0.98 of meeting Kofi on time.

The service system is reorganised and it is observed that 80% of all customers now complete the purchase of food within 250 seconds of entering the canteen.

c) Assuming the standard deviation has remained as 40 seconds, find the new mean time for completing the purchase of food.

d) Henry, an impatient customer, claims that the mean time to complete the purchase of food has not changed.
   i) Assuming that Henry's claim is true, find the new standard deviation.
   ii) Explain why it is very unlikely that Henry's claim is true. *(AQA, 2001)*

12 a) The time, X minutes, taken by Fred Fast to install a satellite dish may be assumed to be a normal random variable with mean 134 and standard deviation 16.
   i) Determine $P(X < 150)$.
   ii) Determine, to one decimal place, the time exceeded by 10 per cent of installations.

b) The time, Y minutes, taken by Sid Slow to install a satellite dish may also be assumed to be a normal random variable, but with:

$$P(Y < 170) = 0.14 \quad \text{and} \quad P(Y > 200) = 0.03$$

Determine, to the nearest minute, values for the mean and standard deviation of Y. *(AQA, 2003)*

5 Estimation

This chapter will show you how to

✦ Understand the terminology associated with sampling
✦ Calculate unbiased estimates of the population mean and variance
✦ Find and use the sampling distribution of the mean
✦ Understand and use the Central Limit Theorem
✦ Calculate confidence intervals

Before you start

S1

You should know how to ...	Check in
1 Calculate the sample mean, $\bar{x}$, the sample variance, s^2, and the sample standard deviation, s.	**1** Calculate the sample mean, $\bar{x}$, the sample variance, s^2, and the sample standard deviation, s, for each of the following cases: a) $n = 10, \sum x = 112.0, \sum(x-\bar{x})^2 = 108.18$. b) $n = 15, \sum x = 120, \sum x^2 = 1245$ c) $x_1 = 1, x_2 = 14, x_3 = 6, x_4 = 2, x_5 = 12, x_6 = 7$.
2 Use tables to calculate probabilities for normal random variables.	**2** a) For $X \sim N(2, 4)$, determine $P(X > 5)$. b) For $X \sim N(5, 9)$, determine $P(0.8 < X < 10.1)$. c) For $X \sim N(6.4, 3.24)$, determine the value of x such that $P(X \leqslant x) = 0.975$.

5.1 Population and sample

Some might say that without sampling the subject of Statistics would not exist. The importance of sampling is that by studying a small amount of data (the **sample**), conclusions may be drawn about a much larger set of data (the **population**), *without* actually studying the whole of that larger set.

For the sample to be useful:

✦ It must *not be biased*.

For example, in determining the distribution of the boot sizes of footballers, the sample should not be restricted to goalkeepers.

✦ It must be taken from the *correct population*.

For example, in determining the characteristics of footballers, a sample of athletes must not be taken.

The simple random sample

Most sampling methods endeavour to give every member of the population the same probability $\left(\frac{1}{N}\text{, where } N \text{ is the size of the population}\right)$ of being included in the sample. If each member of the sample is selected by the equivalent of drawing lots, the sample selected is described as being a **simple random sample**.

One procedure for obtaining a sample of size n by drawing lots, is the following.

1 Make a list of all N members of the population. This list is known as the **sampling frame**.
2 Assign each member of the population a different number.
3 Use a table of random numbers, or the random number generator on a calculator or computer, to decide which members are to be included in the sample. If the number generated is one which has already appeared, or if it is one which has not been assigned, then that number is discarded and a new random number is used in its place.

In reality, there is often no precise sampling frame. For example, in the case of the United Kingdom, a 100% accurate list of every member of the population does not exist. This is because of births, deaths, immigration and emigration.

See Table 13 in the Appendices (page 221) or in the AQA examinations booklet.

Because of the straightforward nature of the simple random sample, most analyses (and almost all examination questions) assume that simple random sampling has been used to obtain the data. The necessary adjustments that may be required when dealing with other methods of sampling are well beyond the scope of this book.

Terminology

Estimation is concerned with using samples to draw conclusions about populations. The two most important population characteristics are probably the mean and the variance, which are known as **population parameters**.

The word 'statistic' applies to any number calculated from, or summarizing, the data in a sample. The mode, the median, the range and the standard deviation are all **statistics**.

To estimate the parameters, an appropriate statistic is chosen. For example, in the case of the mean of a normal distribution, the obvious choice would be the sample mean. Such a statistic is called the **estimate**, while the corresponding random variable is called the **estimator**.

When the average value of an estimator is *exactly equal* to the population parameter, the estimator is described as being **unbiased**. A value of such an estimator is described as being an **unbiased estimate**. The alternative to unbiased is, of course, **biased**.

5.2 Unbiased estimates of a population mean and variance

Consider a random sample of n observations from the distribution of the random variable X.

The key results are the following:

> The sample mean, $\bar{x}$, is an unbiased estimate of the population mean, μ.
>
> The sample variance, s^2, is an unbiased estimate of the population variance, σ^2.

S1

The random variables corresponding to $\bar{x}$ and s^2 will be denoted by $\overline{X}$ and S^2, respectively. Recalling that the random variable corresponding to an estimate is termed an estimator, the key results may be rewritten as follows.

> The random variable $\overline{X}$ is an unbiased estimator of the population mean, μ.
>
> The random variable S^2 is an unbiased estimator of the population variance, σ^2.

If you take lots of samples from a population, you would not expect them to be identical. So, lots of samples implies lots of values for the sample means. In other words, just like any other random variables, the random variables $\overline{X}$ and S^2 have distributions, in this case known as **sampling distributions.**

The term 'population' does not only refer to groups of people, animals or plants. It can also be applied to a group of objects or the theoretically possible set of results from a statistical experiment.

Look now at Example 1, which deals with a simple case of the sampling distribution of $\overline{X}$.

Example 1

For a randomly chosen individual from a very large population, the random variable X is equally likely to take the values 0, 3 or 9.

a) Find the mean, μ, of the population values.

A random sample of two members is chosen from the population.

b) Determine all possible samples.

c) Show that the sample mean, $\overline{X}$, is an unbiased estimator of μ.

d) Determine the sampling distribution of $\overline{X}$.

e) Use bar charts to compare the original distribution with the distribution of $\overline{X}$, stating your conclusions.

a) Suppose that the population contains $3N$ individuals, where N is large. Since the three values are equally likely, there are N individuals having value 0, N having value 3, and N having value 9. The total of the values for the $3N$ individuals is therefore:

$$(0 \times N) + (3 \times N) + (9 \times N) = 12N$$

Therefore, the mean of the population values is:

$$\mu = \frac{12N}{3N} = 4$$

> You do not need to know the value of N, since it cancels out.

b) The first member of the sample is equally likely to have value 0, 3 or 9 (three possibilities). Since the population is very large, the second member is also equally likely to be 0, 3 or 9. Hence, there are nine (3×3) possible samples, all equally likely:

$$(0, 0)\ (0, 3)\ (0, 9)\ (3, 0)\ (3, 3)\ (3, 9)\ (9, 0)\ (9, 3)\ (9, 9)$$

c) The nine samples are listed in the table, together with their sums and the resulting values for $\bar{x}$.

Sample	(0, 0)	(0, 3)	(0, 9)	(3, 0)	(3, 3)	(3, 9)	(9, 0)	(9, 3)	(9, 9)
Σx	0	3	9	3	6	12	9	12	18
$\bar{x}$	0	1.5	4.5	1.5	3	6	4.5	6	9

If you were to perform this sampling experiment $9M$ times, where M is large, each of the nine sample means (0, 1.5, ..., 9) would each occur about M times. The overall mean of these values would therefore be about:

$$\frac{(0 \times M) + (1.5 \times M) + \dots + (9 \times M)}{9M} = \frac{36M}{9M} = 4$$

> As in part a), you do not need to know the value of M.

This value, 4, is exactly equal to the mean of the population. As required, $\bar{X}$ is an unbiased estimator of μ.

d) Since each of the nine samples is equally likely, the sampling distribution for the random variable $\bar{X}$ is:

$\bar{x}$	0	1.5	3	4.5	6	9
$P(\bar{X} = \bar{x})$	$\frac{1}{9}$	$\frac{2}{9}$	$\frac{1}{9}$	$\frac{2}{9}$	$\frac{2}{9}$	$\frac{1}{9}$

e) The diagram shows a bar chart of the original distribution of X, together with that for the distribution of $\bar{X}$.

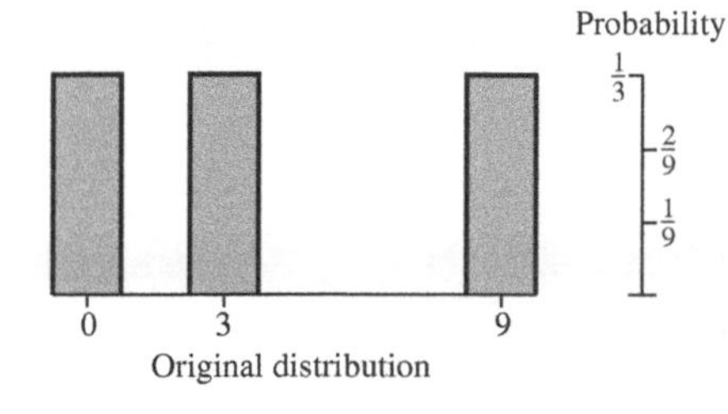

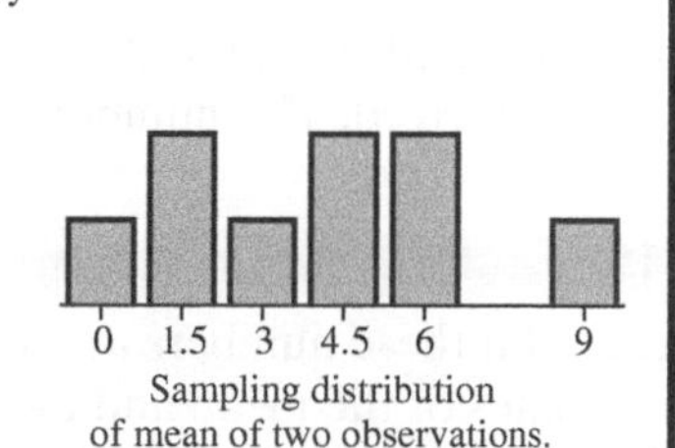

The two distributions have the same range (0 to 9) and the same mean (4). However, the distribution of $\bar{X}$ has the smaller proportion of extreme values. Whereas for X, the probability of a value of 0 or 9 is $\frac{2}{3}$, for $\bar{X}$ this probability is just $\frac{2}{9}$. The implication is that the distribution of $\bar{X}$ has a smaller variance.

S1

The distribution of $\overline{X}$ can never have a larger variance than the distribution of X. In fact, it can be shown that:

> If the distribution of X has variance σ^2, then, for a random sample of size n, the distribution of $\overline{X}$ has variance $\dfrac{\sigma^2}{n}$.

The square root of the variance of the sample mean is $\dfrac{\sigma}{\sqrt{n}}$. It is used in many calculations, and is called the **standard error of the mean.**

When the population variance σ^2 is unknown, it is estimated by s^2, and $\dfrac{s}{\sqrt{n}}$ is called the **estimated standard error of the mean.**

S1

Exercise 5A

1 A random sample of eight satsumas is taken from a large consignment. The weights (in grams) of the satsumas in the sample are:

97 82 88 95 75 89 100 95

Calculate:

a) an unbiased estimate of the mean weight of the satsumas in the consignment

b) an unbiased estimate of the variance of the weights of the satsumas in the consignment

c) the estimated standard error of the mean.

2 A random sample of ten walnuts is taken from the crop on a walnut tree. The weights (in grams) are:

11 4 11 12 15 11 13 7 15 14

For the population of walnuts on the tree, determine the sample values corresponding to unbiased estimators of: a) the population mean; b) the population variance.

3 Sarah asks seven of her 16-year old girl-friends to count the number of Christmas cards which they received. The numbers are:

18 12 21 15 18 10 15

a) State an assumption which is needed if these numbers are to be used to calculate unbiased estimates of the mean and the variance of the number of Christmas cards received by 16-year old girls.

b) Making this assumption, calculate unbiased estimates of: i) the mean; ii) the variance, of the numbers of Christmas cards received by 16-year old girls.

5.3 The sampling distribution of the mean of a random sample from a normal distribution

Suppose the random variable X has a normal distribution with a mean of μ and a variance of σ^2. A total of n independent observations of X are taken. The mean of these observations is calculated as $\bar{x}$. The value of $\bar{x}$ will therefore depend on the sample taken.

The sample mean, $\bar{x}$, is an observation on the random variable $\overline{X}$, whose distribution has a mean of μ and a variance of $\frac{\sigma^2}{n}$. These results involve important features of the distribution, but they do not tell the whole story.

This diagram summarises the results of 8000 observations on a normal random variable having a mean of 24 and a variance equal to 16. All the observations lie between 8 and 40.

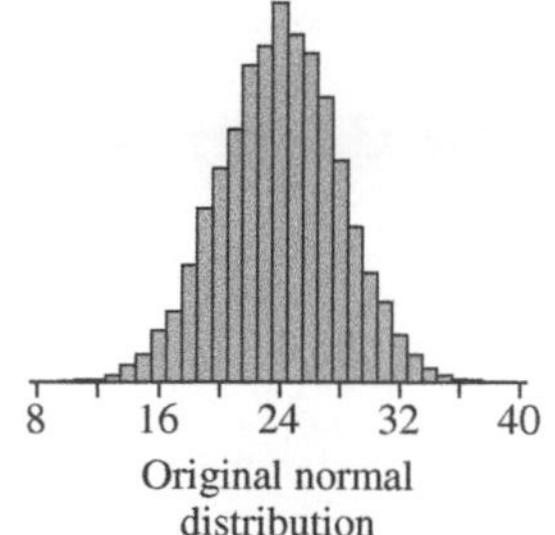

Original normal distribution

This diagram is more peaked. It summarises the sampling distribution of the means of 2000 samples of size 4, using the previous data. The observations are now concentrated between 16 and 32.

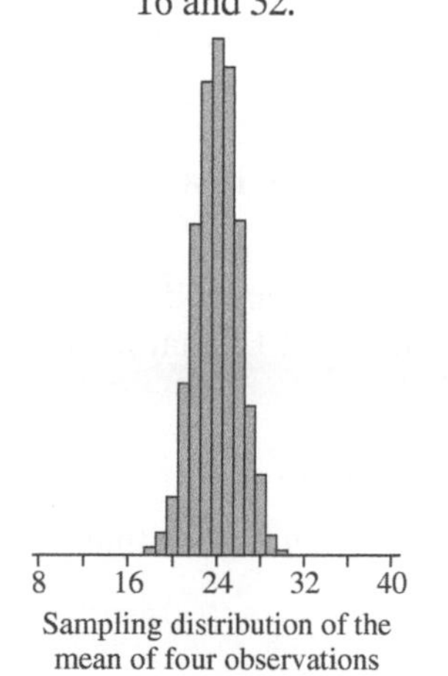

Sampling distribution of the mean of four observations

This diagram summarises the sampling distribution of the means of 500 samples of size 16. The data are still further concentrated, with all the values between 20 and 28.

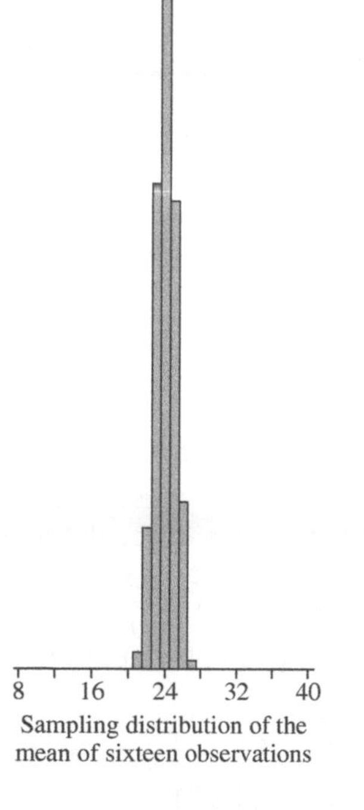

Sampling distribution of the mean of sixteen observations

These histograms emphasise the fact that the variance of the sampling distribution of the mean decreases as the sample size increases. However, it is difficult to see what happens to the shape of the distribution. The next diagrams redisplay the data, using changed scales.

Recall that $\frac{\sigma^2}{n}$ is the variance of the mean of a sample of size n, from a distribution with variance σ^2.

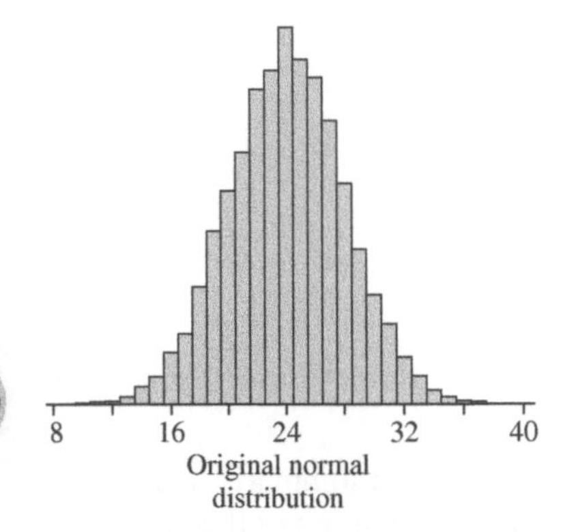

Original normal distribution

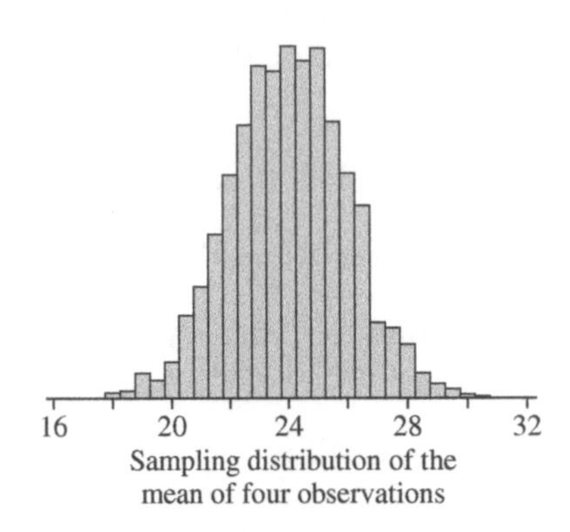

Sampling distribution of the mean of four observations

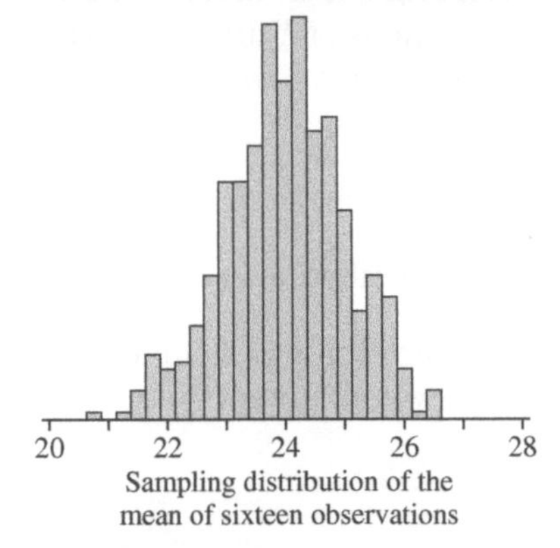

Sampling distribution of the mean of sixteen observations

By changing the scales, the three histograms become similar in shape.

The sampling distribution of the mean of a random sample from a normal distribution appears to be another normal distribution. In fact, this is always true.

The smoother outline of the left-hand diagram is a consequence of its displaying information from 8000 observations, rather than the 500 sample means summarized by the right-hand diagram.

If $X \sim N(\mu, \sigma^2)$ then:

$$\bar{X} \sim N\left(\mu, \frac{\sigma^2}{n}\right)$$

Example 2

The random variable X has a normal distribution, with a mean of 12 and a standard deviation of 6. A random sample of four observations are taken on X. The random variable denoting the mean of these observations is $\bar{X}$. State the distribution of $\bar{X}$, giving the values of its parameters.

Because X has a normal distribution, $\bar{X}$ also has a normal distribution.

The parameters of a normal distribution are its mean and its variance. Since the distribution of X has a mean of 12, that must also be the mean of the distribution of $\bar{X}$.

The variance of $\bar{X}$ is $\frac{\sigma^2}{n}$, where σ^2 is the variance of X and n is the sample size. In this case, $\sigma^2 = 6^2$ and $n = 4$, so that:

$$\frac{\sigma^2}{n} = \frac{36}{4} = 9$$

Thus, $\bar{X} \sim N(12, 9)$.

Example 3

The weights of a particular type of sweet have a normal distribution with a mean of 1 gram and a standard deviation of 0.1 gram. Determine the probability that a randomly chosen selection of 25 sweets has a mean weight which exceeds 1.04 grams, giving your answer to two significant figures.

Since the distribution of the sweet weights, in grams, is $N(1, 0.1^2)$, the distribution of the mean weight of a random sample of 25 sweets is:

$$N\left(1, \frac{0.1^2}{25}\right)$$

The standard error of the mean is, therefore, $\frac{0.1}{\sqrt{25}} = 0.02$.

Denoting the mean weight in grams by $\overline{X}$:

$$P(\overline{X} > 1.04) = P\left(Z > \frac{1.04 - 1}{0.02}\right) = P(Z > 2)$$

where $Z \sim N(0, 1)$. Hence:

$$P(\overline{X} > 1.04) = 1 - \Phi(2) = 1 - 0.977\,25 = 0.022\,75 = 0.023 \text{ (to 2 sf)}$$

The required probability is 0.023 (to 3 dp).

S1

Exercise 5B

1 A random variable has a normal distribution with a mean of 12 and a standard deviation of 3. A random sample of 81 observations is taken.

a) Find the mean and the variance of the distribution of the sample mean.

b) Find the probability that the sample mean is less than 11.5.

2 The weight of a soldier may be taken to be an observation from a normal distribution with a mean of 90 kg, and standard deviation 10 kg. There are 250 soldiers on board an aircraft.

a) Find the mean and the variance of the average weight of the soldiers on the aircraft. State any assumption necessary.

b) Find the probability that the mean weight of the soldiers on the aircraft lies between 89 kg and 91 kg.

3 The amount of fruit juice (in millilitres) in a grapefruit has a normal distribution with a mean of 90 and a variance of 100. The average amount of juice in a random sample of 25 grapefruit is A millilitres.

a) State the distribution of A, and its mean and variance.

b) Find the probability that A differs from 90 by more than 4.

4 A random variable X has a normal distribution with a mean of 150 and a standard deviation of 2. A random sample of n observations of X is taken.

Find the smallest value of n such that the standard deviation of the sample mean is less than 0.1.

S1

5.4 The Central Limit Theorem

An informal statement of this extremely important theorem is as follows.

> Suppose a random sample of n independent observations is taken from the distribution of X. As n increases, the distribution of the sample mean $\overline{X}$ comes increasingly to resemble a normal distribution, regardless of the distribution of X.

The importance of the **Central Limit Theorem** lies in these facts:

- Means are quantities of interest.
- The theorem does not require the distribution of X to be known. It can be almost *any* distribution.
- The resemblance to a normal distribution holds for remarkably small values of n. The approximation usually improves as the sample size (n) increases, and a normal distribution is generally taken to be a good approximation to the distribution of $\overline{X}$ for sample sizes of 30 or more.

As an example, consider a continuous random variable, X, for which:

$$f(x) = \begin{cases} 1 & \text{for } 0 < x < 1 \\ 0 & \text{otherwise} \end{cases}$$

The graph of f(x) is shown on the right.

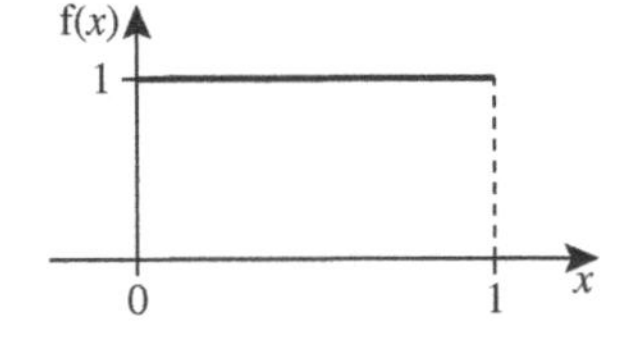

The data in the following table constitute part of a random sample of observations on X.

Original observations	0.020		0.706		0.536		0.580
Means of pairs		0.363				0.558	
Means of fours				0.4605			
Original observations	0.290		0.302		0.776		0.014
Means of pairs		0.296				0.395	
Means of fours				0.3455			

The successive diagrams which follow show a histogram of the first 50 randomly chosen single observations from that distribution, a histogram of the first 50 means of pairs of observations from the distribution, the same for groups of four observations, and finally, the same for groups of eight observations.

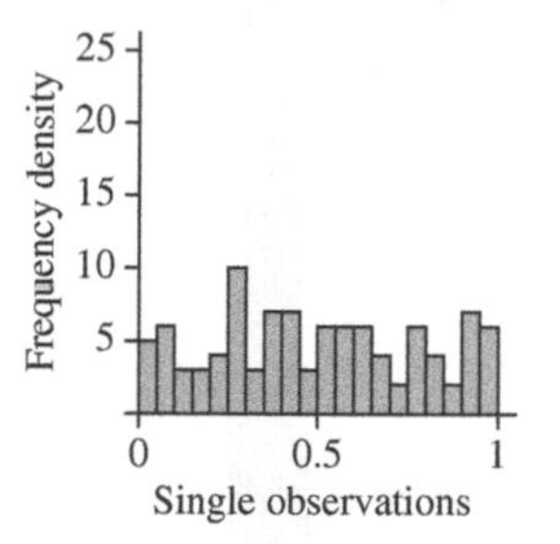

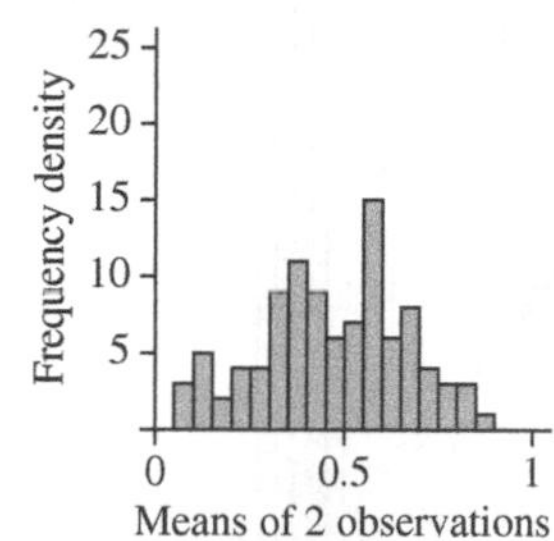

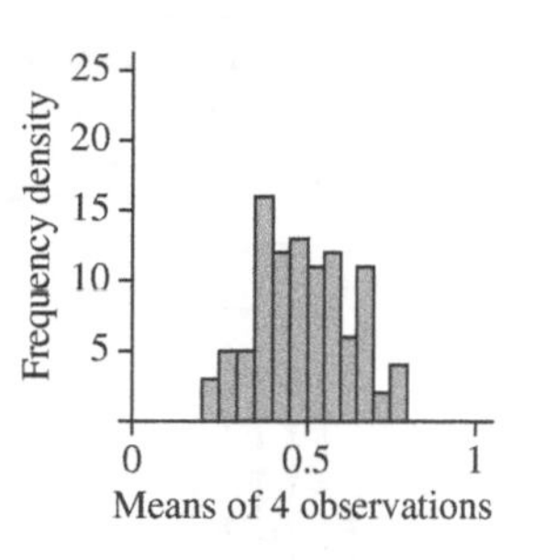

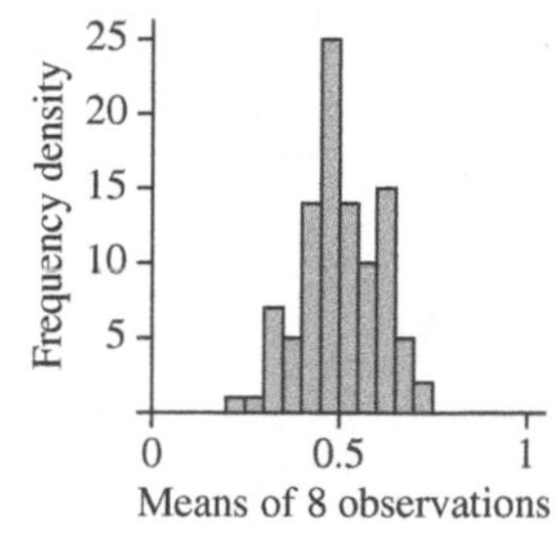

As the group size increases, so the means become increasingly clustered in a symmetrical fashion about 0.5 (the mean of the original population).

As a second example, consider means of observations from a V-shaped distribution with its probability density function illustrated by the graph on the right.

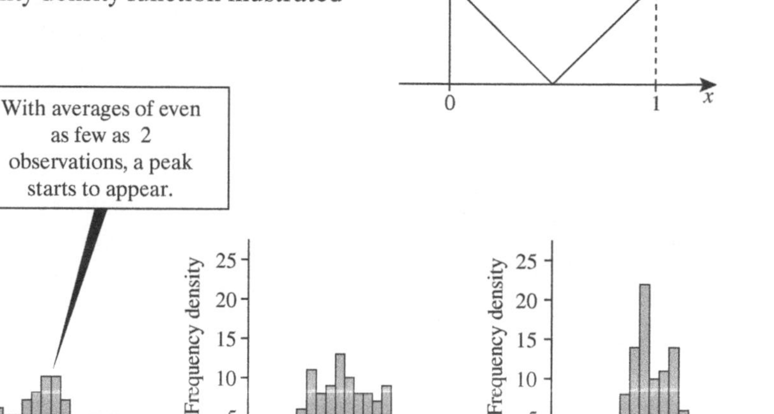

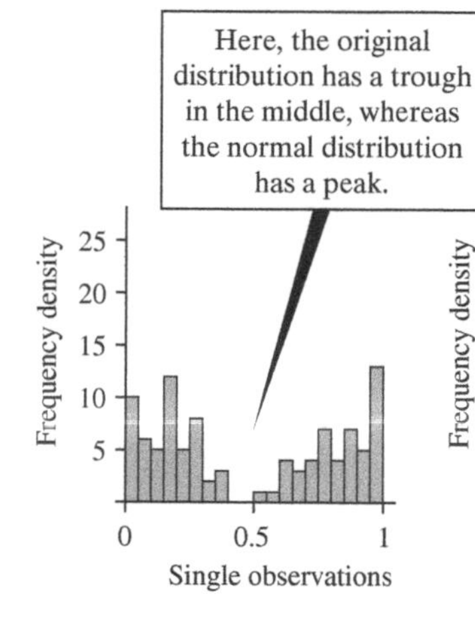

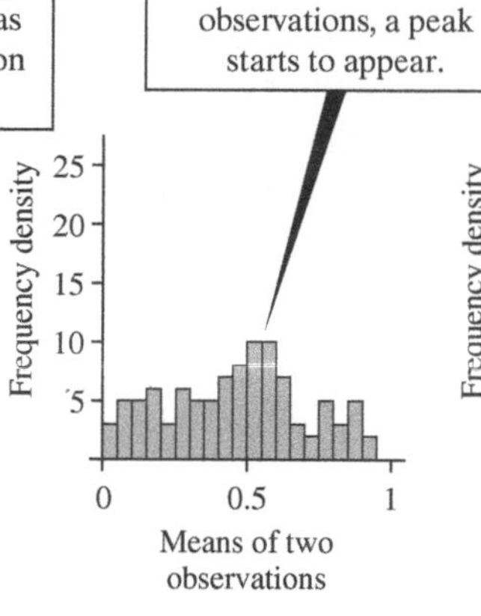

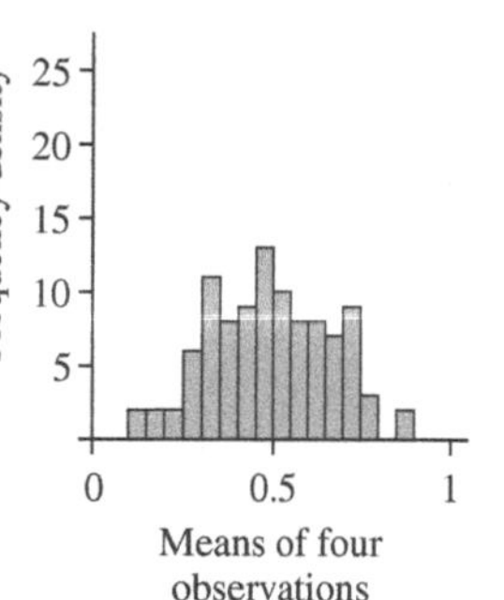

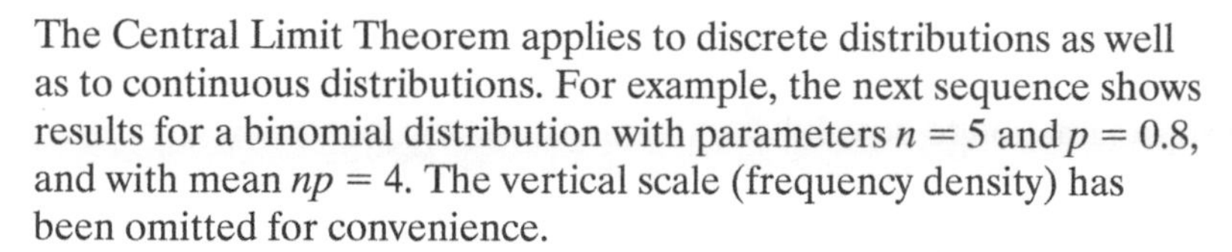

The Central Limit Theorem applies to discrete distributions as well as to continuous distributions. For example, the next sequence shows results for a binomial distribution with parameters $n = 5$ and $p = 0.8$, and with mean $np = 4$. The vertical scale (frequency density) has been omitted for convenience.

S1

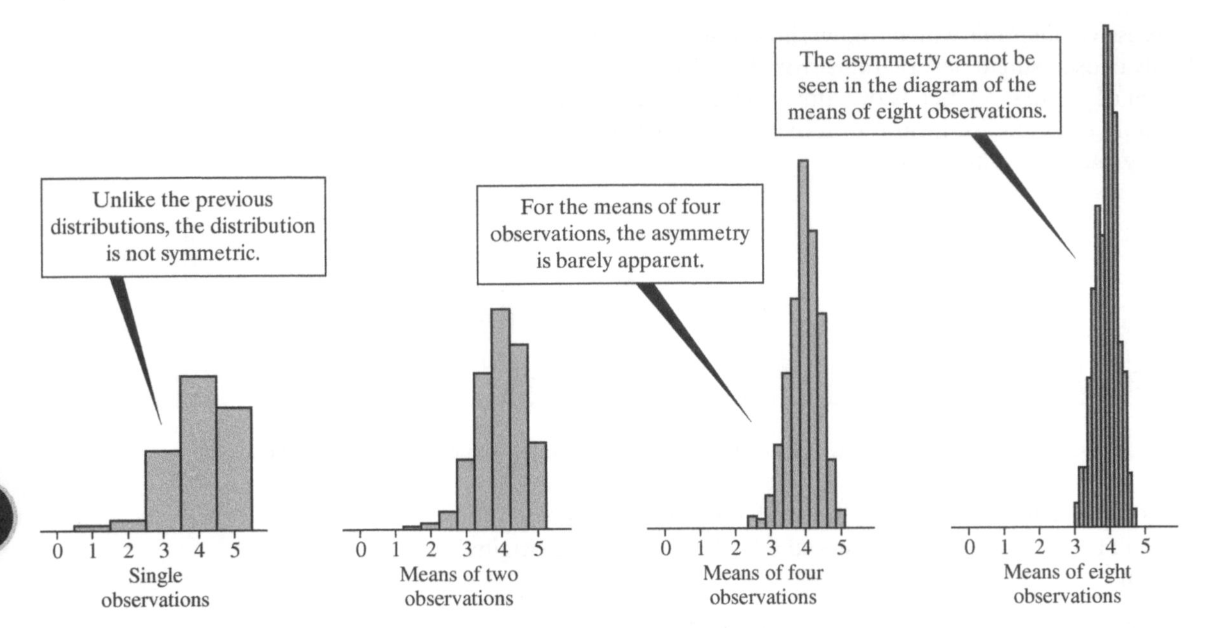

S1

In each of these sequences of histograms, as the sample size increases the values of the sample mean become increasingly concentrated about the centre (the mean) of the original distribution. It is this central tendency that leads to the name of the theorem.

The Central Limit Theorem
For a large sample of n independent observations of a random variable X, where X has a distribution with a mean of μ and a variance of σ^2, the distribution of $\overline{X}$ is given approximately by:

$$\overline{X} \sim \mathrm{N}\left(\mu, \frac{\sigma^2}{n}\right)$$

This result holds *irrespective* of the distribution of X.

An equivalent statement is that, for large n:

$$Z = \frac{\overline{X} - \mu}{\frac{\sigma}{\sqrt{n}}} \sim \mathrm{N}(0, 1)$$

Note that the size of n for the above approximation to be valid depends on the distribution of X.

- When the distribution of X is normal, the distribution of $\overline{X}$ is exactly normal for *all* n.
- When the distribution of X is nearly symmetric, the approximation is usually good, even for n as small as 10. If the distribution is very asymmetric, then a much bigger value (say, $n = 100$) might be needed. In general, its use is recommended for any case where $n \geqslant 30$.

S1

Example 4

The random variable X has a mean of 5 and a variance of 25. A random sample of 100 observations is taken on X. Determine an approximate value for the probability that the sample mean exceeds 5.4.

The random variable $\overline{X}$ has a mean of 5 and a variance of $\frac{25}{100} = \frac{1}{4} = 0.25$. By the Central Limit Theorem, this distribution is approximately normal.

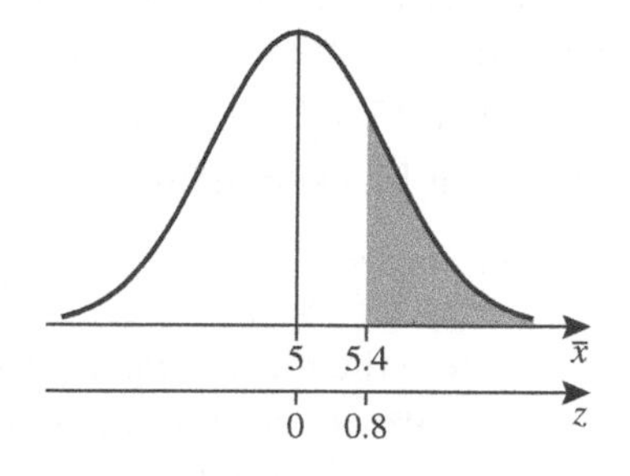

Using this approximation:

$$\begin{aligned} P(\overline{X} > 5.4) &= P\left(Z > \frac{5.4 - 5}{\sqrt{0.25}}\right) \\ &= 1 - \Phi\left(\frac{0.4}{0.5}\right) \\ &= 1 - \Phi(0.8) \\ &= 1 - 0.788\,14 \\ &= 0.211\,86 \end{aligned}$$

So, the required probability is 0.212 (to 3 dp).

Example 5

The random variable X has a probability distribution with a mean of 1.1 and a variance of 0.9. Determine an approximation to the probability for which a random sample of 500 observations on X will have a mean less than 1.04, giving the answer to the nearest percentage point.

Let $\overline{X}$ be the random variable corresponding to the mean of the 500 observations.

The distribution of $\overline{X}$ has a mean of 1.1 and a variance $\frac{0.9}{500} = 0.0018$.

By the Central Limit Theorem, the distribution of $\overline{X}$ will be approximately normal. Using this approximation:

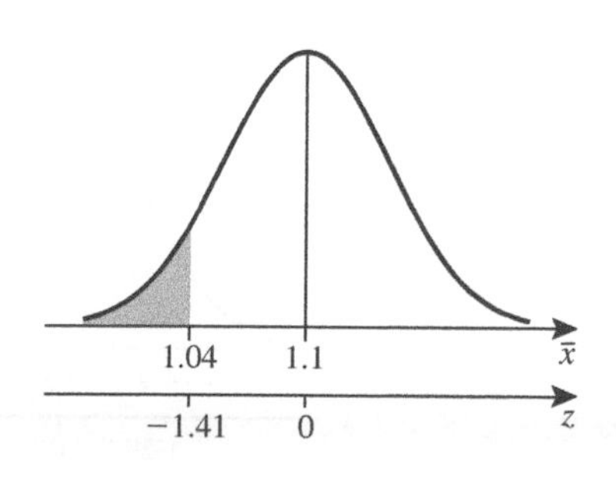

$$\begin{aligned} P(\overline{X} < 1.04) &= P\left(Z < \frac{1.04 - 1.1}{\sqrt{0.0018}}\right) \\ &= \Phi(-1.4142) \\ &= 1 - \Phi(1.4142) \end{aligned}$$

Table 3 gives $\Phi(1.41) = 0.920\,73$, so that the required probability is $1 - 0.920\,73 = 0.079\,27$, which is about 8%.

Note that the z-values in Table 3 are given to two decimal places.

Example 6

A builder orders 200 planks of walnut. The mean and standard deviation of the distribution of the weights (in kilograms) of the planks are 15 and 1.1, respectively. Assuming that the planks delivered to the builder are a random sample from the population of planks, calculate the approximate probability that the mean weight of the planks delivered is:

a) less than 15.025 kilograms,

b) between 14.9 kilograms and 15 kilograms.

Give your answers to two decimal places.

Let $\overline{X}$ denote the mean weight (in kilograms) of the planks. Since the sample size, n, is large (200), the Central Limit Theorem applies and the distribution of $\overline{X}$ is approximately normal. The mean of this distribution is 15 and the variance is $\frac{1.1^2}{200} = 0.006\,05$.

Note that, in this question, you are given the standard deviation, not the variance. Using one in place of the other is a frequent source of error in this type of calculation.

S1

a) Since $\overline{X} \sim \mathrm{N}(15, 0.006\,05)$:

$$\mathrm{P}(\overline{X} < 15.025) = \mathrm{P}\left(Z < \frac{15.025 - 15}{\sqrt{0.006\,05}}\right)$$
$$= \Phi(0.3214)$$

From Table 3, $\Phi(0.32) = 0.625\,52$. So, the required probability is 0.63, to two decimal places.

b) By a similar calculation:

$$\mathrm{P}(14.9 < \overline{X} < 15) = \mathrm{P}(\overline{X} < 15) - \mathrm{P}(\overline{X} < 14.9)$$
$$= \mathrm{P}\left(Z < \frac{15 - 15}{\sqrt{0.006\,05}}\right) - \mathrm{P}\left(Z < \frac{14.9 - 15}{\sqrt{0.006\,05}}\right)$$
$$= \Phi(0) - \Phi(-1.2856)$$

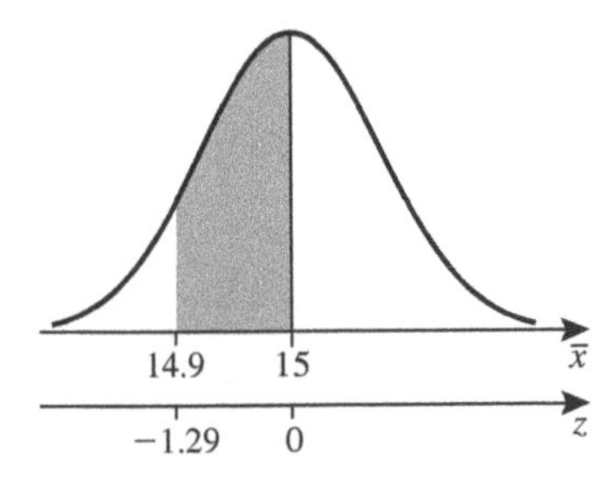

Rounding 1.2856 to 1.29, Table 3 gives $\Phi(1.29) = 0.901\,47$. Since $\Phi(0) = 0.5$, and $\Phi(-1.29) = 1 - \Phi(1.29)$, the required probability is:

$$0.5 - (1 - 0.901\,47) = 0.401\,47$$
$$= 0.40 \text{ (to 2 dp)}$$

Exercise 5C

1 The random variable X has a mean of 15 and a variance of 25. The random variable $\overline{X}$ denotes the mean of a random sample of 70 observations on X.

State the approximate distribution of $\overline{X}$ and hence find an approximate value for $P(15 < \overline{X} < 16)$.

2 The random variable Y has a mean of 50 and a standard deviation of 20. The random variable $\overline{Y}$ denotes the mean of a random sample of n observations on Y.

Find an approximate value for $P(45 < \overline{Y} < 55)$ in the cases:
a) $n = 50$, b) $n = 100$.

3 Let W denote the weight (in grams) of a Size 2 egg. The mean and the variance of the distribution of W are, respectively, 67.5 and $\frac{25}{12}$.

Find the approximate probability that the mean weight, in grams, of 120 randomly chosen Size 2 eggs, lies between 67.2 and 67.8.

5.5 Confidence intervals for the mean of a normal distribution with known variance

Suppose a random sample of n observations is taken from a $N(\mu, \sigma^2)$ distribution, where σ^2 is known, but μ is unknown. Denoting the random variable corresponding to the sample mean by $\overline{X}$:

$$\overline{X} \sim N\left(\mu, \frac{\sigma^2}{n}\right)$$

Let:

$$Z = \frac{\overline{X} - \mu}{\frac{\sigma}{\sqrt{n}}}$$

Table 4 in the Appendices (page 220) gives $P(Z \leqslant 1.9600) = 0.975$. So:

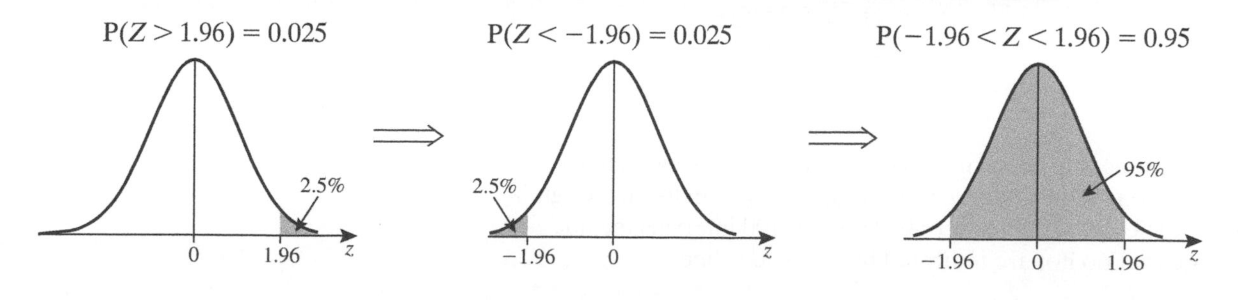

Substituting for Z:

$$P\left(-1.96 < \frac{\overline{X} - \mu}{\frac{\sigma}{\sqrt{n}}} < 1.96\right) = 0.95$$

Multiplying the inequality through by $\frac{\sigma}{\sqrt{n}}$, this statement becomes:

$$P\left(-1.96\frac{\sigma}{\sqrt{n}} < \overline{X} - \mu < 1.96\frac{\sigma}{\sqrt{n}}\right) = 0.95$$

In words, this states that the probability that the distance between μ and $\overline{X}$ is less than $1.96\frac{\sigma}{\sqrt{n}}$ is 0.95. You can rewrite this statement as:

$$P\left(\overline{X} - 1.96\frac{\sigma}{\sqrt{n}} < \mu < \overline{X} + 1.96\frac{\sigma}{\sqrt{n}}\right) = 0.95$$

It is important to know that this is a probability statement concerning the random variable $\overline{X}$. It is *not* a probability statement about μ. The mean, μ, is a constant and is not a variable.

S1

Suppose you now use the n observations on X, and compute the observed sample mean, $\bar{x}$. The interval:

$$\left(\bar{x} - 1.96\frac{\sigma}{\sqrt{n}}, \bar{x} + 1.96\frac{\sigma}{\sqrt{n}}\right) \qquad (5.1)$$

is called a **95% symmetric confidence interval** for μ. The two limiting values that define the interval are known as the **95% confidence limits.**

Often the adjective 'symmetric' is omitted, to give:
95% confidence interval

The next diagram shows one hundred 95% confidence intervals, all based on samples of the same size and from the same population. Each has been calculated using Equation (5.1).

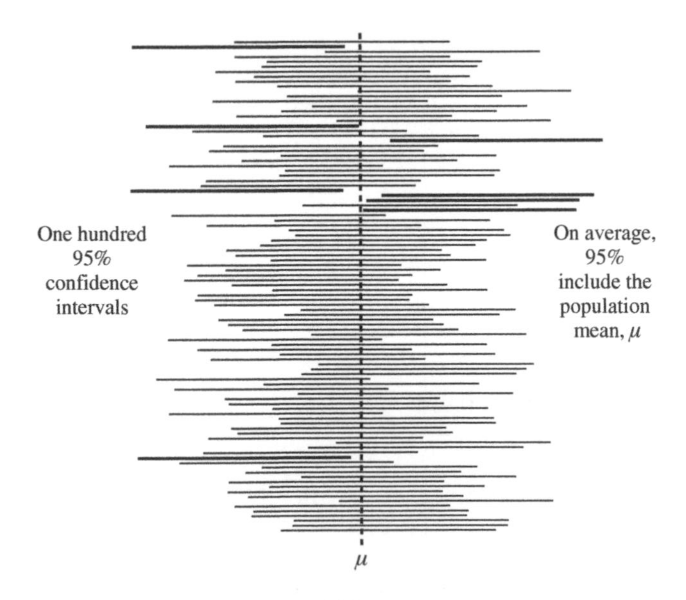

You can see that most of the confidence intervals overlap the population mean value, μ. On average, 95% will do so, though in this particular set of trials only 92 of the 100 intervals include μ. Those that do not are indicated by the bolder lines.

The 95% confidence interval for the unknown mean, μ, of a normal distribution with known variance σ^2, based on a random sample of n observations having a mean of $\bar{x}$, is:

$$\left(\bar{x} - 1.96\frac{\sigma}{\sqrt{n}}, \bar{x} + 1.96\frac{\sigma}{\sqrt{n}}\right)$$

This is often written as:

$$\bar{x} \pm 1.96\frac{\sigma}{\sqrt{n}}$$

If you want to be more confident that an interval includes μ, all you need do is replace 1.96 by a larger value. This will widen the intervals. One common alternative to the 95% confidence interval is the 99% confidence interval. On average, this fails to include μ just 1% of the time.

S1

In order to have an interval corresponding to 99% probability, just 0.5% is needed in each tail. Now $0.5\% = \frac{0.5}{100} = 0.005$ and the value of z for which $P(Z > z) = 0.005$, is the value for which $P(Z \leqslant z) = 0.995$.

Table 4 gives this value as 2.5758. The remainder of the argument follows as before.

The 99% confidence interval for the unknown mean, μ, of a normal distribution with known variance, σ^2, based on a random sample of n observations having mean $\bar{x}$, is:

$$\left(\bar{x} - 2.5758\frac{\sigma}{\sqrt{n}}, \bar{x} + 2.5758\frac{\sigma}{\sqrt{n}}\right)$$

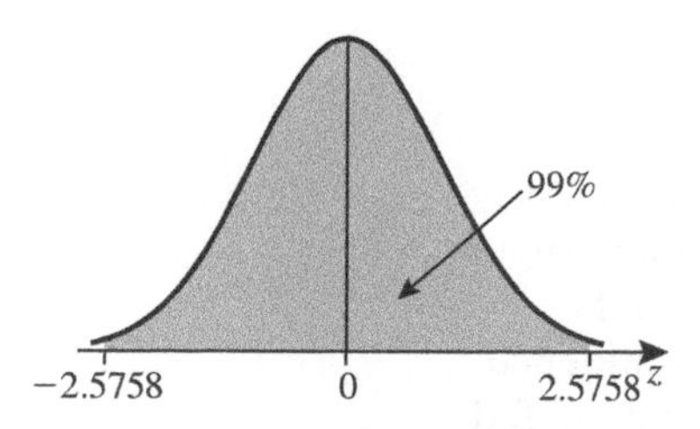

Reducing the confidence level means reducing confidence that the procedure gives an interval which includes μ.

If you want to have a smaller interval, then you must either take a larger sample or reduce the confidence level.

Confidence intervals could be calculated corresponding to any specified level. Some common choices are tabulated below.

Confidence level	90%	95%	98%	99%	99.8%
z-value	1.6449	1.9600	2.3263	2.5758	3.0902

Example 7

A machine cuts metal tubing into pieces. It is known that the lengths of the pieces have a normal distribution with a standard deviation of 4 mm. After the machine has undergone a routine overhaul, a random sample of 25 pieces are found to have a mean length of 146 cm. Assuming the overhaul has not affected the standard deviation of the tube lengths, determine a 99% symmetric confidence interval for the population mean length, giving your answer to the nearest centimetre.

Working in centimetres, $\bar{x} = 146$ and $\sigma = 4$, so that the confidence interval is:

$$\left(146 - 2.5758 \times \frac{4}{\sqrt{25}}, 146 + 2.5758 \times \frac{4}{\sqrt{25}}\right)$$

which simplifies to (143.94, 148.06) or (144, 148) to the nearest centimetre.

This particular interval either does or does not include the population mean length – you cannot say which has occurred. What you *can* say is that 99% of the intervals constructed in this way will include the population mean length, μ. This is sometimes described as: 'Being 99% confident that the calculated interval contains μ'.

S1

Exercise 5D

1 The random variable X has a normal distribution with a mean of μ and a variance of 9. A random sample of ten observations of X has a mean of 8.20. Find:

a) a 95% symmetric confidence interval for μ

b) a 99% symmetric confidence interval for μ

2 The weights of four-months-old pigs are known to be normally distributed with a standard deviation of 4 kilograms. A new diet is suggested and, in a sample of 25 pigs given this new diet, the average weight is 30.42 kilograms. Determine a 99% confidence interval for the mean weight of four-months-old pigs that are fed this diet.

3 A machine measures out quantities of dough to make loaves of bread. The mean weight of a loaf is set by a control. The weight of a loaf has a normal distribution with a standard deviation of 25 grams. With the control at a particular setting, a sample of 16 loaves is taken. The total weight is 29.120 kilograms.

Find a 90% confidence interval for the mean weight of a loaf.

5.6 Confidence intervals for the mean of a distribution with unknown variance using a normal approximation

Suppose X is a random variable with a mean of μ and a variance of σ^2. If the sample size, n, is sufficiently large ($n \geqslant 30$, say) then, because of the Central Limit Theorem, the distribution of the sample mean $\overline{X}$ is approximately:

$$N\left(\mu, \frac{\sigma^2}{n}\right)$$

X can be a discrete or continuous random variable.

When the variance, σ^2, of the distribution is known, an approximate 95% confidence interval for the unknown population mean, μ, is:

$$\left(\bar{x} - 1.96\frac{\sigma}{\sqrt{n}}, \bar{x} + 1.96\frac{\sigma}{\sqrt{n}}\right)$$

This result is exact if the distribution of X is normal.

When σ^2 is unknown, the unbiased estimate s^2 is used.

An approximate 95% confidence interval for μ is:

$$\left(\bar{x} - 1.96\frac{s}{\sqrt{n}}, \bar{x} + 1.96\frac{s}{\sqrt{n}}\right) \qquad (5.2)$$

Confidence intervals for other levels of confidence are given in a similar way.

Using s^2 rather than σ^2 is an approximation, but, if the sample size is reasonably large ($n \geqslant 30$, say), the approximation should not be bad.

In general, this case involves *two* approximations: the normal approximation to the distribution of the mean, and the approximation of σ by s.

The *S2* module yields a more appropriate interval by replacing 1.96 by a value derived from the *t*-distribution.

S1

Example 8

A random sample of 64 sweets is selected. The sweets are found to have a mean weight of 0.932 grams, and the value of s is 0.100 gram. Determine an approximate 99% confidence interval for the population mean weight.

The sample size is large enough ($n = 64$) for the Central Limit Theorem to apply. Although σ is unknown, the sample size is sufficiently large to use s as an approximation. The sample mean, $\bar{x}$, is equal to 0.932 gram. The interval is therefore:

$$\left(0.932 - 2.5758 \times \frac{0.100}{\sqrt{64}}, 0.932 + 2.5758 \times \frac{0.100}{\sqrt{64}}\right)$$

which simplifies to:

(0.900, 0.964)

giving the 99% confidence limits in grams to three significant figures.

Example 9

A random sample of 100 men is taken. The men have heights (x cm) summarized by $\sum x = 17\,280$ and $\sum x^2 = 2\,995\,400$.

a) Determine an unbiased estimate of the population variance of height.

b) Determine also an approximate 98% confidence interval for the population mean height. Give the limits, in cm, to one decimal place.

a) The unbiased estimate of the population variance is s^2 (cm^2), given by:

$$s^2 = \frac{1}{99}\left\{2\,995\,400 - \frac{17\,280^2}{100}\right\}$$

$$= 95.11$$

b) The sample size, 100, is sufficiently large for the Central Limit Theorem to apply. It is also large enough to use s^2 as an approximation to σ^2. Since the sample mean is 172.8, the approximate 98% confidence interval for the population mean height, in cm, is:

$$\left(172.8 - 2.3263\sqrt{\frac{95.11}{100}},\ 172.8 + 2.3263\sqrt{\frac{95.11}{100}}\right)$$

which simplifies, correct to one decimal place, to (170.5, 175.1).

In this case, with $n = 100$, the normal approximation to the distribution of the mean should be very accurate. The same is likely to be true of s as an approximation to σ.

S1

Exercise 5E

1 The random variable W has a distribution with a mean of μ and an unknown variance. A random sample of 150 observations of W gives $\sum w = 1601$, $\sum w^2 = 18\,048$. Giving your answers to two decimal places, find:

a) an approximate 90% confidence interval for μ,

b) an approximate 95% confidence interval for μ.

2 The random variable Y has a normal distribution with a mean of μ and an unknown variance. A random sample of 200 observations of Y gives $\sum y = 541.2$, $\sum(y - \bar{y})^2 = 366.9328$, where $\bar{y}$ denotes the sample mean. Find:

a) an approximate 90% confidence interval for μ,

b) an approximate 98% confidence interval for μ.

3 An airline is concerned about the mean turn-round time, μ, of its aircraft. For a random sample of 50 turn-rounds, the mean turn-round time was 55.2 minutes and the value of s was 13.4 minutes. Giving your answer to the nearest minute, find an approximate 95% confidence interval for μ.

5.7 Inferences from confidence intervals

Suppose that it has been claimed that the mean of a distribution is 80. However, a random sample of observations from the distribution yields (83.0, 85.1) as the 95% confidence interval for μ. This suggests that the claim is false. There are reasonable grounds for rejecting the claim that $\mu = 80$. By definition, however, 5% of 95% confidence intervals will not include μ. The observed interval might be one of those 5%, so you cannot be *certain* that μ is not 80.

Indeed, *any* claim that the value of μ is greater than 85.1, or is less than 83.0, must be doubted.

When a confidence interval for an unknown population mean, μ, does not include the value claimed for μ, there are grounds for rejecting the claim.

Example 10

A machine cuts wood to form stakes, which are supposed to be 200 cm long. A random sample of 40 stakes is taken and the stakes are accurately measured. Their lengths x (in cm, after subtracting 200 cm from each measurement) are summarized by:

$$\sum x = 41.56 \quad \sum x^2 = 107.4673$$

a) Determine an approximate 95% confidence interval for the mean stake length.
b) Does it appear likely that the lengths of stakes cut by the machine have the required mean length?

a) The unbiased estimate of the population variance of the x-values is given by:

$$s^2 = \frac{1}{39}\left(107.4673 - \frac{41.56^2}{40}\right) = 1.6484$$

This is, therefore, the estimated variance of the distribution of stake lengths.

The sample size is sufficiently large that the distribution of the sample mean can be taken to be normal (because of the Central Limit Theorem).

Therefore, the approximate 95% confidence interval for the mean of the population of x-values is:

$$\left(\frac{41.56}{40} - 1.9600\sqrt{\frac{1.6484}{40}}, \frac{41.56}{40} + 1.9600\sqrt{\frac{1.6484}{40}}\right)$$

which gives (0.64, 1.44).

The corresponding 95% confidence interval for the mean stake length is:

$$(200 + 0.64, 200 + 1.44) \text{ cm} = (200.64, 201.44) \text{ cm}$$

b) This interval does not include 200 cm, the supposed mean. Therefore, it is not likely that the lengths of the stakes cut by the machine have the required mean length.

Remember Subtraction of a constant (in this case, 200 cm) from each observation leaves the variance unchanged (see pages 26–28).

Acceptance of a claim should not be interpreted as proving that the claim is correct. It is always possible that, although the claim is incorrect, the sample has nevertheless led to an interval which, by (mis)chance, happens to include the claimed value.

Exercise 5F

1 Jars of honey are filled by a machine. It has been found that the quantity of honey in a jar has a mean of 460.3 grams, with a standard deviation of 3.2 grams. It is believed that the controls have been altered in such a way that, although the standard deviation is unaltered, the mean quantity may have changed. A random sample of 60 jars is taken and the mean quantity of honey per jar is found to be 461.2 grams. By constructing a 95% confidence interval for the mean, decide whether to accept the claim that the mean is 460.3 grams.

2 Observations of the time taken to test an electrical circuit board show that it has a mean of 5.82 minutes with a standard deviation of 0.63 minute. A new board inspection routine is introduced. It is found that, for a random sample of 150 tests with the new scheme, the mean time taken is 5.68 minutes.

a) Assuming that the standard deviation is unaltered, construct a 95% confidence interval for the mean time using the new scheme.

b) Does it seem reasonable to suppose that the mean time taken to test a board is still 5.82 minutes?

3 A light bulb manufacturer has established that the life of a bulb has a mean of 95.2 days with a standard deviation of 10.4 days. Following a change in the manufacturing process, a random sample of 96 bulbs has a mean life of 96.6 days.

a) Assuming that the population standard deviation is unchanged, construct a 99% confidence interval for the mean lifetime following the change.

b) Does it appear that there has been a change in the average lifetime?

4 It is claimed that Size 1 eggs have a mean weight of 70.0 grams. An inspector weighs a random sample of 200 Size 1 eggs and obtains results summarized by $\sum x = 13\,824$, $\sum x^2 = 957\,320$, where x is the weight of an egg in grams.

a) Determine an approximate 99% confidence interval for the mean weight of Size 1 eggs.

b) Hence, state your conclusions about the claimed mean weight.

5 Rumour has it that the average length of a leading article in the *Daily Intellectual* is 960 words. As part of a project, a student counts the number of words in each of 55 randomly chosen leading articles from the paper. The student's results are summarized by $\sum x = 51\,452$, $\sum(x - \bar{x})^2 = 1\,013\,851$, where $\bar{x}$ denotes the sample mean. Decide whether to accept the truth of the rumour, by finding an approximate 90% confidence interval.

Summary

You should know how to ...	Check out
1 Calculate unbiased estimates of the population mean and variance.	**1** Calculate unbiased estimates of the population mean and variance in each of the following cases: a) $n = 20$, $\sum x = 234.5$, $\sum(x - \bar{x})^2 = 1045.38$ b) $n = 15$, $\sum x = 143.2$, $\sum x^2 = 3245.8$ c) $x_1 = 11, x_2 = 13, x_3 = 6, x_4 = 9, x_5 = 12,$ $x_6 = 5$.
2 Calculate the estimated standard error of the mean.	**2** Calculate the estimated standard error of the mean, for each of Question **1** a) to c).
3 Use the Central Limit Theorem.	**3** The random variable X has an unknown distribution with mean 5 and variance 25. A random sample of 49 observations are to be taken on X. Use the Central Limit Theorem to state the approximate distribution of the mean of these observations.
4 Construct a confidence interval for the mean of a normal distribution with known variance.	**4** The random variable X has a normal distribution with mean μ and variance 16. A random sample of 100 observations from this distribution has mean 82.4. Determine a 95% confidence interval for μ.
5 Determine a confidence interval for the mean of a distribution with unknown variance by using a normal approximation.	**5** A sample of 81 observations are taken from the distribution of X, which has unknown mean and variance. The sample is summarised by: $\sum x = 372.6 \quad \sum(x - \bar{x})^2 = 462.40$ Determine a 95% confidence interval for the mean of the distribution of X.
6 Draw inferences from a confidence interval.	**6** Based on a random sample of 50 observations, the 99% confidence interval for the mean of the distribution of X is (87.4, 94.6). It has been claimed that the distribution has mean 100. Does this seem reasonable?

Revision exercise 5

1 Explain the difference between a parameter and a statistic. *(AQA, 2003)*

2 A machine dispenses peanuts into bags so that the weight, in grams, of peanuts per bag is normally distributed with a mean of μ. An inspector needs to obtain an estimate of μ with a standard error of 0.1. To decide on the size, n, of his main sample, the inspector measured the weight, x grams, of peanuts in each bag from a pilot random sample of 50 bags. The data obtained are summarized below.

$$\sum x = 3830 \quad \sum x^2 = 293\,770$$

a) Use these data to show that an unbiased estimate of the population variance is 8.

b) Hence calculate a value of n in order to meet the inspector's needs. *(AQA, 1999)*

S1

3 The weight, x kg, is measured for each sack of potting compost in a sample of 25 sacks, giving the following results.

$$\sum x = 1263.5 \quad \sum (x - \bar{x})^2 = 345.6$$

where $\bar{x}$ denotes the sample mean.

a) Calculate unbiased estimates of the mean and the variance for the weight of a sack of potting compost.

b) State the assumption you needed to make in answering part a).

c) A random sample of 16 sacks of compost is taken and the mean weight for the sample is calculated. Assuming that the weight of a sack of compost is a normal random variable with a mean and a variance equal to the estimates you obtained in part a), determine the probability that the calculated sample mean is less than 50 kg. *(AQA, 2000)*

4 The volume of soft drink in a can is a normally distributed random variable with a mean of 336 ml and a standard deviation of 3.2 ml.

a) A random sample of 16 cans of soft drink is taken. Determine the probability that the mean volume of drink per can exceeds 335 ml.

b) State why, in answering part a), you did not need to use the Central Limit Theorem. *(AQA, 2001)*

5 A firm has cars available for hire. The distance travelled per day by a hire car has a mean of 236 miles and a standard deviation of 80 miles.

a) For a random sample of 100 such distances, determine the probability that its mean is less than 250 miles.

b) Name the theorem which you have used, and explain why it is applicable in this case. *(AQA, 2000)*

6 A study showed that the time, T minutes, spent by a customer between entering and leaving Fely's department store has a mean of 20 with a standard deviation of 6. Assume that T may be modelled by a normal distribution.

a) Find the value of T exceeded by 20% of customers.

b) i) Write down the standard deviation of the mean time spent in Fely's store by a random sample of 90 customers.

ii) Find the probability that this mean time will exceed 21 minutes.

(*AQA, 2002*)

7 A group of 65 students are asked to guess the length of a particular object and their answers are recorded as x cm, with the following results:

$$\sum x = 6019.0 \quad \sum(x - \bar{x})^2 = 374.4$$

where $\bar{x}$ denotes the sample mean.

a) Show that the estimated standard error of the sample mean is 0.3 cm.

b) Determine an approximate symmetric 95 per cent confidence interval for the mean of the population of all such guesses, giving your limits correct to two decimal places.

c) State one assumption which you have made in your calculations.

(*NEAB, 1997*)

S1

8 Pencils produced on a certain machine have lengths, in millimetres, which are normally distributed with a mean of μ and a standard deviation of 3.

A random sample of 16 pencils was taken and the length, x millimetres, measured for each pencil, giving

$$\sum x = 2848$$

a) State why $\bar{X}$, the mean length, in millimetres, of a random sample of 16 pencils produced on the machine, is normally distributed.

b) Construct a 99% confidence interval for μ.

(*AQA, 2002*)

9 Kevin uses his mobile phone for X minutes each day. X is a random variable which may be modelled by a normal distribution with a mean of 28 minutes and a standard deviation of 8 minutes.

a) Find the probability that on a particular day Kevin uses his mobile phone for i) less than 30 minutes; ii) between 10 and 20 minutes.

b) Calculate an interval, symmetrical about 28 minutes, within which X will lie on 80% of days.

c) Find the probability that on seven randomly selected days the mean time Kevin spends on his mobile phone is at least 30 minutes.

(*AQA, 2003*)

10 The contents of each of a random sample of 100 cans of a soft drink are measured. The results have mean 331.28 ml and give 8.91 ml^2 as an unbiased estimate of the population variance.

a) Construct a 99% confidence interval for the population mean, giving the limits to two decimal places.

b) Explain why, in answering part a), an assumption regarding the distribution of the contents of cans was **not** necessary. *(AQA, 2003)*

11 A company has three machines, I, II and III, each producing chocolate bar ice creams of a particular variety.

a) Machine I produces bars whose weights are normally distributed with a mean of 48.1 grams and a standard deviation of 0.25 gram. Determine the probability that the weight of a randomly selected bar is less than 47.5 grams.

b) Machine II produces bars whose weights are normally distributed with a standard deviation of 0.32 gram. Given also that 85 per cent of bars have weights below 50.0 grams, determine the mean weight of bars.

c) From a random sample of 36 bars, selected at random from those produced on Machine III, calculations gave a mean weight of 52.46 grams and an unbiased estimate of the population variance of 0.1764 $gram^2$.

i) Construct a 95% confidence interval for the mean weight of bars produced on Machine III, giving the limits to two decimal places.

ii) Name the theorem that you have used and explain why it was applicable in this case. *(AQA, 2001)*

12 The weight, in grams, of Italian grated cheese in cartons may be assumed to be normally distributed with a mean of μ and a standard deviation of 1.6. From a random sample of 64 such cartons, the mean weight of grated cheese per carton is found to be 80.8 grams.

Construct a 95% confidence interval for μ. *(AQA, 2003)*

6 Correlation and regression

This chapter will show you how to

- ✦ Calculate and interpret the product moment correlation coefficient
- ✦ Identify response and explanatory variables in regression
- ✦ Find and interpret the least-squares regression line
- ✦ Calculate residuals
- ✦ Apply linear scaling to correlation and regression

Before you start

You should know how to ...	Check in
1 Represent data on a scatter diagram.	**1** Plot the following data on a scatter diagram. x: 1 2 3 4 5 6 7 8 y: −4 −1 0 5 3 7 7 9
2 Calculate a mean.	**2** Calculate the mean of the following data: 5 8 12 16 24 40
3 Use sigma notation.	**3** There are six observations on y: 11 3 4 6 7 8 Calculate the values of $\sum y$ and $\sum y^2$.
4 Use linear scaling.	**4** Use linear scaling to calculate the mean of the following observations: 999772 999771 999778 999777 999773 999770 999779

6.1 Introduction

Previous chapters have concentrated on developing methods and models for a *single* random variable. This chapter focuses on methods suitable for use with two continuous or discrete random variables, usually denoted by X and Y, where the observations consist of a pair of values (x, y).

Often, all the data are collected at more or less the same time, as exemplified in the following table.

X	Y
Take-off speed of ski-jumper	Distance jumped
Number of red blood cells in blood sample	Number of white blood cells in the sample
Hand span	Foot length
Size of house	Value of house

However, sometimes data are collected on one variable later than the other variable, though the link (the same individual, the same plot of land, the same family, and so on) is clear:

X	Y
Mark in mock examination	Mark in real examination (three months later)
Weight of fertilizer per hectare	Yield of crop in kilograms per hectare
Height of father	Height of son when aged 18

To quantify the extent to which there is an association between X and Y, you can use the idea of **correlation**.

6.2 Calculation and interpretation of the product moment correlation coefficient

When data consists of pairs of (x, y) values, the first thing you should do is to plot the data on a **scatter diagram**, which will give an idea of the association (if any) between the two variables. The scatter diagram will also help you to identify any unusual data items.

The following data were collected in September 2002 at a weather station near Bolton. The data were gathered at midday on each day of the month. The variables are the amount of solar energy received during the last hour (measured in hundreds of kilojoules) and the average temperature during that hour (measured in degrees Celsius).

Energy	23.5	23.1	20.5	13.2	16.7	8.1	9.0	18.2	5.5	17.6
Temperature	15.5	18.9	18.4	18.6	17.8	14.2	14.4	15.6	14.4	16.4
Energy	22.8	9.0	21.0	22.1	20.7	7.8	7.6	11.4	7.3	7.3
Temperature	19.7	19.0	18.5	16.2	15.3	15.1	15.4	14.9	14.2	15.0
Energy	19.1	8.7	21.1	17.0	11.2	20.5	6.5	4.1	9.2	18.1
Temperature	16.5	14.1	15.3	15.0	14.1	14.3	15.2	15.0	15.4	18.4

The data are summarised on a scatter diagram.

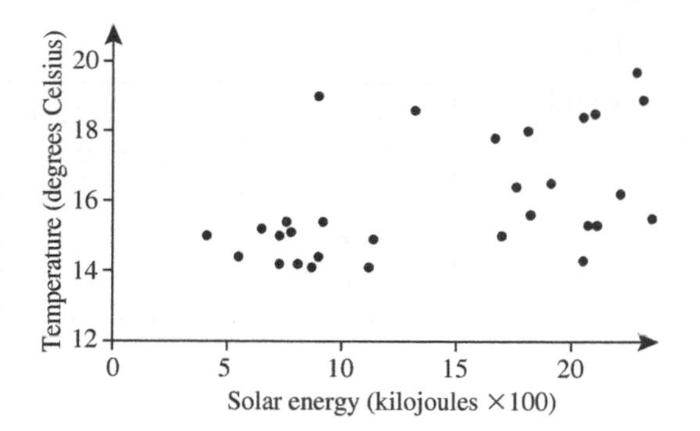

Each point on the diagram represents a data pair.

This scatter diagram of temperature and solar energy reveals a great deal of variation. Although the colder hours tend mostly to be those during which less solar energy has been received, the association between the variables is not as clear as might have been expected.

The fall-off in solar energy is due to increasing cloud cover.

S1

The next scatter diagram provides an example where the association is quite obvious. In this case, two different methods of estimating the cumulative rainfall in each of a series of rain storms are being compared, using data from the same Bolton weather station.

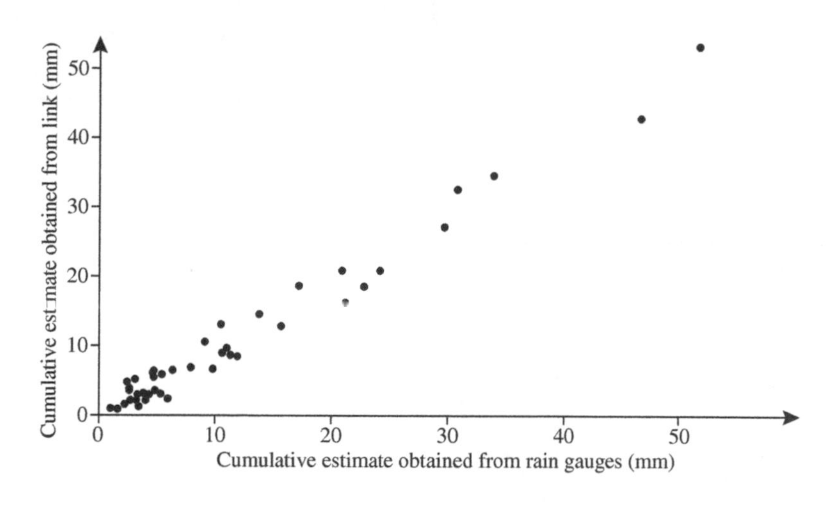

Naturally, the individual points lie quite close to a straight line, whereas, for the temperature data, the scatter was much greater. The next section introduces a measure that quantifies how closely the data fit a straight line.

The product moment correlation coefficient

The **product moment correlation coefficient**, r, is a measure of the extent to which any association between the observed values of the random variables X and Y is linear.

The product moment correlation coefficient is sometimes referred to simply as the **correlation coefficient**.

Many calculators can provide the value of r at the push of a button, once all the data points have been input. However, you may have to calculate r from scratch, so the relevant formulae are given below.

Suppose that there are n pairs of (x, y) values, with the x-values and y-values having means $\bar{x}$ and $\bar{y}$, respectively. The quantities S_{xx}, S_{yy} and S_{xy} are defined as follows:

The *AQA Statistics 1* specification states: 'Candidates should be encouraged to obtain correlation coefficient values directly from calculators'.

$$S_{xx} = \sum(x_i - \bar{x})^2 = \sum x_i^2 - \frac{(\sum x_i)^2}{n} \qquad (6.1)$$

$$S_{yy} = \sum(y_i - \bar{y})^2 = \sum y_i^2 - \frac{(\sum y_i)^2}{n} \qquad (6.2)$$

$$S_{xy} = \sum(x_i - \bar{x})(y_i - \bar{y}) = \sum x_i y_i - \frac{(\sum x_i)(\sum y_i)}{n} \qquad (6.3)$$

S1

These equations can be simplified slightly by omitting the i suffices. For example:

$$S_{xx} = \sum x^2 - \frac{(\sum x)^2}{n}$$

The product moment correlation coefficient, r $(-1 \leqslant r \leqslant 1)$, is given by:

$$r = \frac{S_{xy}}{\sqrt{S_{xx}S_{yy}}}$$

where, for example,

$$S_{xy} = \sum xy - \frac{(\sum x)(\sum y)}{n}$$

Since $\sqrt{S_{xx}S_{yy}}$ is positive, it is the sign of S_{xy} that determines whether the correlation coefficient is negative, zero, or positive.

The value of r cannot be less than -1 nor greater than 1. These extremes are only attained when all the data points lie on a straight line, as shown in these diagrams. In other cases, $-1 < r < 1$.

Correlation coefficient = -1

Correlation coefficient = -0.8

Correlation coefficient = 0.3

Correlation coefficient = 1

In cases where increasing values of one variable are associated with generally decreasing values of the other variable, $r < 0$ and the variables are said to display **negative correlation**.

In cases where increasing values of one variable are associated with generally increasing values of the other variable, $r > 0$ and the variables are said to display **positive correlation**.

Examples of **uncorrelated variables**, where the data have zero correlation ($r = 0$), are shown in the next two diagrams:

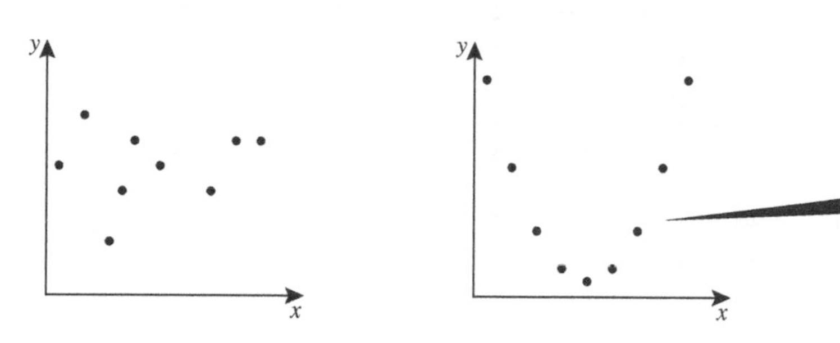

While a zero correlation implies that the data show no evidence of linear association, it does not rule out a non-linear relationship. This is one reason why it is always useful to plot the data.

Some suggested descriptions of correlation are:

- When r is between -0.2 and 0.2, the correlation might be described as *weak* or *very weak*.
- When r is between 0.2 and 0.7, or between -0.2 and -0.7, the correlation might be described as *moderate*.
- When r is between 0.7 and 0.9, or between -0.7 and -0.9, the correlation might be described as *strong*.
- When r is above 0.9 or below -0.9 the correlation might be described as *very strong*.

S1

The value of r is unaffected by changes in the units of measurement.

Example 1

A class of students takes examinations in both mathematics and physics. The marks that they obtain are as follows.

Student	1	2	3	4	5	6	7	8	9	10
Mathematics	65	45	40	55	60	50	80	30	70	65
Physics	60	60	55	70	80	40	85	50	70	80

a) Plot the data on a scatter diagram.

b) Determine the value of the product moment correlation coefficient, using the formula.

c) Interpret this value in the context of the question.

a)

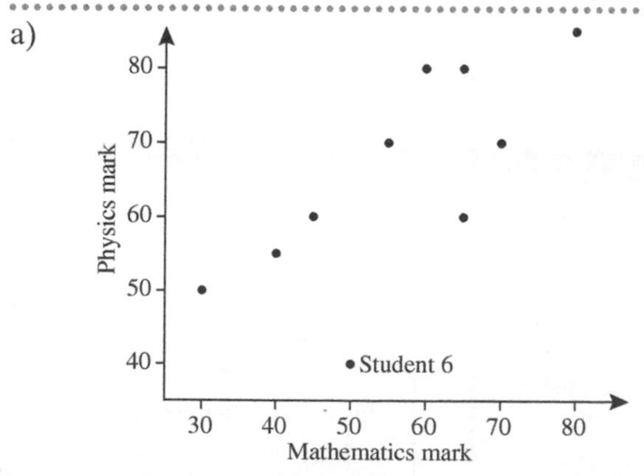

With the exception of Student 6, there is a strong correspondence between the two sets of marks. The students who do well at mathematics are those who also do well at physics. You should therefore expect a rather large positive value for r.

b) The necessary calculations can be set out as follows:

Student	Maths x	Physics y	xy	x^2	y^2
1	65	60	3900	4225	3600
2	45	60	2700	2025	3600
3	40	55	2200	1600	3025
4	55	70	3850	3025	4900
5	60	80	4800	3600	6400
6	50	40	2000	2500	1600
7	80	85	6800	6400	7225
8	30	50	1500	900	2500
9	70	70	4900	4900	4900
10	65	80	5200	4225	6400
Total	560	650	37 850	33 400	44 150

S1

Now calculate S_{xy}, S_{xx} and S_{yy} using Equations (6.1) to (6.3):

$$S_{xy} = \sum xy - \frac{(\sum x)(\sum y)}{n} = 37\,850 - \frac{(560 \times 650)}{10} = 1450$$

$$S_{xx} = \sum x^2 - \frac{(\sum x)^2}{n} = 33\,400 - \frac{560^2}{10} = 2040$$

$$S_{yy} = \sum y^2 - \frac{(\sum y)^2}{n} = 44\,150 - \frac{650^2}{10} = 1900$$

Hence:

$$r = \frac{1450}{\sqrt{2040 \times 1900}} = 0.736\,51 = 0.737 \quad \text{(to 3 dp)}$$

c) As anticipated, the two sets of marks do display a positive correlation, which could reasonably be described as strong. The implication is that students who are good at one subject are generally good at the other, while those who are weak at one subject are likely to be weak at the other.

Since S_{xx} and S_{yy} are sums of squares, they are *never negative*. If you have found a negative value, then you have made an error. S_{xy} may be positive or negative.
If your value of r is greater than 1, or less than -1, then you have made an error.

Calculator practice

Many calculators have in-built routines for calculating the value of r. If you have a calculator of this type, make sure that you know how to find the value of r. You could start with the exam mark data in Example 1. Note that these calculators, when calculating r, usually store the values of n, $\sum x$, $\sum x^2$, $\sum y$, $\sum y^2$ and $\sum xy$ in accessible memories. As well as $\bar{x}$ and $\bar{y}$, they often also give $s_x = \sqrt{\frac{S_{xx}}{n-1}}$ and $s_y = \sqrt{\frac{S_{yy}}{n-1}}$, the sample standard deviations of the x-values and the y-values.

The values of n, $\sum x$, $\sum y$, $\sum x^2$, $\sum y^2$, $\sum xy$, S_{xx}, S_{yy} and S_{xy} may be referred to as **summary statistics**.

Example 2

On page 145 are presented scatter diagrams of two sets of data derived from observations made at a Bolton weather station. By comparing the scatter diagrams for each Bolton data set with that for the marks data of Example 1 ($r = 0.737$) and with the diagrams corresponding to correlations of -1, -0.8, 0.3 and 1 (page 146), suggest approximate values for the correlation coefficient in each case.

For the temperature and solar energy data, while there is a good deal of scatter, it does appear that the higher temperatures are associated with higher amounts of solar energy. This implies that $r > 0$. The association does not appear as obvious as it does for the marks data, implying that $r < 0.737$. The diagram is quite similar to that for the case where $r = 0.3$. It seems likely, therefore, that r lies between 0.2 and 0.7.

The two sets of rainfall estimates are in nearly perfect agreement, with high values of one estimate corresponding to high values of the other, so that $r > 0$. The agreement is certainly much better than for the marks example, so $r > 0.737$. The scatter diagram is similar (with opposite slope) to that for the case $r = -0.8$, but the scatter is less. The conclusion is that r lies between 0.8 and 1.

In fact, the two correlation coefficients are 0.502 and 0.991 (to 3 dp).

S1

Exercise 6A

1 The moisture content, m, of core samples of mud is measured as a percentage. It is believed that m is related to the depth, d metres, at which the core is collected. The results for eight samples are given in the table.

d	0	5	10	15	20	25	30	35
m	90	82	56	42	30	21	21	18

a) Calculate the value of r.

b) Draw a scatter diagram, and comment, in the context of the data, on your value of r.

2 The data in the following table relates the average temperature (in degrees Celsius) and the average butterfat content for a group of cows (expressed as a percentage of the milk).

Temperature (°C)	17	16	13	4	8	14	16	3	3	16
Butterfat (%)	4.65	4.83	4.55	5.44	4.69	4.65	4.65	4.95	4.66	4.60

a) Draw a scatter diagram.

b) Calculate the value of the product moment correlation coefficient, and comment on its value.

3 A survey of common garden birds in Great Britain gave figures for each species, comparing the total number recorded with the percentage of gardens where each species was seen. The figures for nine species are given in the following table.

Number recorded (thousands)	702	673	308	156	455	411	370	230	196
Percentage of gardens	53.9	64.0	47.4	50.3	81.8	89.0	59.2	57.4	80.0

a) Draw a scatter diagram for the data.

b) Calculate the value of r.

c) Comment, in the context of the question, on your value of the correlation coefficient.

S1

4 The following table gives the numbers of households living in their own properties, and the numbers that are not doing so (both in thousands), for selected regions of East Anglia.

Region	Southend	Colchester	Kings Lynn	St Albans	Ipswich
Owner-occupied	51.6	46.1	41.8	40.6	32.4
Other	19.4	17.6	16.5	12.1	17.5

Region	Cambridge	Hertsmere	Harlow	Brentwood	Maldon
Owner-occupied	22.8	28.5	19.8	22.8	19.5
Other	19.8	9.4	13.4	6.0	4.7

Source: *Office of National Statistics*

a) Display these data on a scatter diagram.

b) Determine the value of r, the correlation coefficient.

c) Interpret your value of r in the context of the data.

d) Suppose that the correlation coefficient had been equal to 1. What would this imply about the households?

5 The following table contrasts the rates of two types of crime (violence against the person and robbery) for various London districts. The rates, per 1000 population, apply to the year starting April 2000.

District	Westminster	Islington	Hounslow	Brent	Croydon
Violence	36.6	30.9	25.5	22.9	18.7
Robbery	10.3	8.6	3.4	7.7	4.6

District	Kingston	Bexley	Havering	Richmond
Violence	16.6	14.6	12.1	10.4
Robbery	1.6	1.9	1.7	1.2

Source: *Office of National Statistics*

a) Display these data on a scatter diagram.
b) Calculate the value of r.
c) Interpret your value of r in the context of the data.

Correlation and nonlinear relations

Although the value of the correlation coefficient is a measure of the extent to which the variables X and Y are linearly associated, its interpretation often needs care.

- A near-zero value of r should not be interpreted (without reference to the data) as implying that the variables are unrelated.
- A value of r near 1 or -1 should not be interpreted (without reference to the data) as implying that the variables are exactly linearly related, though clearly a straight-line relationship will be a good approximation (see Examples 3 and 4).

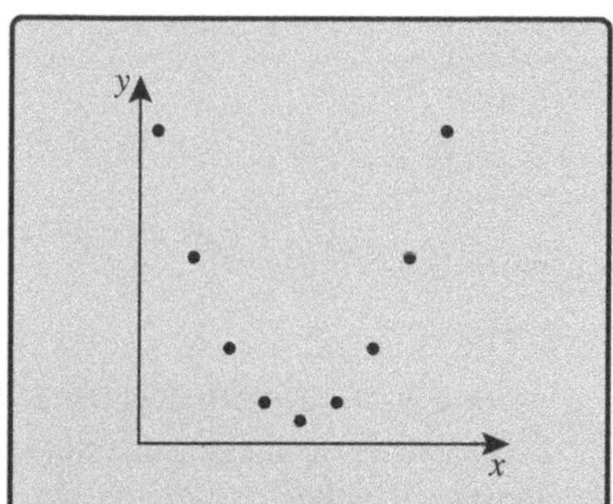

This scatter diagram (also shown on page 147) indicates a simple non-linear relation connecting X and Y, and yet the correlation is zero.

S1

Example 3

A scientist is measuring the effect of gravity in a near vacuum. A ball-bearing is dropped down a tube, and the distance fallen, d cm, is recorded for a series of increasing times, t (measured in 10^{-2} seconds). The results are as follows.

t	1	2	3	4	5	6	7	8
d	0	25	50	75	125	175	250	325

a) Use a calculator to determine the value of the correlation coefficient for the (t, d) values.
b) Plot the values on a scatter diagram.
c) Comment on the results.

a) The summary statistics are:

$$n = 8 \quad \sum t = 36 \quad \sum t^2 = 204$$

$$\sum d = 205 \quad \sum d^2 = 8925 \quad \sum dt = 1305$$

These give $S_{tt} = 42$, $S_{dd} = 3671.875$ and $S_{td} = 382.5$.

Hence, the value of the correlation coefficient is 0.974 (to 3 dp), indicating a very strong linear relation between t and d.

It would be tempting to conclude that, were it not for round-off errors, or other measurement errors, the relation would be exactly linear.

Check that these figures are correct by using your calculator.

b)

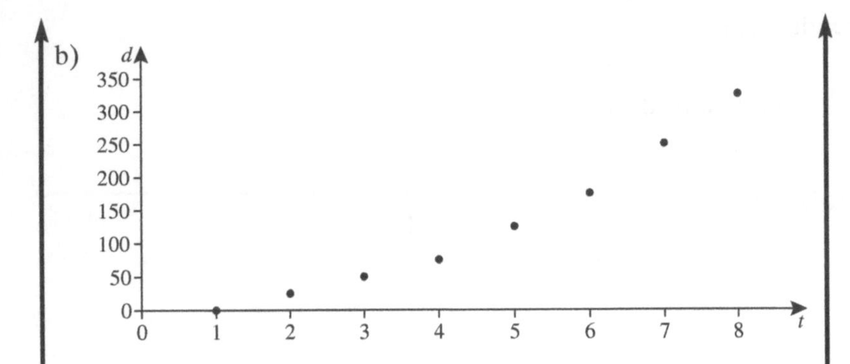

c) The diagram below shows that, although the points are very close to a straight line over the given range of values of t (which is why r is so large and close to 1), they are even closer to the curve $d = 5t^2$.

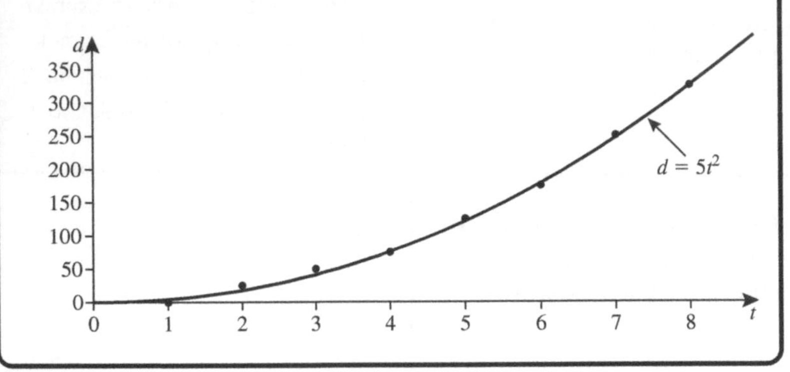

Example 4

a) Use a calculator to determine the value of the correlation coefficient for the following pairs of (x, y) values.

x	5	6	7	8	9	10	11	12	13	14	24
y	5	8	7	9	9	4	6	9	7	8	20

b) Plot the values on a scatter diagram.

c) Comment on the results.

a) The summary statistics are:

$$n = 11 \quad \sum x = 119 \quad \sum x^2 = 1561$$

$$\sum y = 92 \quad \sum y^2 = 946 \quad \sum xy = 1722$$

These give (to 5 sf) $S_{xx} = 273.64$, $S_{yy} = 176.55$ and $S_{xy} = 176.73$. The value of the correlation coefficient, r, is 0.804 (to 3 dp). This is a high value that might suggest a strong linear association between x and y.

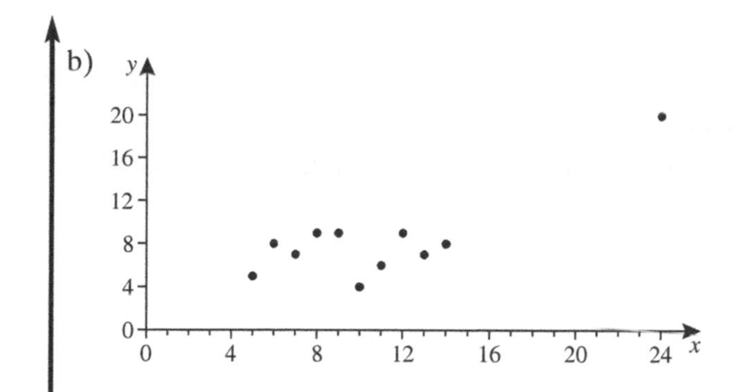

c) A glance at the scatter diagram shows that the high value of r is a consequence of the single data point (24, 20).

Further examples of influential data points are given in Section 6.5, pages 173–175.

S1

Since, in Example 4, 24 is much the largest x-value and 20 is much the largest y-value, the data point (24, 20) is described as **influential**. If you ignore this point, there is no obvious relation between x and y. Indeed, if this point were to be removed from the data, the value of the correlation coefficient would drop to 0.168 (to 3 dp).

More information would be needed about the values taken by Y when X is greater than 14 before you can draw any safe conclusions. The relationship *may* be linear, but the high value of r is largely due to a single data point and this conclusion must therefore be treated with caution.

Whenever possible, you should plot the data *before* carrying out any analysis. Sometimes the plot shows that no analysis is required, or reveals errors in the data that need correction before the analysis commences.

The influence of a background variable

It is often the case that the two variables of interest, X and Y, are each strongly correlated with an unmeasured background variable, Z. The result is that any changes in Z affect each of X and Y, which are therefore strongly correlated with each other, even though there may be no direct connection.

Often this is incorrectly interpreted as meaning that X 'causes' Y (or vice-versa) when in fact it is Z that 'causes' both.

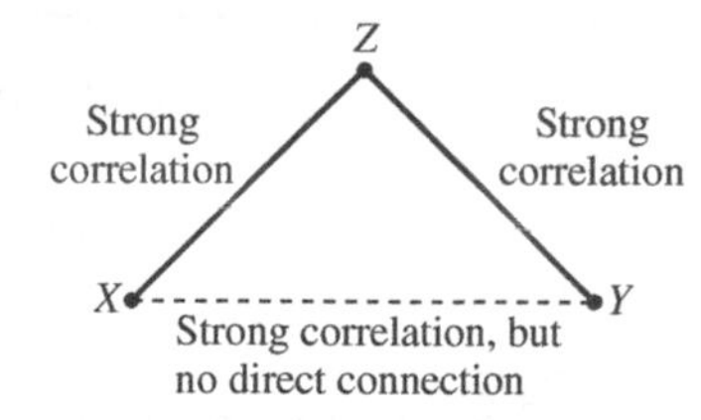

Example 5

The table records (in years) the life expectancies at birth of males (x) and females (y), based on data supplied by the Office for National Statistics.

	1972–76	1977–81	1982–86	1987–91	1992–96	1997–99
All males	69.2	70.0	71.4	72.3	73.9	75.0
All females	75.1	76.3	77.1	77.9	79.3	79.7

Source: *Longitudinal Study, Office for National Statistics*

a) Plot the data on a scatter diagram.

b) Determine the value of the correlation coefficient.

c) Comment on your results. Would it be reasonable to claim that either variable influenced the other?

a)

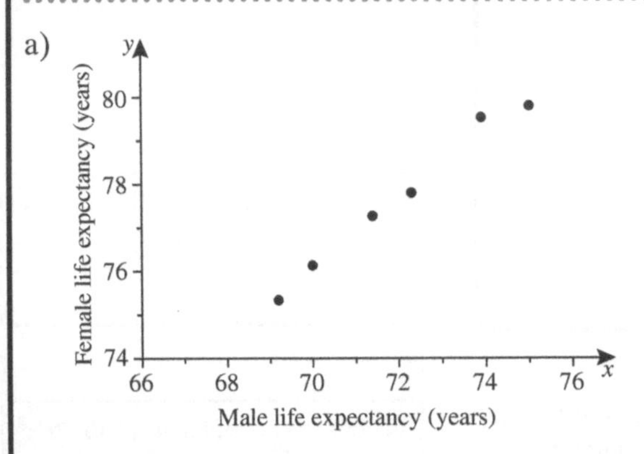

b) In this case:

$$n = 6 \quad \sum x = 431.8 \quad \sum x^2 = 31\,100.1$$
$$\sum y = 465.4 \quad \sum y^2 = 36\,115.1 \quad \sum xy = 33\,512.8$$

These give (to 5 sf) $S_{xx} = 24.893$, $S_{yy} = 15.573$ and $S_{xy} = 19.513$, leading to the extremely high value for the correlation coefficient, r, of 0.991 (to 3 dp).

c) The scatter diagram suggests that the near-linear relationship is perfectly genuine. Even so, it is not reasonable to claim that either variable influences the other. What has happened is that improved medical facilities and living conditions have resulted in longer lives for all people, so that both males and females show a steady rise in life expectancy. The background variable in this case is the unmeasured state of human welfare.

Sometimes the variables X and Y make a very curious or comical pair, as the next example illustrates. In this case, the correlation between X and Y may be referred to as being a **spurious correlation** (also called a **nonsense correlation**).

Example 6

The table records the life expectancies at birth of males (x years) and the North Sea stocks of haddock (y thousands of tonnes averaged over the time periods given).

Time period	1972–76	1977–81	1982–86	1987–91	1992–96	1997–99
Male life expectancy (x)	69.2	70.0	71.4	72.3	73.9	75.0
Haddock stocks (y)	1439	765	933	595	704	535

Sources: *Longitudinal Study, Office for National Statistics; Centre for Environment, Fisheries and Aquaculture Science*

a) Plot the data on a scatter diagram.

b) Determine the value of the correlation coefficient.

c) Comment on the value obtained.

a)

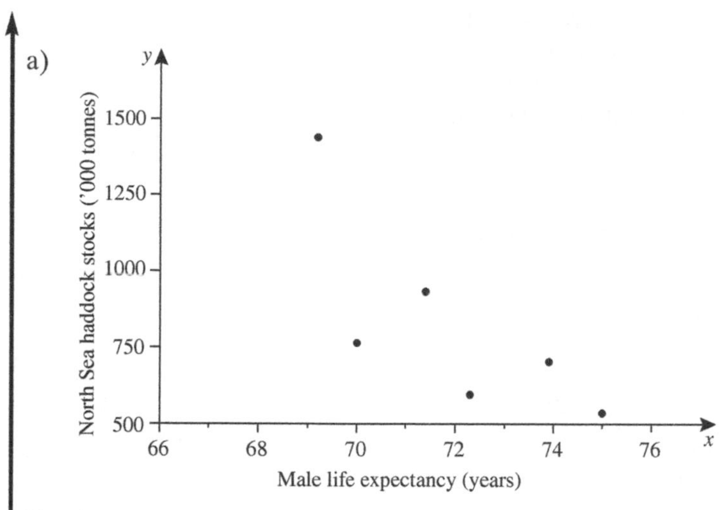

b) The summary statistics are:

$n = 6 \quad \sum x = 431.8 \quad \sum x^2 = 31\,100.1$

$\sum y = 4971 \quad \sum y^2 = 4\,662\,301 \quad \sum xy = 354\,914.1$

These give (to 5 sf) $S_{xx} = 24.893$, $S_{yy} = 543\,830$ and $S_{xy} = -2832.2$. So, $r = -0.770$ (to 3 dp).

c) The rather strong negative correlation between the variables might be interpreted as suggesting either that the haddock stocks would be increased by decreasing male life expectancy, or that the elimination of haddock from the North Sea would be accompanied by a further increase in male life expectancy.

In fact, as is often the case, the third variable is time. Over time, there have been improvements in medicine leading to increased life expectancy. Meanwhile, consistent over-fishing of the North Sea has resulted in reduced fish stocks. The activities of the health service and the fishing industry are quite unrelated, but both have changed with time. These simultaneous but unconnected changes have led to the high spurious correlation obtained here.

Exercise 6B

1 A particular model of car is available with engines of various sizes. Measurements of fuel economy for each engine size are given in the table.

Engine size (cm^3)	1390	1595	1598	1781
Fuel economy (mpg)	51	48	49	45

Engine size (cm^3)	1896	1984	2324	2792
Fuel economy (mpg)	64	46	42	34

a) Calculate the value of the product moment correlation coefficient, r.

b) Draw a scatter diagram for the data, and identify a point which is likely to be influential.

c) i) Remove the corresponding data point (which corresponds to the only diesel engine) and calculate the value of the product moment correlation coefficient for the remaining data, confirming that the diesel engine gives an influential point.
ii) Comment on your value of r.

2 The following table reports annual expenditure (in £millions), by the Department for Culture, Media and Sport, on the arts and on sport.

Year ending	1992	1993	1994	1995	1996
Arts (x, £millions)	212	235	235	195	200
Sport (y, £millions)	47	50	54	53	54
Year ending	**1997**	**1998**	**1999**	**2000**	**2001**
Arts (x, £millions)	195	196	198	232	240
Sport (y, £millions)	52	59	49	52	53

S1

a) Plot a scatter diagram for the data.
b) Calculate the value of the product moment correlation coefficient, r, and comment on its value.

3 The table gives the current prices of second-hand cars, all in first-class condition. The figures are for a particular luxury model and a particular standard model, made by different manufacturers. Each data point gives the price for the luxury model and the standard model of the same age.

Luxury model price (£)	16 090	16 805	18 765	19 670	22 100
Standard model price (£)	5720	5950	6700	6985	7850
Luxury model price (£)	23 120	25 995	27 270	27 950	
Standard model price (£)	8195	9070	9465	9655	

a) Draw a scatter diagram for the data, and comment on what it reveals.
b) Calculate the value of the product moment correlation coefficient, and comment, in context, on its value.

4 The following data refer to the incidence of burglaries and vehicle thefts per 10 000 households, for nine English regions.

Region	NE	NW	Yorkshire	E Mid	W Mid
Burglary	621	589	585	396	467
Vehicle thefts	1448	1943	1559	1254	1684
Region	**East**	**London**	**SE**	**SW**	
Burglary	299	512	292	395	
Vehicle thefts	1048	2141	1299	1268	

a) Plot the data on a scatter diagram.
b) Calculate the value of the product moment correlation coefficient.
c) Interpret your result in the context of the data.

5 The following data refer to the annual use of natural gas in the United Kingdom (in 10^4 GWh) and the North Sea herring stocks (in '000 tonnes).

Year	1992	1993	1994	1995
Natural gas use	54.25	59.66	63.50	67.23
Herring stocks	2991	2961	2380	1977

Year	1996	1997	1998	1999
Natural gas use	78.35	80.66	85.25	91.20
Herring stocks	1585	1958	2005	2440

a) Plot the data on a scatter diagram.

b) Calculate the value of the product moment correlation coefficient.

c) Interpret your result in the context of the data.

6 Figures for the numbers killed, and the numbers seriously injured, in road accidents in Great Britain, in the last quarter of each year, are given in the table.

	1990	1991	1992	1993	1994
Killed (x)	1418	1349	1176	1117	1049
Seriously injured (y)	15 402	14 261	12 857	12 061	12 868

	1995	1996	1997	1998
Killed (x)	1011	1023	985	940
Seriously injured (y)	12 038	12 209	11 469	10 520

Source: *Transport Statistics, Department for Transport*

a) Plot a scatter diagram for the data.

b) Calculate the value of the product moment correlation coefficient, r.

c) Comment on the data and on your value of r.

d) Plot a scatter diagram of numbers killed against year, and of numbers seriously injured against year. Comment on the relationship between the three scatter diagrams which you have drawn.

7 Various A-level Statistics books were compared for price and length. The results are in the following table.

Price (£x)	18.75	13.75	8.99	8.99	19.99
Length (y pages)	768	208	215	136	687

Price (£x)	7.95	10.99	9.95	19.50	21.00
Length (y pages)	222	144	192	480	670

a) Plot a scatter diagram for the data.

b) Calculate the value of the product moment correlation coefficient, r.

c) Comment on your value of r.

8 Measurements of hand-span and arm-length were carried out for 11 members of a family, with the following results.

Span (x cm)	25.1	20.6	19.4	24.1	22.3	20.9
Length (y cm)	49.5	42.9	42.2	49.9	42.2	45.1
Span (x cm)	19.4	23.3	21.5	23.1	21.4	
Length (y cm)	38.5	47.0	45.1	46.8	42.8	

a) Plot a scatter diagram for the data.

b) Calculate the value of the product moment correlation coefficient, r.

c) Comment on your value of r.

S1

6.3 Identification of response and explanatory variables

In the measurement of correlation, the two variables are treated in the same way, which is reflected by the formula for r, which would be unaltered if x and y were interchanged.

Often, however, it is interesting to find out about the way that the values of one variable (usually Y) change as the values of the other variable change. This is emphasized by referring to Y and X as the **response variable** and the **explanatory variable**, respectively.

Former terminology referred to the response variable as the **dependent variable**, and the explanatory variable as the **independent variable**.

Here are some examples.

Explanatory variable	Response variable
Time for which a chemical reaction is allowed to proceed	Weight of chemical compound produced
Weight of chemical compound required	Time taken to produce this weight
An interval of time	Number of cars passing during this interval
Number of cars passing a junction	Time taken for these cars to pass

To decide which variable is which requires some knowledge of how and why the data were collected. Often, the explanatory variable takes some specified value, while the value taken, as a consequence, by the response variable is subject to random variation. The response variable is, therefore, denoted by Y, rather than y, since it is a random variable. Conversely, x rather than X is used for the explanatory variable to emphasize that it is *not* a random variable. Here are some examples.

x	Y
Number of bricks in pile	Weight of pile of bricks
Price of a commodity	Number sold
Capacity of a car engine	Average miles/gallon

The first example is a particularly obvious one. A lot of piles could contain precisely 10 bricks. However, each of those piles would have a different weight (because of the variations in the weights of individual bricks). Thus, while x is a fixed quantity (for example, 10) for each pile, y is an observation on a random variable Y.

6.4 Calculation of least squares regression lines

In this section you will learn how to fit a straight line to a set of data pairs.

The equation of a straight line

In Statistics, a linear relationship is denoted by:

$$y = a + bx$$

where a is a constant known as the **intercept** (with the y-axis) and b is a constant known as the **slope** or **gradient**. Either, or both, of a and b can be negative.

You should already be familiar with the equation of a straight line in the form:

$y = mx + c$

S1

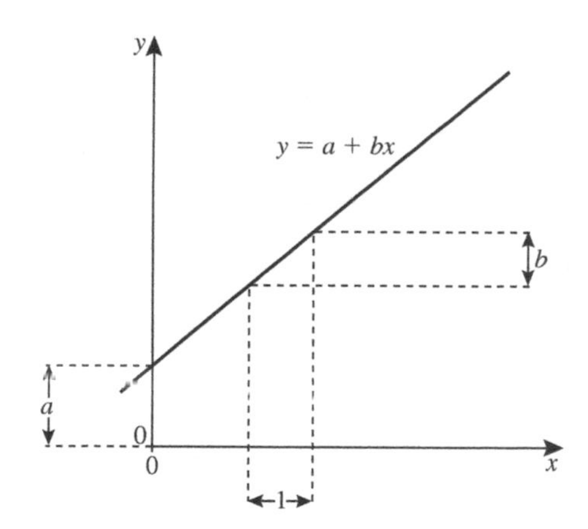

If x increases to $(x + 1)$, y increases from $a + bx$ to $a + b(x + 1)$, which is an increase of:

$$(a + bx + b) - (a + bx) = b$$

Thus the slope b measures the amount of change in y for unit change in x. A negative value of b means that y decreases as x increases.

The intercept a represents the value of y when x is zero, and so $(0, a)$ is the point where the line crosses the y-axis. A negative value of a means that the line crosses the y-axis below the origin.

Calculation of the least squares regression line

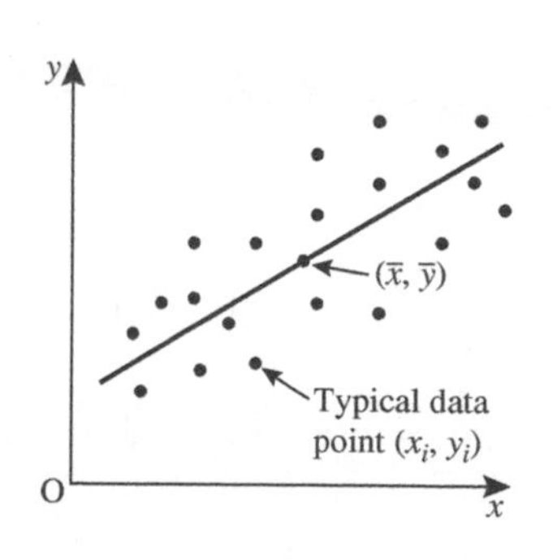

A typical pair of values is denoted by (x_i, y_i). Denoting the means of the x-values and the y-values by $\bar{x}$ and $\bar{y}$, respectively, the 'centre' of the scatter diagram can be represented by the point $(\bar{x}, \bar{y})$. It would therefore seem sensible that a line summarizing the relation between x and y should pass through this point. The condition for this to occur is that a and b satisfy:

$$\bar{y} = a + b\bar{x}$$

which gives:

$$a = \bar{y} - b\bar{x} \qquad (6.4)$$

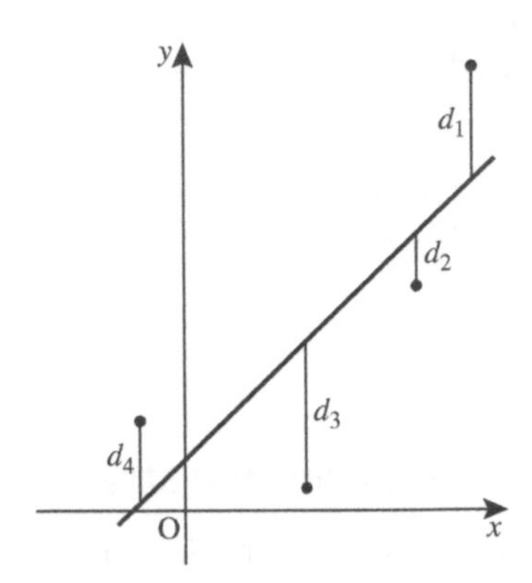

To fix the line, a value is needed for b. This should be chosen so that the line $y = a + bx$ is as close as possible to all the n data points in the scatter diagram. This process is often referred to as **fitting the data** and the line is called the **regression line**.

For each data point (x_i, y_i), the difference between y_i and the value given by the regression line is denoted by d_i. Thus:

$$\begin{aligned} d_i &= y_i - (a + bx_i) \\ &= y_i - a - bx_i \qquad (6.5) \end{aligned}$$

The line should be such that the n differences are as small as possible. Avoiding sign problems by using squares, this can be achieved by minimizing $\sum d_i^2$.

The quantity d_i is called a **residual** (see Section 6.5, page 173).

It turns out that the value for b which minimizes $\sum d_i^2$ is given by:

$$b = \frac{S_{xy}}{S_{xx}} \qquad (6.6)$$

Proof of this result is beyond the scope of this book.

where S_{xy} and S_{xx} are given by Equations (6.3) and (6.1).

The resulting line is described as the **least squares regression line of y on x**. The slope b is often called the **regression coefficient**.

To find the least squares regression line of y on x:

- Calculate S_{xx} and S_{xy}.
- From these values, work out b.
- Calculate $\bar{x}$ and $\bar{y}$.
- From these values, work out a.

The values of the intercept, a, and the slope, b, in the least squares regression line of y on x, $y = a + bx$, are given by:

$$b = \frac{S_{xy}}{S_{xx}} \quad \text{and} \quad a = \bar{y} - b\bar{x} = \frac{\sum y}{n} - b\left(\frac{\sum x}{n}\right)$$

where $\bar{x}$ and $\bar{y}$ are the means of the x-values and the y-values, respectively, and:

$$S_{xx} = \sum(x - \bar{x})^2 = \sum x^2 - \frac{(\sum x)^2}{n}$$

$$S_{xy} = \sum(x - \bar{x})(y - \bar{y}) = \sum xy - \frac{(\sum x)(\sum y)}{n}$$

Example 7

Cars are driven around a test circuit at a variety of constant speeds and the corresponding fuel consumptions are monitored. The results are summarized in the table.

Speed (miles/hour)	35	35	35	35	40	40	40	40
Fuel consumption (miles/gal)	48.4	47.6	47.8	46.2	45.8	45.6	45.0	44.9
Speed (miles/hour)	**45**	**45**	**45**	**45**	**50**	**50**	**50**	**50**
Fuel consumption (miles/gal)	43.0	42.8	42.7	42.2	39.9	40.3	38.9	39.6

a) Identify the explanatory variable, x, and the response variable, Y.

b) Plot the data on a scatter diagram.

c) Comment on whether there appears to be a linear relationship.

d) Find the least squares regression line of y on x.

e) Plot this line on the scatter diagram and comment on its fit.

a) It is speed that affects fuel consumption, thus the explanatory variable, x, is speed (in miles/hour) and the response variable, Y, is fuel consumption (in miles/gal).

b) The scatter diagram is as shown.

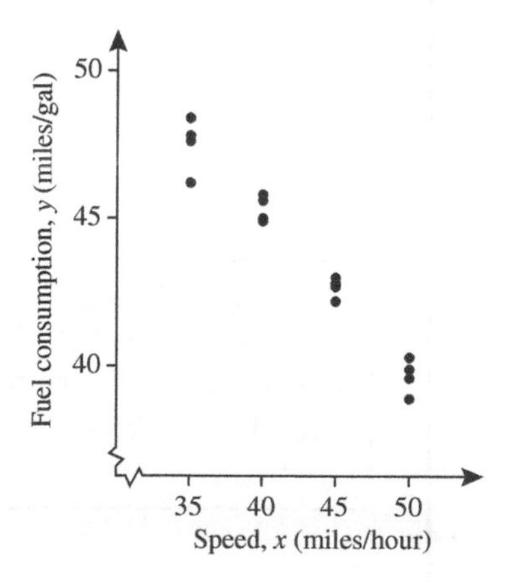

Many calculators are programmed to calculate the values of a and b as a result of a few button pushes. Often, intermediate values (such as $\sum x$, $\sum xy$) can also be recovered from the calculator. For this first example, however, working is shown in detail. This would be a good approach if you are working with a spreadsheet.

c) Although there is some variation from car to car in the fuel consumption at each of the fixed speeds, the general relationship does appear to be linear.

S1

d) First, arrange the data in a table, as shown.

	x	y	x^2	xy
	35	48.4	1225	1694
	35	47.6	1225	1666
	35	47.8	1225	1673
	35	46.2	1225	1617
	40	45.8	1600	1832
	40	45.6	1600	1824
	40	45.0	1600	1800
	40	44.9	1600	1796
	45	43.0	2025	1935
	45	42.8	2025	1926
	45	42.7	2025	1921.5
	45	42.2	2025	1899
	50	39.9	2500	1995
	50	40.3	2500	2015
	50	38.9	2500	1945
	50	39.6	2500	1980
Total	680	700.7	29 400	29 518.5

Next, calculate S_{xy} and S_{xx}, using $n = 16$:

$$S_{xy} = 29\,518.5 - \frac{680 \times 700.7}{16} = -261.25$$

$$S_{xx} = 29\,400 - \frac{680^2}{16} = 500$$

Hence, the values of b and a are given by:

$$b = \frac{S_{xy}}{S_{xx}} = -\frac{261.25}{500.00} = -0.5225$$

$$a = \bar{y} - b\bar{x} = \frac{\sum y}{n} - b\left(\frac{\sum x}{n}\right)$$

$$= \frac{700.7}{16} - (-0.5225) \times \frac{680}{16}$$

$$= 66.0 \text{ (to 3 sf)}$$

The value of b is given to four significant figures, since there is no way of deciding whether it should be rounded to -0.523 or to -0.522.

So, the least squares regression line is:

$$y = 66.0 - 0.5225x$$

e) To plot the least squares line, calculate two points that lie on the line and then draw the line through these points. Choose values of x that lie in the range of values observed. Two possibilities are $x = 40$, which gives:

$$y = 66 - 0.5225 \times 40 = 45.1$$

and $x = 50$, which gives:

$$y = 66 - 0.5225 \times 50 = 39.9 \text{ (to 3 sf)}$$

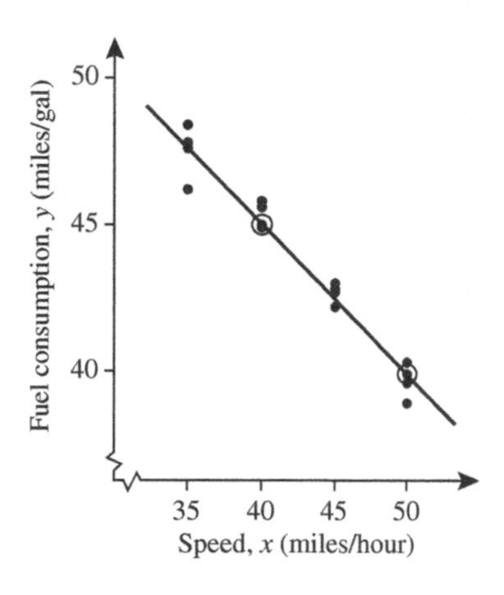

The least squares regression line is seen to provide a good fit to the data, since it is close to all the points.

Example 8

A company has a fleet of similar cars of different ages. Examination of the company records reveals that the cost of replacement parts for the older cars is generally greater than that for the newer cars. A random sample of the records is reported in the table.

Age, x (years)	1	1	2	2	2	3
Cost, y (£)	163	382	478	466	549	495
Age, x (years)	3	3	4	4	4	5
Cost, y (£)	723	681	619	1049	1033	890

a) Plot the data on a scatter diagram and comment.

b) Determine the parameters, a and b, of the regression line, $y = a + bx$.

c) Plot this line on your scatter diagram and comment on how well it fits the data.

a) The scatter diagram shows the cost, y, plotted against age, x, for each car in the sample.

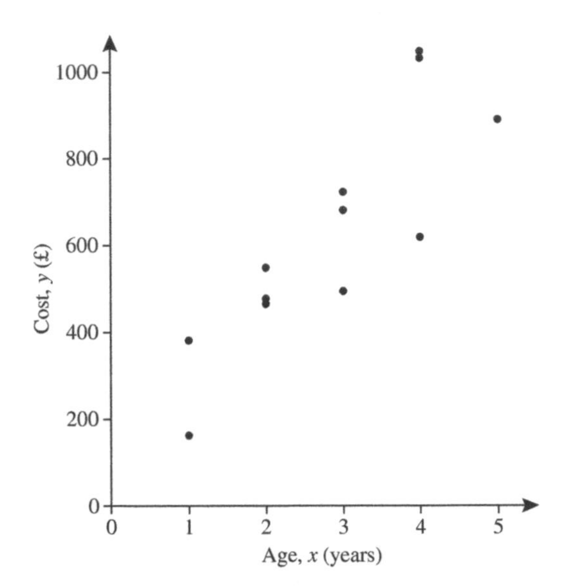

There appears to be a roughly linear relation between the variables, with the y-values (cost) generally increasing with the increasing x-values (age).

b) The summary statistics are:

$$n = 12 \quad \sum x = 34 \quad \sum x^2 = 114 \quad \sum y = 7528 \quad \sum xy = 24\,482$$

These give $S_{xx} = 17.666\,7$ and $S_{xy} = 3152.666\,7$. Hence:

$$b = \frac{3152.666\,7}{17.666\,7} = 178.452\,8 = 178.5 \quad \text{(to 1 dp)}$$

$$a = \frac{7528}{12} - b\left(\frac{34}{12}\right) = 121.717\,0 = 121.7 \quad \text{(to 1 dp)}$$

Note that the calculations retain many significant figures in order to avoid errors due to premature rounding.

c) Choose two x-values (which fall in the range of the original x-values) and calculate the corresponding y-values. When $x = 1$:

$$y = 121.7 + 178.5 = 300$$

When $x = 5$:

$$y = 121.7 + (178.5 \times 5) = 1014$$

Note that both values are given to the nearest whole number.

In selecting values for x for plotting two points on the regression line, choose values near to the minimum and maximum values of x. The values should also be easy to use, hence the choices of 40 and 50 for Example 7, and of 1 and 5 for Example 8.

S1

Draw the line through the points, (1, 300) and (5, 1014).

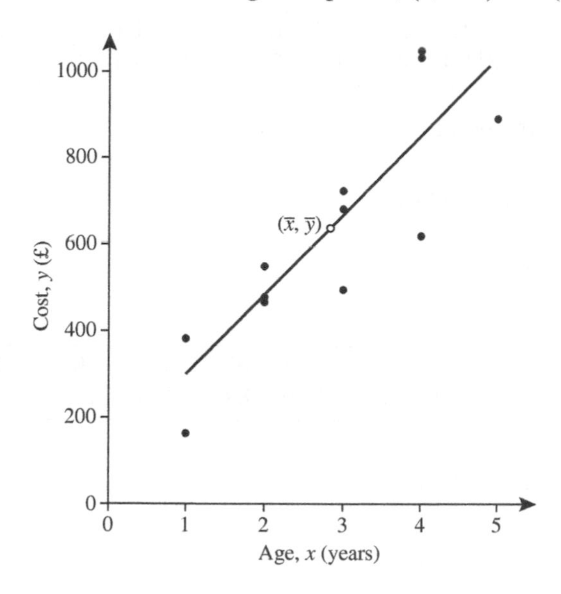

The line does seem to provide a reasonable fit to the data, though not as good as the line in Example 7.

Note If the least squares line does not pass through $(\bar{x}, \bar{y})$, you have made an error.

S1

The extent to which the least squares regression line is a good fit to the data is related to the value of r, the correlation coefficient. When $r = 1$ or $r = -1$, the line is a perfect fit to the points and the points are said to be **collinear**. As r decreases in magnitude, so the fit worsens.

The fit is excellent in Example 7 ($r = -0.981$) and very good in Example 8 ($r = 0.854$).

Calculator practice

Many calculators have in-built routines for calculating least squares regression lines. Often, the values of summary statistics are stored in memories which can be accessed by the user. Such calculators usually provide the values of a and b (and also the correlation coefficient, r). If you have this type of calculator, you should practise using it to do regression calculations. Start by using the data from Examples 7 and 8.

If you have a graphical calculator, you can plot the data as a scatter diagram and you can superimpose the calculated least squares regression line. If everything is correct, then the line will go through $(\bar{x}, \bar{y})$.

Exercise 6C

1 A random sample of eight pairs of (x, y) values are given in the table.

x	1.2	0.5	0.8	0.1	2.3	1.1	1.8	2.2
y	8.1	4.3	7.1	3.5	12.8	8.4	9.9	11.4

a) Plot a scatter diagram.
b) Find the coordinates of the point $(\bar{x}, \bar{y})$ and mark the point on your scatter diagram.
c) Find the values of a and b for the least-squares regression line $y = a + bx$.
d) Draw the regression line on your diagram, verifying that it passes through the point $(\bar{x}, \bar{y})$.

2 A random sample of six pairs of (g, h) values are given in the table.

g	55.7	10.4	67.1	91.2	30.8	72.1
h	21.2	45.9	88.3	11.4	75.4	21.4

a) Plot a scatter diagram, with values of g on the horizontal axis.
b) Find the coordinates of the point $(\bar{g}, \bar{h})$ and mark the point on your scatter diagram.
c) Using your calculator, find the equation of the regression line of h on g.
d) Draw the regression line on your diagram and verify that it passes through the point $(\bar{g}, \bar{h})$.

3 A random sample of five pairs of (w, z) values are given in the table.

w	357.2	284.3	435.8	571.9	101.2
z	0.0149	0.0375	−0.0172	−0.0345	0.0651

a) Plot a scatter diagram, with values of z on the horizontal axis.
b) Find the coordinates of the point $(\bar{w}, \bar{z})$ and mark the point on your scatter diagram.
c) Using your calculator, find the equation of the regression line of w on z.
d) Draw the regression line on your diagram and verify that it passes through the point $(\bar{w}, \bar{z})$.

4 The yield (per hectare) of a crop, y, is believed to be dependent upon the September rainfall, s. At eight locations, the average values for the last 20 years are given in the table.

y	8.2	10.1	6.5	15.0	9.9	11.9	12.3	12.4
s	14.8	10.3	13.2	18.6	12.1	11.8	13.8	15.5

a) Plot a scatter diagram with values of s on the horizontal axis.
b) Find the coordinates of the point $(\bar{s}, \bar{y})$ and mark the point on your scatter diagram.
c) Using your calculator, find the equation of the regression line of y on s.
d) Draw the regression line on your diagram and verify that it passes through the point $(\bar{s}, \bar{y})$.

5 Metal plates are immersed in an acid which erodes the plates. Six plates, each weighing 1 kg, are immersed in the acid at the same time. They are withdrawn after varying lengths of time and weighed again, with the results given in the table.

Time, t (hours)	1	2	3	4	5	6
Weight loss, w (grams)	23	42	60	79	100	115

a) Plot a scatter diagram, with values of t on the horizontal axis.

b) Find the coordinates of the point $(\overline{w}, \overline{t})$ and plot it on your scatter diagram.

c) Using your calculator, find the equation of the regression line of w on t.

d) Draw the regression line on your diagram and verify that it passes through the point $(\overline{w}, \overline{t})$.

6 A company makes small numbers of specialist farm equipment. The number sold, x, in each quarter for two years, together with the total company profits on the sales, y (£millions) of this type of equipment is given in the table.

x	11	25	22	16	18	33	32	24
y	1.8	2.6	2.7	2.2	2.3	3.1	3.7	2.4

a) Plot a scatter diagram, with values of x on the horizontal axis.

b) Find the coordinates of the point $(\overline{x}, \overline{y})$ and mark the point on your scatter diagram.

c) Using your calculator, find the equation of the regression line of y on x.

d) Draw the regression line on your diagram and verify that it passes through the point $(\overline{x}, \overline{y})$.

Prediction and extrapolation

Prediction means estimating a future value of Y given the value of x.

Suppose that you want to predict a value for Y for a future observation at x_0. Because of random variation, you cannot be sure exactly what value will occur. However, an estimate is obtained by the substitution of x_0 in the least squares regression line:

$$y_0 = a + bx_0$$

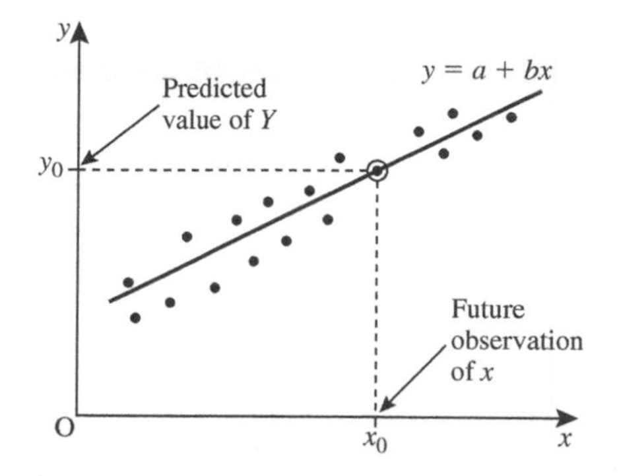

For this estimate to be a good one, the following criteria should apply.

- The least squares regression line is a good fit to the data.
- The future observation will be taken on the population from which the current data were obtained.
- The value of x for the future observation should lie in (or close to) the range of values of x used in the calculation of the least squares regression line.

If the third criterion is not satisfied, you are said to be extrapolating. **Extrapolation** can lead to seriously incorrect estimates of y if, in fact, the relation between y and x is approximately linear only in the range of the original x-values.

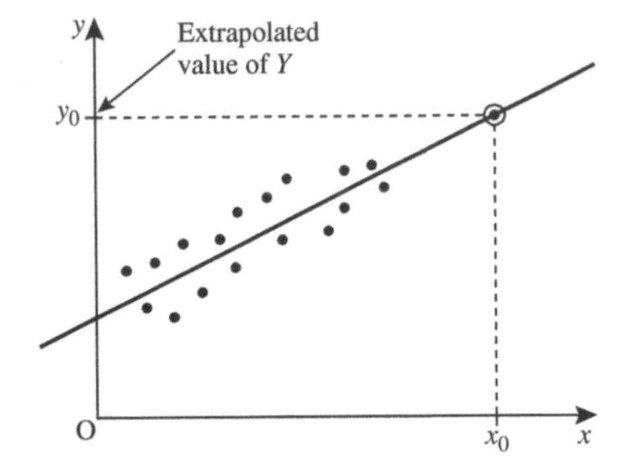

Example 9

The data in the table refer to a chain of shops in the London area. The figures reported are the numbers of sales staff (x) and the average daily takings in thousands of pounds (y) for a random sample of shops.

x	17	39	32	17	25	43	25	32
y	7	17	10	5	7	15	11	13

x	48	10	48	42	36	30	19
y	19	3	17	15	14	12	8

a) Plot the data on a scatter diagram and verify that there is an approximate linear relation between x and y.

b) Determine the least squares regression line of y on x.

c) Use your equation to estimate the average daily takings of a shop with 21 staff.

d) The company proposes opening a new superstore in Birmingham. Explain, with a reason, why it would be unwise to use the result in part b) to estimate the daily takings in the new store.

a)

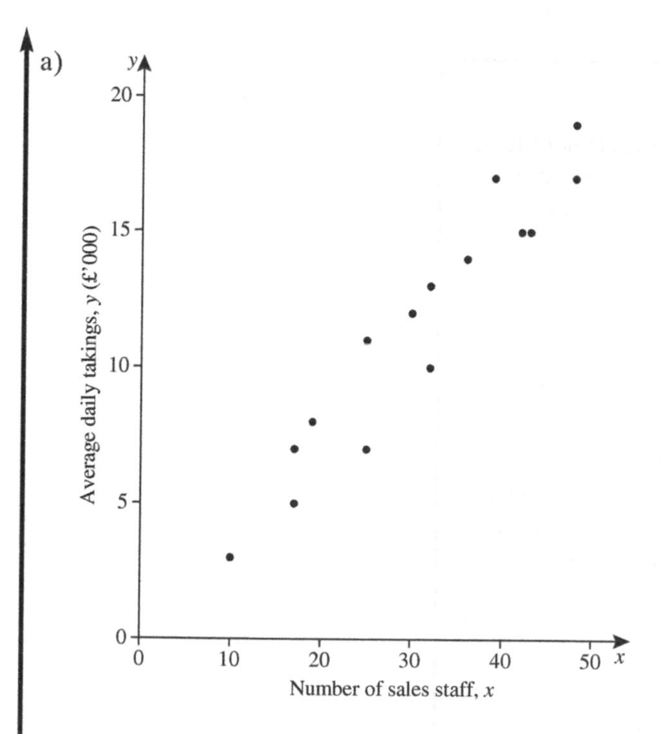

The scatter diagram shows that a linear relation between x and y is a good description of the data.

b) The summary statistics are:

$$n = 15 \quad \sum x = 463 \quad \sum x^2 = 16\,275 \quad \sum y = 173 \quad \sum xy = 6102$$

from which $S_{xy} = 762.07$ and $S_{xx} = 1983.7$ (to 5 sf). These give:

$$b = \frac{762.07}{1983.7} = 0.384\,16 \text{ and } a = \frac{173}{15} - b \times \frac{463}{15} = -0.324\,34$$

To three significant figures, the least squares regression line is:

$$y = -0.324 + 0.384x$$

c) The value of y corresponding to $x = 21$ is given by:

$$y = -0.324 + 0.384 \times 21$$
$$= 7.74 \quad \text{(to 3 sf)}$$

The average daily takings are estimated to be a little under £7750.

d) There are two reasons. First, the customers in Birmingham and London may not have the same pattern of spending – the populations are different. Second, a superstore is very much bigger than an ordinary shop, so the x-value will be much greater. Using the least squares regression line would amount to foolish extrapolation.

Although the final answers are given to three significant figures, the intermediate calculations use greater accuracy. This is always a good idea, since premature approximation can lead to considerable errors.

Many calculators provide the possibility of accurate calculation of a y-value for a given x-value using the least squares regression line. Check whether your calculator has this facility.

Example 10

A chemist conducts a series of experiments, using the same quantities of reactants in each experiment. Each experiment lasts exactly 30 minutes, at the end of which the amount of compound formed is measured. Each experiment takes place at a different temperature. The results are as follows.

Temperature, x (°C)	20	30	40	50	60	70
Amount formed, y (grams)	0.4	1.1	1.6	2.4	3.0	3.4

a) Plot the data on a scatter diagram and comment thereon.

b) Calculate the equation of the least squares regression line.

c) Use the regression line to estimate the amount of compound that would be formed in 30 minutes at a temperature of 35°C.

d) Use the regression line to estimate the amount of compound that would be formed in 30 minutes at a temperature of 10°C. Comment on your result.

S1

a)

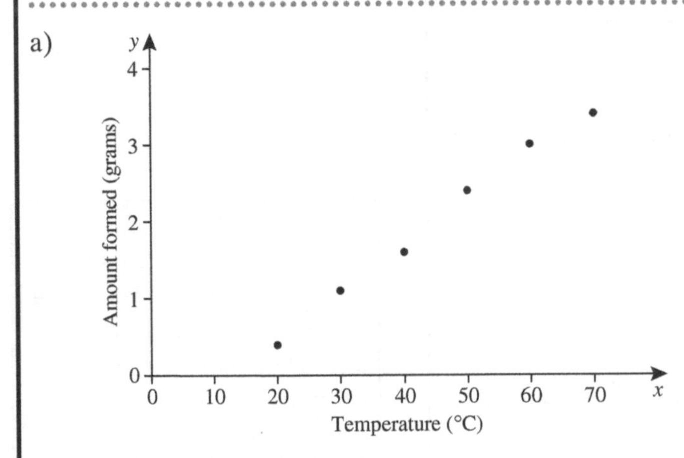

The scatter diagram illustrates the steadily increasing amounts of compound which are formed as the temperature is increased.

b) The summary statistics are:

$$n = 6 \quad \sum x = 270 \quad \sum x^2 = 13\,900 \quad \sum y = 11.9 \quad \sum xy = 643$$

which give $S_{xx} = 1750$ and $S_{xy} = 107.5$. To five significant figures, the slope and intercept are respectively:

$$b = \frac{S_{xy}}{S_{xx}} = 0.061\,429 \quad \text{and} \quad a = \frac{11.9}{6} - 0.061\,429 \times \frac{270}{6}$$

$$= -0.780\,95$$

Thus the regression line is:

$$y = -0.781 + 0.0614x$$

with the coefficients given to 3 sf.

c) Substituting $x = 35$ gives:

$$y = -0.781 + 0.0614 \times 35 = 1.37 \text{ (to 3 sf)}$$

So, at 35°C, an estimated 1.37 grams of compound will be formed in 30 minutes.

d) Substituting $x = 10$, gives:

$$y = -0.781 + 0.0614 \times 10 = -0.167 \text{ (to 3 sf)}$$

So, at 10°C, an estimated −0.167 gram of compound will be formed in 30 minutes!

This is obviously impossible. It is a case of extrapolation beyond the x-values used in the calculation of the regression line. While a straight line may be a reasonable description of the relation between temperature and the amount of compound formed, for the range 20°C to 70°C, it cannot be assumed to hold for temperatures much below 20°C, or for temperatures much above 70°C.

Exercise 6D

1 In the following six pairs of data points, the values of x are exact, but the values of y are liable to error.

x	1	2	3	4	5	6
y	4.61	18.13	32.35	45.29	48.61	72.13

a) Plot a scatter diagram.

b) Calculate the equation of the least squares regression line of y on x.

c) Estimate the value of y corresponding to $x = 3.5$.

2 In the following twelve pairs of data points, the values of u are exact but the values of v are liable to error.

u	5	5	5	6	6	6
v	0.71	0.63	0.46	0.56	0.82	0.71

u	7	7	7	8	8	8
v	1.03	0.99	0.98	1.05	1.42	1.07

a) Plot a scatter diagram.

b) Calculate the equation of the least squares regression line of v on u.

c) Plot your regression line on your scatter diagram.

d) Estimate the value of v when $u = 9$.

3 A factory uses steam to keep its radiators hot. Records are kept of y, the monthly consumption of steam for heating purposes (measured in kilograms of water) and of x, the average monthly temperature (in degrees C). The results are set out in the table.

x	1.8	−1.3	−0.9	14.9	16.3	21.8	23.6	24.8
y	11.0	11.1	12.5	8.4	9.3	8.7	6.4	8.5

x	21.5	14.2	8.0	−1.7	−2.2	3.9	8.2	9.2
y	7.8	9.1	8.2	12.2	11.9	9.6	10.9	9.6

a) Plot the data on a scatter diagram.

b) Determine the least squares regression line of y on x.

c) Plot this line on your scatter diagram.

d) Given that the average temperature one month was 12.5°C, use your estimated regression line to predict the consumption of steam for heating purposes during that month.

4 The table shows the annual pensions that can be obtained for an investment, at ages 60 and 70, of £100 000, from various insurance companies. The two figures in each column are for the same insurance company.

	M	F	M	M	F
Age 60 (£x)	6605	6290	6464	6607	6144
Age 70 (£y)	8552	7724	8630	8595	7968

	M	F	F	F	M
Age 60 (£x)	6235	6424	6105	6395	6411
Age 70 (£y)	8369	7682	7523	7904	8615

a) Draw a scatter diagram for the data, labelling the points M and F, as indicated.

b) Comment on your scatter diagram.

c) Calculate the least squares regression line for the complete set of data.

d) Calculate the least squares regression line for the data points labelled M and the least squares regression line for the data points labelled F.

e) Data points labelled M are for males and data points labelled F are for females. Give a reason for the fact that the two lines are very different.

f) Two females, one aged 60 and the other aged 70, invest £100 000 in a particular insurance company. Use the appropriate regression line to estimate the annual pension payable to the 70-year-old, given that the pension payable to the 60-year-old is £6250.

5 The acidity/alkalinity of a liquid is measured by its pH value (pure water has a pH value of 7 and lower values indicate acidity). The data in the table refer to measurements of the pH values of samples of water collected from random locations in lakes in the vicinity of a Canadian copper smelting plant. It is believed that debris and dust from the smelter will be carried through the atmosphere and will contaminate the neighbourhood. The data in the table shows d, the distance (in km) of a lake from the smelter, and p, the pH value.

d	3.9	6.5	13.5	41.9	47.7	52.3	61.3	75.5	90.3
p	3.40	3.20	4.20	5.19	4.41	6.75	7.01	6.40	4.75

a) Which is the response variable?

b) Plot the data using a scatter diagram. Comment on any key features.

c) Determine the value of the correlation coefficient, r. Explain carefully how this value should be interpreted.

d) Find an appropriate regression line of the form $y = a + bx$, giving the values of a and b to the accuracy that you feel is appropriate. Plot your line on your scatter diagram.

e) Explain carefully what the values of a and b mean in the context of the question.

f) Where you feel that it is appropriate, give the estimated pH values for lakes at distances of 0 km, 50 km, 100 km and 200 km from the smelter. If you do not feel that it is appropriate to provide an estimated pH value, explain the basis for your decision.

6.5 Calculation of residuals

You have seen that the true relation between x and y may not be exactly linear, or may be linear only for a restricted range of x-values. However, plotting the data, calculating the least squares regression line and plotting the line on the scatter diagram, does *not* complete the statistical analysis.

There are two reasons for plotting the line.

- To make sure that there are no gross errors in the calculations.
- To examine the **residuals**.

A **residual** is an observed y-value minus the value given by the regression line.

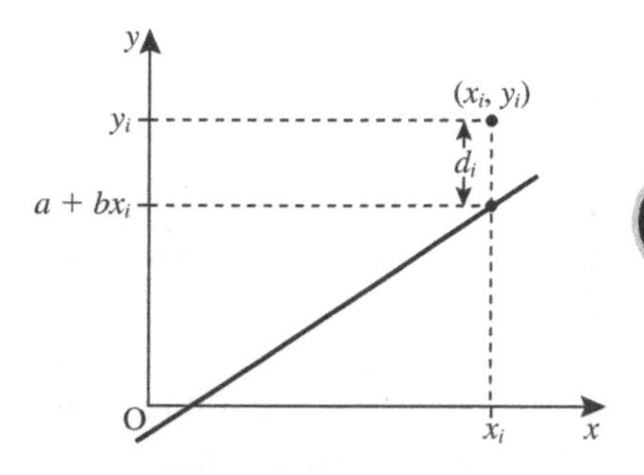

S1

The residual associated with the data point (x_i, y_i) is d_i, given by:

$$d_i = y_i - (a + bx_i) = y_i - a - bx_i$$

A large (positive or negative) value of d_i therefore indicates a data point which is not well 'explained' by the regression line.

When the magnitude of the residual associated with one data point is much larger than that for any of the others, the data point is described as being an **outlier**.

If there is a single outlier, you should check for errors. Maybe 9.2 has been recorded as 99.2, or 2.9. Or maybe this observation was taken under different conditions from all the others. For example, it might be the only measurement taken on a winter's day, with the remainder being taken in June.

An **outlier** is a data point having a relatively large residual.

Having identified one or more outliers, you should look for explanations. When the explanation is a simple error, you correct it. If you find that the data comes from more than one population, you could analyse each population separately.

Example 11

Ten randomly chosen observations on the explanatory variable, x, and the response variable, y, had the following values:

x	132	246	188	343	512	442	377	413	421	334
y	116	188	136	215	300	266	239	253	180	218

a) Plot the data using a scatter diagram and verify that the diagram suggests that there is an outlier.

b) Obtain the least squares regression line of y on x, using all ten pairs of data points. Plot this line on your scatter diagram.

c) Determine the residuals corresponding to the points (421, 180) and (512, 300).

d) Obtain the least squares regression line omitting the point (421, 180).

e) Plot this line on your scatter diagram. Determine the revised residual corresponding to the point (512, 300).

f) Comment on the consequences of removing the outlier.

a)

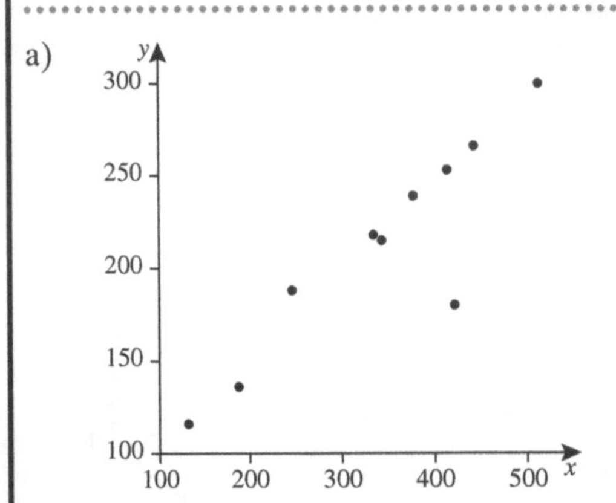

The diagram shows that all the data points except (421, 180) lie close to a straight line, suggesting that (421, 180) is an outlier.

In a real situation, you would now move straight to part d) of the question, removing the outlier.

b) With $n = 10$, you have:

$$\sum x = 3408 \quad \sum x^2 = 1\,289\,936 \quad \sum y = 2111 \quad \sum xy = 775\,229$$

These give $S_{xx} = 128\,489.6$ and $S_{xy} = 55\,800.2$. The regression line has a slope of 0.434 28 (to 5 sf) and an intercept of 63.098 (to 5 sf). Using three significant figures, the equation of the regression line is:

$$y = 63.1 + 0.434x$$

The diagram displays the line and the residuals.

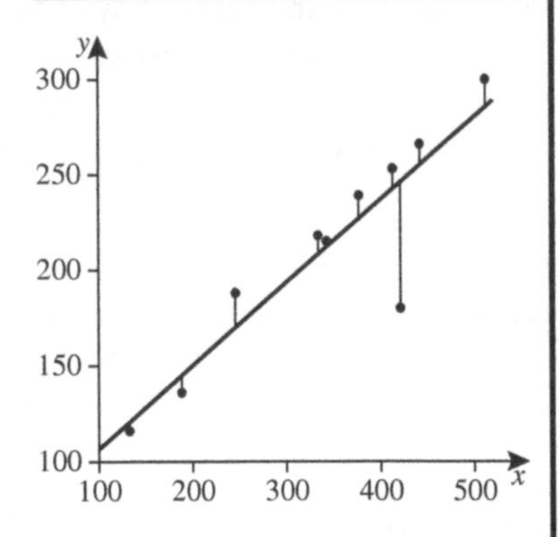

c) From the regression line, the value of y that corresponds to $x = 421$ is:

$$63.098 + 0.434\,28 \times 421 = 245.93 \text{ (to 5 sf)}$$

Since the observed value of y is 180, the residual for this data point is:

$$180 - 245.93 = -65.9 \text{ (to 3 sf)}$$

The corresponding calculation for the data point (512, 300) gives the residual:

$$300 - (63.098 + 0.434\,28 \times 512) = 14.6 \text{ (to 3 sf)}$$

d) Having removed the data point (421, 180), the summary statistics become:

$$n = 9 \quad \sum x = 3408 - 421 = 2987 \quad \sum x^2 = 1\,112\,695$$
$$\sum y = 1931 \quad \sum xy = 699\,449$$

These give (to 5 sf) $S_{xx} = 121\,342.9$ and $S_{xy} = 58\,571.6$. The revised slope and intercept are respectively (to 5 sf) 0.482 69 and 54.355. Using three significant figures, the equation of the new regression line is:

$$y = 54.4 + 0.483x$$

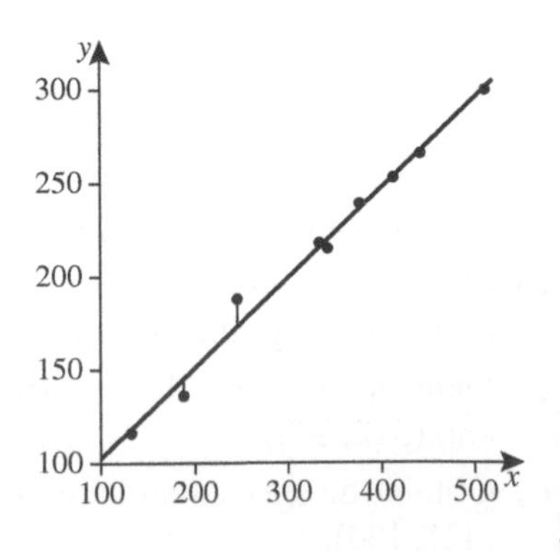

S1

e) The revised residual for the data point (512, 300) is given by:

$$300 - (54.355 + 0.482\,69 \times 512) = -1.49 \text{ (to 3 sf)}$$

f) The removal of the outlier point (421, 180) reduces the sizes of most of the residuals, so that, visually, the line appears to be a much better fit to the remaining data points.

The formula:

$$(\text{residual})_i = y_i - a - bx_i$$

is **not** included in the formula booklet but should be learnt.

When a data point has an x-value that is much bigger than (or much smaller than) all the other x-values, it will always have a big influence on the least squares line. The next pair of diagrams provide examples of **influential data points.**

In these diagrams, fifteen of the sixteen points have the same values in both cases. These values show no special relation between x and y. The regression line is principally determined by the location of the influential point.

S1

A data point may be both influential and an outlier.

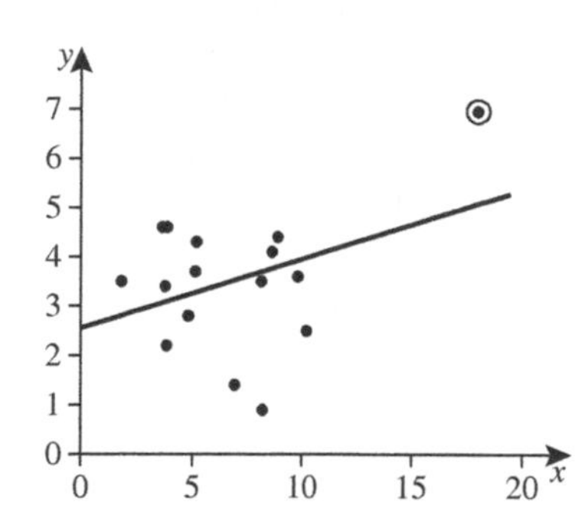

However, an influential data point need not be a outlier.

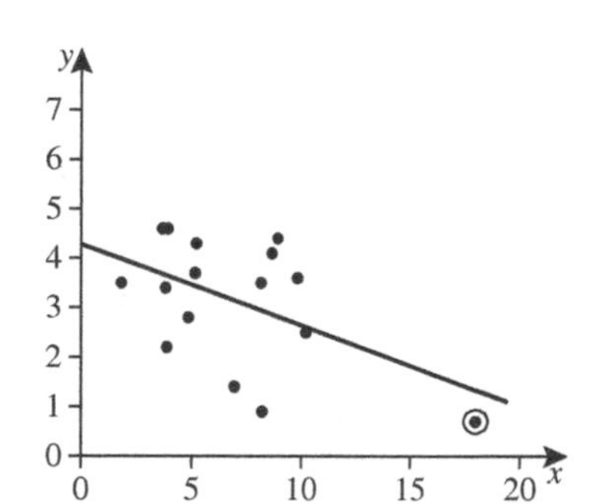

An **influential** data point has an x-value much greater (or less) than the other x-values.

Exercise 6E

1 The times taken by children of various ages to run 100 m were noted and recorded in the table.

Age (months)	88	101	120	171	98	112	90	117	106
Time (seconds)	18.7	17.7	18.6	19.5	18.7	17.3	18.3	17.3	17.2

a) Plot a scatter diagram for the data.

b) Identify an influential point. Remove this point from the data, and calculate the least squares line of regression of time on age, for the remaining data.

c) Plot this line on your scatter diagram.

2 The rents per week, in the Low Season and the High Season, for a random sample of French holiday homes are given in the table.

Low Season (£x)	130	154	235	350	680
High Season (£y)	275	266	420	595	1780
Low Season (£x)	490	450	700	350	375
High Season (£y)	2460	1000	1300	625	375

a) Draw a scatter diagram for the data.

b) Calculate the least squares regression line and, by drawing it on your scatter diagram, identify the largest residual, giving its value.

c) Given that this large residual is due to an accidental transposition of the first two digits in the value of x, calculate the least squares regression line for the corrected data.

S1

3 The populations and areas of 11 European countries are given in the table.

	Greece	France	Germany	UK	Moldavia	Russia
Area, x ('0000 km^2)	13.2	54.5	35.7	24.4	3.4	1707.5
Population, y (millions)	10.5	58.8	82.1	59.1	4.2	146.9
	Belgium	**Neth'ds**	**Denmark**	**Portugal**	**Spain**	
Area, x ('0000 km^2)	3.1	4.2	4.3	9.2	50.5	
Population, y (millions)	10.2	15.7	5.3	9.9	39.4	

a) Plot a scatter diagram for the data, using a scale of 1 cm per 100 units of x and 1 cm per 20 units of y. Identify the influential point.

b) Remove this influential point from the data, and calculate the least squares line of regression of y on x, for the remaining data. Calculate the value of y predicted by this regression line when $x = 1707.5$. Comment on this value of y in the light of the given data.

c) Calculate the value of the product moment correlation coefficient, r, for the original data set. Repeat your calculation for the reduced data set from which the influential point has been removed. Comment on the two values, explaining the difference.

6.6 Linear scaling

Sometimes correlation and regression calculations are greatly simplified by using a linear scaling of one or both of the variables.

Recall that: $r = \dfrac{S_{xy}}{\sqrt{S_{xx}S_{yy}}}$

Linear scaling is covered on pages 26–28.

where:

$$S_{xy} = \sum(x - \bar{x})(y - \bar{y}) \qquad S_{xx} = \sum(x - \bar{x})^2 \qquad S_{yy} = \sum(y - \bar{y})^2$$

If a constant, k, is added to every x-value, their mean, $\bar{x}$, increases by k. Writing $x_s = x + k$, the mean $\bar{x}_s$ is given by $\bar{x}_s = \bar{x} + k$. It follows that:

$$x_s - \bar{x}_s = (x + k) - (\bar{x} + k) = x - \bar{x}$$

Thus, the scaling does not change the values of S_{xx} and S_{xy} and hence r is unaltered.

Similarly, adding a constant to every y-value has no effect on r, and the same is true if constants are added to both the x-values and the y-values.

If each x-value is multiplied by a positive constant, c, then their mean is also multiplied by c. Writing $x_s = cx$, you have $\bar{x}_s = c\bar{x}$ and hence:

$$x_s - \bar{x}_s = cx - c\bar{x} = c(x - \bar{x})$$

In this case, therefore, S_{xx} is multiplied by c^2 and $\sqrt{S_{xx}}$ is multiplied by c. Similarly, S_{xy} is multiplied by c. Thus, in the formula for r, both numerator and denominator are multiplied by c. These changes cancel and the value of r is again unaffected.

Once again, this argument applies to scaling of the y-values, and also to scaling of both the x-values and the y-values.

The correlation coefficient, r, is unaffected by linear scaling.

S1

Example 12

a) Use linear scaling to determine the value of the correlation coefficient for the following eight pairs of (x, y) values.

x	1 230 005	1 230 007	1 230 009	1 230 010
y	0.0003	0.0004	0.0009	0.0011
x	1 230 002	1 230 004	1 230 001	1 230 007
y	0.0001	0.0009	0.0004	0.0008

b) Find the equation of the regression line for these data.

a) There are two obvious linear scalings:

$$x_s = x - 1\,230\,000 \quad y_s = y \times 10\,000$$

Using these, the original data simplify to the following:

x_s	5	7	9	10	2	4	1	7
y_s	3	4	9	11	1	9	4	8

which are obviously going to be much easier to deal with.

Of course, it is entirely possible to type all these digits accurately into the calculator without making an error, but it requires considerable concentration. However, even when the entries are made correctly, many calculators will be unable to obtain the correct result.

For the scaled data, you have:

$$n = 8 \quad \sum x_s = 45 \quad \sum x_s^2 = 325 \quad \sum y_s = 49$$
$$\sum y_s^2 = 389 \quad \sum x_s y_s = 332$$

These give: $S_{x_s x_s} = 71.875$, $S_{x_s y_s} = 56.375$, and $S_{y_s y_s} = 88.875$.
The correlation coefficient, r, is given by:

$$r = \frac{56.375}{\sqrt{71.875 \times 88.875}} = 0.705 \text{ (to 3 sf)}$$

So, the correlation coefficient for the original data is also 0.705 (to 3 sf).

b) The regression line for the (x_s, y_s) data is given by:

$$y_s = 1.713\,043 + 0.784\,3478 x_s$$

with coefficients given to 7 sf.

For the original data, the regression line is therefore given by:

$$y \times 10\,000 = 1.713\,043 + 0.784\,3478 \times (x - 1\,230\,000)$$
$$= -964\,746.081 + 0.784\,3478x$$

and becomes:

$$y = -96.4746 + 0.000\,078\,4348x$$

where the final coefficients are given to 6 sf.

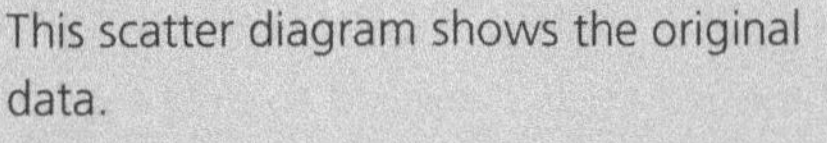
This scatter diagram shows the original data.

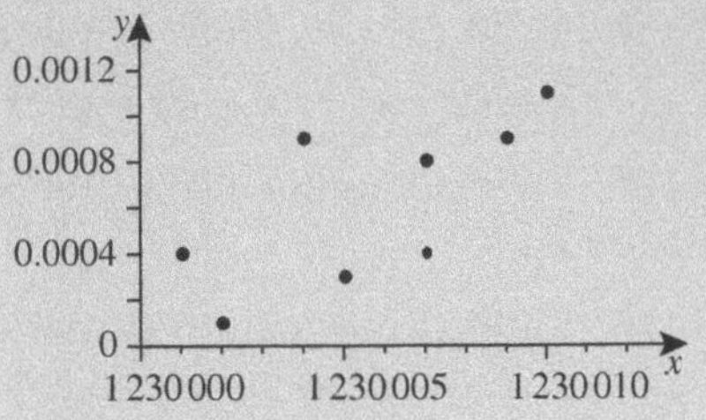

This scatter diagram shows the scaled data.

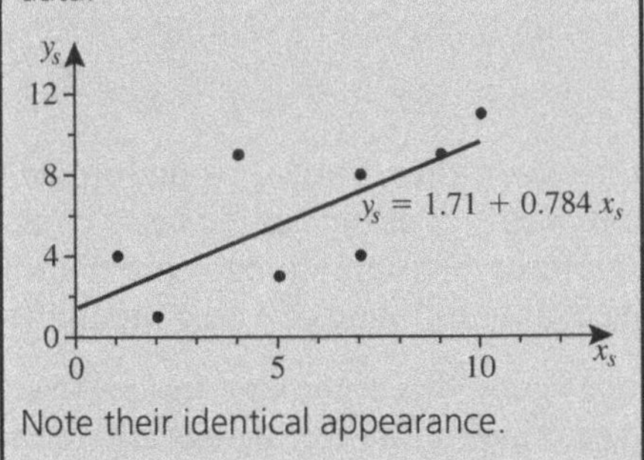

Note their identical appearance.

The large number of significant figures are necessary, so that any y-values calculated from the regression line can be obtained with reasonable accuracy.

Exercise 6F

This exercise is intended to provide practice in using scaling. It is not, however, intended to provide examples of questions likely to be set on an AQA examination paper.

1 The domestic sales of gas (x gigawatt hours) and electricity (y terawatt hours) in the first quarters of the years 1993 to 1999 are given in the table.

Gas (x)	124 905	131 225	134 293	160 624
Electricity (y)	30.03	31.31	31.90	33.90
Gas (x)	137 264	132 260	133 903	
Electricity (y)	31.54	32.26	33.14	

a) Calculate the value of the product moment correlation coefficient, and the values of the slope and intercept of the least squares line of regression of y on x.

b) Calculate the scaled data resulting from:

$$x_s = \frac{x}{1000} - 120 \qquad y_s = y - 30$$

and draw a scatter diagram for the scaled data.

c) For the scaled data, calculate the value of the product moment correlation coefficient, and verify that its value is unchanged by the scaling.

d) Calculate values for the slope and the intercept of the line of regression of y_s on x_s.

e) Use the regression line obtained in part a) to find the estimated domestic sale of electricity (in terawatt hours) when $x = 32.5$. Verify that the same estimate is obtained using the regression line in part d).

2 The December figures for mean rainfall and minimum temperature in various Mediterranean countries are given in the table.

Rainfall, x (mm)	68	77	71	7	8	127	73	47	48
Min temp, y (°C)	7	2	8	10	12	11	9	9	−2

a) Calculate the value of r and the equation of the least squares regression line of y on x.

b) Calculate the scaled data resulting from the scaling

$$x_s = \frac{x}{25.4} \qquad y_s = 1.8y + 32$$

so that x_s is the rainfall in inches, and y_s is the minimum temperature in °F. Draw a scatter diagram for the scaled data.

c) For the scaled data, calculate the value of r, verifying that its value is unchanged by the scaling.

d) Calculate the equation of the least squares line of regression of y_s on x_s.

e) Use the regression line obtained in part a) to find the estimated value of y when $x = 80$. Verify that the same estimate is obtained using the regression line in part d).

3 A car is driven on a test track at a steady speed and the fuel economy in miles per gallon is noted. The test is repeated for various speeds, with the results given in the table.

Speed, x (mph)	70	65	60	55	50	45	40	35
Economy, y (mpg)	32.1	34.3	37.8	40.2	44.5	47.9	51.2	55.2

a) Calculate the value of r and the equation of the least squares regression line of y on x.

b) Calculate the scaled data resulting from the scaling

$$x_s = 1.61x \qquad y_s = 0.425y$$

so that x_s is the speed in km per hour, and y_s is the economy in km per litre. Draw a scatter diagram for the scaled data.

c) For the scaled data, calculate the value of r, confirming that its value is unchanged by the scaling.

d) Calculate the equation of the least squares line of regression of y_s on x_s.

e) Use the regression line obtained in part a) to find the estimated value of y when $x = 53$. Verify that the same estimate is obtained using the regression line in part d).

f) Use the regression line obtained in part a) to find the predicted economy when the car is stationary: that is, travelling at 0 mph. Comment on the result.

Summary

You should know how to ...	Check out
1 Calculate S_{xx}, S_{xy}, and S_{yy}.	**1** Calculate S_{xx}, S_{xy}, and S_{yy} for the following data: (see table 1 below)
2 Calculate and interpret the product moment correlation coefficient.	**2** Calculate the product moment correlation coefficient, given that: $S_{xy} = 2345 \quad S_{xx} = 1800 \quad S_{yy} = 4100$
3 Distinguish between response and explanatory variables.	**3** In each of the following cases distinguish between response and explanatory variables: a) During a traffic census, observers watch for various periods of time, counting the numbers of cars in each period. b) Apple pickers are paid according to the amount they pick each day. At the end of each day, the total weight of the apples and their resulting pay are recorded.
4 Determine the least squares regression line.	**4** With Y as the response variable, determine the least squares regression line in each of the following cases: a) (see table 4a below) b) $n = 12$, $\sum x = 15.4$, $\sum y = 8.2$, $S_{xy} = 47.23$, $S_{xx} = 12.1$

Check out 1:

x	33	40	44	50	56	65
y	2.4	3.8	4.9	3.9	5.0	4.0

Check out 4 a):

x	1	2	3	4	5	6	7	8
y	1.4	2.2	3.5	3.8	4.2	4.0	5.0	5.9

5 Use a least squares regression line for prediction, and understand the dangers of extrapolation.	**5** The least squares regression line $y = 4.1 + 8.2x$ has been calculated from twenty observations, with the values of x being 21, 22, …, 40, and the correlation coefficient being 0.83 a) A future observation will be taken at $x = 28.2$. Predict the value of y. b) For what range of values of x might it be reasonable to use the above line?

Revision exercise 6

S1

1 Estimate, **without undertaking any calculations**, the values of the product moment correlation coefficient between the variables X and Y in **each** of the scatter diagrams below.

a)

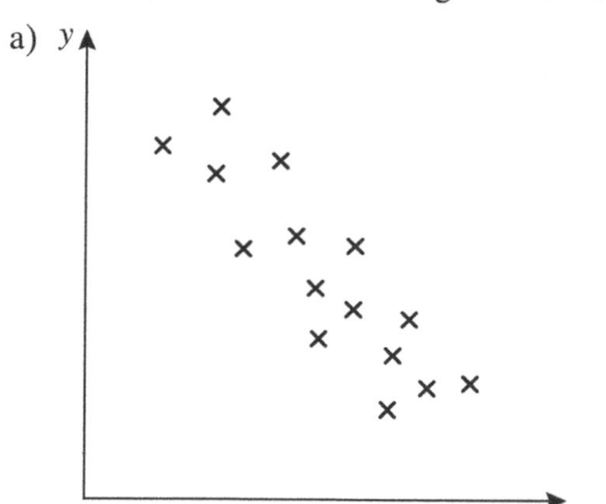

b)

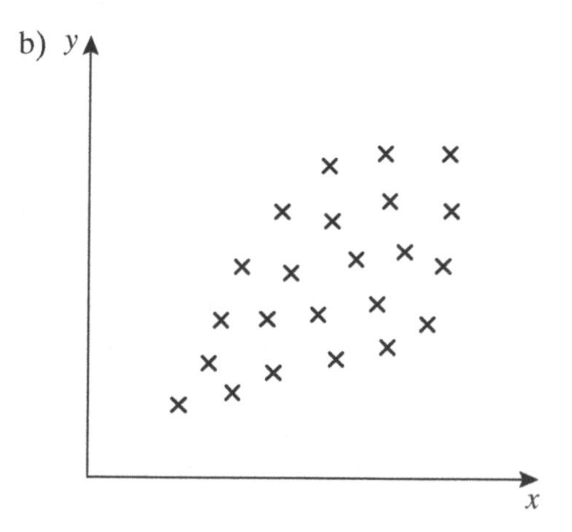

c)

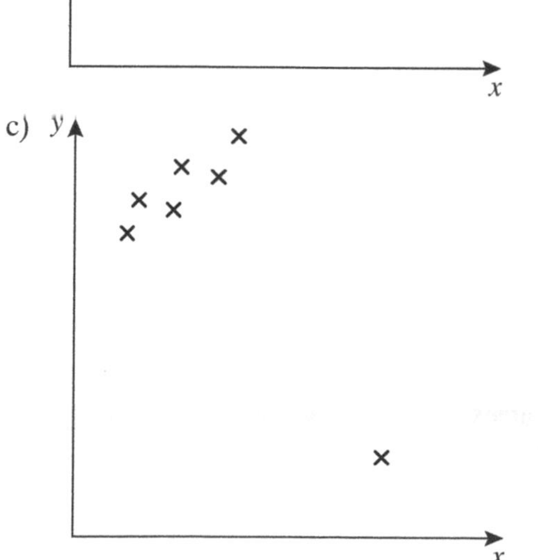

(*AQA, 2002*)

2 The scatter diagram shows, for a sample of countries, average annual income per head, x, and the percentage of children in full-time education, y.

a) Describe the relationship between x and y.

b) Comment on the suggestion that the strength of the relationship should be measured by calculating the product moment correlation coefficient between x and y.

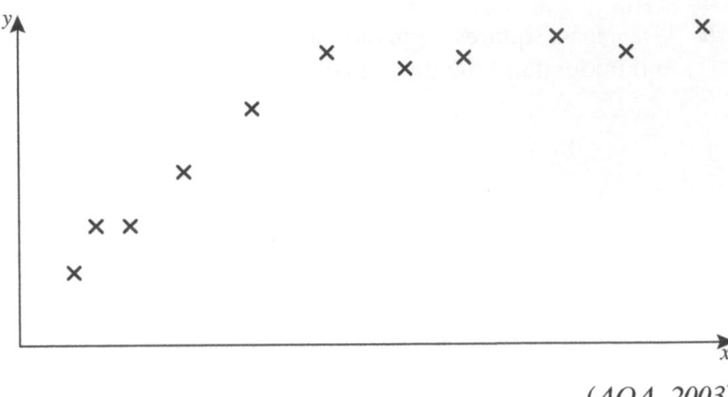

(AQA, 2003)

3 A class of Statistics students, studying correlation, obtains data by completing a questionnaire and by reference to the register. They use the data collected to practise their calculations.

A student calculates that the product moment correlation coefficient for the class is:

a) 1.17 between average journey time to school and distance travelled,

b) −0.34 between height and weight,

c) 0.75 between marks in the last test and number of days absent last term.

For **each** calculation, state, giving a reason, whether the result is probably correct, probably incorrect or definitely incorrect.

(AQA, 2001)

4 The age, x years, and the number of half-day absences from school through illness, y, are recorded for 28 school pupils, covering the age range five to eighteen.

The data are summarised as follows:

$\sum x = 322$ $\quad \sum y = 238$ $\quad \sum xy = 2485$

$\sum x^2 = 4158$ $\quad \sum y^2 = 2932$ $\quad n = 28$

Calculate the value of the product moment correlation coefficient for these data.

(AQA, 2003)

5 Over a period of one year, a greengrocer sells tomatoes at six different prices (x pence per kilogram). He calculates the average number of kilograms, y, sold per day at each of the six different prices. From these data the following are calculated.

$\sum x = 200$ $\quad \sum y = 436$ $\quad \sum xy = 12\,515$

$\sum x^2 = 7250$ $\quad \sum y^2 = 39\,234$ $\quad n = 6$

Calculate the value of the product moment correlation coefficient.

(AQA, 2002)

6 The table shows a Verbal Reasoning test score, x, and an English test score, y, for each of a random sample of eight children who took both tests.

Child	*A*	*B*	*C*	*D*	*E*	*F*	*G*	*H*
x	112	113	110	113	112	114	109	113
y	69	65	75	70	70	75	68	76

a) Calculate the value of the product moment correlation coefficient between the scores in Verbal Reasoning and English.

b) Comment briefly, in context, on the result obtained in part a). *(AQA, 2003)*

S1

7 The following table shows, for a sample of towns in Great Britain, the number of solicitors, x, and the number of cars stolen last week, y.

x	12	7	11	19	5	21	3	4	17
y	14	3	21	28	6	43	1	12	30

a) i) Calculate the value of the product moment correlation coefficient for the data.

ii) Interpret your result from part a) i) in the context of the question.

b) Comment on the suggestion that most car thieves are solicitors. *(AQA, 2003)*

8 A school owns a minibus, which is used for transporting students to sports fixtures and on school visits. It is the practice that for each trip the mileage and the petrol consumption are recorded. The tank is topped up with petrol at the end of each trip.

A statistics teacher decides to record, for each trip, the number of students transported, x, and the petrol consumption, y, in km per litre. The following table shows the data recorded for a number of trips.

Trip	*A*	*B*	*C*	*D*	*E*	*F*	*G*	*H*	*I*	*J*
x	14	2	16	9	12	5	7	7	15	11
y	8.07	8.98	8.02	8.42	8.39	8.21	8.69	8.85	8.13	8.19

a) Draw a scatter diagram of the data.

b) Calculate the equation of the regression line in the form $y = a + bx$ and draw it on your scatter diagram.

c) Interpret, in the context of this question, the value of a.

d) On one of the trips, a large amount of heavy equipment was carried in addition to the students. Identify the most likely trip, giving a reason. *(AQA, 2003)*

9 Megan and David run a small business installing double glazing. They give each job a score based on the size, number and accessibility of the windows to be double glazed. The price charged is related to this score.

The following table shows the score, x, given to each of nine jobs and the time, y hours, taken by Megan and David, working as a team, to complete each job.

Job	1	2	3	4	5	6	7	8	9
x	23	34	47	44	57	16	73	40	28
y	8.5	14.0	22.5	28.0	33.5	6.0	40.0	17.5	12.5

a) Draw a scatter diagram of these data.

b) Find the equation of the regression line of y on x and draw this line on your scatter diagram.

c) Evaluate the residual for Job 4.

d) The next job is given a score of 52.
   i) Use your regression equation to estimate the time taken to complete this job.
   ii) Also, bearing in mind your result in part c), comment on Megan's claim that it is very unlikely that this job will take more than 34 hours.

(AQA, 2002)

S1

10 One end A of an elastic string was attached to a horizontal bar and a mass, m grams, was attached to the other end B. The mass was suspended freely and allowed to settle vertically below A. The length AB, l mm, was recorded for various masses as follows.

m	100	200	300	400	500	600
l	228	236	256	278	285	301

a) Draw a scatter diagram to illustrate the above information.

b) Calculate the least squares line of regression of l on m, and plot this line on your scatter diagram.

c) Give, in context, interpretations for: i) the gradient of the line; ii) the intercept of the line on the l-axis.

d) Estimate the length of the string when a mass of 360 grams is attached at B.

e) State a physical limitation that there might be in using your equation to estimate the length of the string when a mass of 1200 grams is attached at B.

(AQA, 2002)

11 Packers at a mail-order firm select items requested by customers and pack them into parcels for posting. The time taken to pack a parcel will depend to some extent on the number of items, x, which have been ordered. A new packer is employed and after initial training, her times, y minutes, to pack a number of parcels are recorded. The parcels are listed in order of packing.

Parcel number	1	2	3	4	5	6	7	8	9	10
x	4	13	2	7	23	1	14	17	7	29
y	35	49	23	35	71	19	44	43	24	64

a) Draw a scatter diagram of the data. Label the points 1 to 10.

b) Calculate the equation of the regression line of y on x and draw the line on your scatter diagram.

c) Describe briefly the relationship suggested by your scatter diagram.

d) If the regression line is denoted $y = a + bx$, give, in the context of this question: i) an interpretation to b; ii) an interpretation to a or an explanation of why this is not possible.

e) Calculate the residuals for parcels numbered 8, 9 and 10.

f) The next parcel to be packed is to contain 12 items.
   i) Use your regression equation to predict the time taken to pack this parcel.
   ii) Modify your prediction in part i) to take account of your answers in part e).

(AQA, 2001)

S1

MS1A Practice Paper (with coursework)

75 minutes *60 marks* *You may use a graphics calculator.*

*Answer **all** questions.*

1 The following table shows the gas consumption, x kWh, and the electricity consumption, y kWh, for a house in Manchester for a sample of nine weeks in 2001.

Week	1	2	3	4	5	6	7	8	9
x	312	46	23	406	350	67	295	247	110
y	84	57	54	96	82	63	59	73	60

(a) Calculate the value of the product moment correlation coefficient for these data. *(3 marks)*

S1

(b) The householder expects that, for weeks when the gas consumption is high, the electricity consumption will be low and vice versa.

(i) Explain to what extent the value you calculated in part (a) confirms or denies the householder's expectation. *(2 marks)*

(ii) Give a reason why the value you calculated in part (a) is plausible. *(1 mark)*

2 Charlotte is a dentist. The time that each patient, attending for an appointment, spends in her surgery may be modelled by a normal distribution with mean 23 minutes and standard deviation 4 minutes.

(a) Find the probability that a randomly chosen patient, attending for an appointment, will spend between 20 and 30 minutes in her surgery. *(4 marks)*

(b) Find the length of time spent in her surgery that will be exceeded by 1% of patients. *(4 marks)*

3 A random sample of 170 students aged between 16 and 21 years was asked their opinions regarding the level of the student loan available to students in higher education.

They were asked to comment on whether they felt that the level of the loan was too low, about right or too high.

The following table summarizes their replies.

		Reply		
		Too low	**About right**	**Too high**
Age of student	**16 to 17 years**	45	17	8
	18 to 21 years	40	35	25

A student is chosen at random.

B is the event 'the student is aged 16 to 17 years'.
C is the event 'the student replied about right'.
D is the event 'the student replied too high'.
C' is the event 'not C'.

(a) Find:
   (i) $P(C)$; *(1 mark)*
   (ii) $P(B \cap D)$; *(1 mark)*
   (iii) $P(B \cup C')$; *(2 marks)*
   (iv) $P(D|B)$. *(2 marks)*

(b) Define in words the event $B \cup D$. *(2 marks)*

4 A manufacturer of balloons produces 40 per cent that are oval and 60 per cent that are round. Packets of 20 balloons are assumed to contain random samples of balloons.

(a) Determine the probability that such a packet contains:
   (i) an equal number of oval balloons and round balloons; *(3 marks)*
   (ii) fewer oval balloons than round balloons. *(2 marks)*

(b) Jack selects packets of 20 balloons at random from a large consignment until he finds a packet with exactly 12 round balloons.

Give a reason why a binomial distribution is **not** an appropriate model for the number of packets selected by Jack. *(1 mark)*

(c) Jill selects a random sample of 100 packets of 20 balloons from another large consignment and counts the number of round balloons in each packet. Her results are tabled below.

Number of round balloons	10	11	12	13	14	15
Number of packets	15	20	33	18	10	4

   (i) Find the mean and variance of these data. *(2 marks)*
   (ii) Obtain values for the mean and variance of the binomial distribution $B(20, 0.6)$. *(2 marks)*
   (iii) Hence comment on the assumption that packets of 20 balloons contain random samples of balloons. *(2 marks)*

S1

5 The following table shows the hours of sunshine, x, during nine days in August and the number of ice creams, y, sold by a beach shop in Yorkshire.

x	4.3	6.9	0.0	10.4	5.2	1.8	8.0	9.2	2.1
y	224	208	123	419	230	184	362	351	196

(a) Plot a scatter diagram of these data. *(3 marks)*

(b) Calculate the equation of the least squares regression line of y on x and draw the line on your scatter diagram. *(6 marks)*

(c) Calculate the residual for the day when the number of hours of sunshine was: (i) 8.0; (ii) 6.9. *(3 marks)*

(d) On one of the days, the shop closed early to allow the owner to attend a funeral. Suggest, giving a reason, which day this was. *(2 marks)*

(e) The owner asks you to use your regression line to forecast the daily sales when there is 20 hours of sunshine. Give **two** reasons why it would be inappropriate to do this. *(2 marks)*

6 The volume, X millilitres, of hand cream in tubs is normally distributed with mean μ and variance σ^2.

(a) From a random sample of 50 tubs, the following information was determined, where $\bar{x}$ denotes the sample mean.

$$\sum x = 25\,065 \quad \text{and} \quad \sum(x-\bar{x})^2 = 384.16$$

(i) Construct a 99% confidence interval for μ, giving the limits to two decimal places. *(6 marks)*

(ii) State why, in answering part (a) (i), you did **not** need to use the Central Limit Theorem. *(1 mark)*

(b) It is proposed that, from a second random sample of 50 tubs, **both** a 99% confidence interval and a 90% confidence interval for μ be constructed.

State the probability that **neither** of these confidence intervals will contain μ. *(1 mark)*

S1

(c) It is also proposed that, from a third random sample of 50 tubs, a 99% confidence interval for μ be constructed and that, from a fourth, independent, random sample of 50 tubs, a 90% confidence interval for μ be constructed.

Find the probability that **neither** of these confidence intervals will contain μ. *(2 marks)*

MS1B Practice Paper (without coursework)

90 minutes *75 marks* *You may use a graphics calculator.*

*Answer **all** questions.*

1 The following table shows the gas consumption, x kWh, and the electricity consumption, y kWh, for a house in Manchester for a sample of nine weeks in 2001.

Week	1	2	3	4	5	6	7	8	9
x	312	46	23	406	350	67	295	247	110
y	84	57	54	96	82	63	59	73	60

(a) Calculate the value of the product moment correlation coefficient for these data. *(3 marks)*

(b) The householder expects that, for weeks when the gas consumption is high, the electricity consumption will be low and vice versa.

(i) Explain to what extent the value you calculated in part (a) confirms or denies the householder's expectation. *(2 marks)*

(ii) Give a reason why the value you calculated in part (a) is plausible. *(1 mark)*

2 Paper clips are produced in a variety of colours.

(a) The proportion of pink paper clips produced is 0.15. Calculate the probability that, in a random sample of 24 coloured paper clips, exactly 4 are pink. *(3 marks)*

(b) The proportion of blue paper clips produced is 0.2. Determine the probability that, in a random sample of 40 coloured paper clips, at most 10 are blue. *(2 marks)*

(c) The proportion of dark coloured paper clips is 0.55. Determine the probability that, in a random sample of 50 coloured paper clips, more than 20 but fewer than 30 are dark coloured. *(4 marks)*

3 A company sells clothes by mail order catalogue. The sizes of skirts are defined by the hip measurement; thus customers of the same size will have different heights. The heights, to the nearest centimetre, of a sample of female customers of size 16 were recorded and are summarized in the table below. The sample is thought to be representative of the heights of all female customers of size 16.

Height (cm)	Frequency
131–140	6
141–150	21
151–155	19
156–160	16
161–170	24
171–190	14

(a) Identify the modal class of the heights of female customers of size 16. *(2 marks)*

(b) Calculate estimates of the mean and the standard deviation of the heights of female customers of size 16. *(5 marks)*

(c) The company decides that it is not economic to produce a range of skirts designed for customers of the same size but different heights. For each size, skirts will be designed for customers of the same height. With the intention of maximising sales, it is proposed, for customers of size 16, to make skirts suitable for those of mean height.

Without further calculation, suggest a more appropriate height. Explain your answer. *(2 marks)*

4 Jennifer attends college five days a week. Each day she is either on time or late. The following table shows the probability that she is late for each day that she attends college.

Day	Monday	Tuesday	Wednesday	Thursday	Friday
Probability late	0.4	0.1	0.1	0.1	0.55

(a) Assuming independence find the probability that, during a particular week, Jennifer is:
(i) late on both Monday and Tuesday;
(ii) on time every day. *(4 marks)*

(b) The probability that Jennifer's friend, Hassan, is late for college is 0.7 on days when Jennifer is late and 0.05 on days when Jennifer is on time.

Assuming independence, find the probability that on a particular Monday:
(i) both Jennifer and Hassan are on time; *(1 mark)*
(ii) one is on time and the other is late; *(3 marks)*
(iii) Jennifer is on time, given that only one is on time. *(3 marks)*

S1

5 Charlotte is a dentist. The time that each patient, attending for an appointment, spends in her surgery may be modelled by a normal distribution with mean 23 minutes and standard deviation 4 minutes.

(a) Find the probability that a randomly chosen patient, attending for an appointment, will spend between 20 and 30 minutes in her surgery. *(4 marks)*

(b) Find the length of time spent in her surgery that will be exceeded by 1% of patients. *(4 marks)*

(c) Charlotte has her first appointment at 9 am. Rupert has an appointment with her at 10 am. Charlotte sees three patients before Rupert. Assume that these three patients may be regarded as a random sample from all patients.
(i) Find the probability that the mean time spent in Charlotte's surgery by these three patients is less than 20 minutes. *(4 marks)*
(ii) Explain whether it is likely that Charlotte will see Rupert on time. *(2 marks)*

6 The following table shows the hours of sunshine, x, during nine days in August and the number of ice creams, y, sold by a beach shop in Yorkshire.

x	4.3	6.9	0.0	10.4	5.2	1.8	8.0	9.2	2.1
y	224	208	123	419	230	184	362	351	196

(a) Plot a scatter diagram of these data. *(3 marks)*

(b) Calculate the equation of the least squares regression line of y on x and draw the line on your scatter diagram. *(6 marks)*

(c) Calculate the residual for the day when the number of hours of sunshine was: (i) 8.0; (ii) 6.9. *(3 marks)*

(d) On one of the days, the shop closed early to allow the owner to attend a funeral. Suggest, giving a reason, which day this was. *(2 marks)*

(e) The owner asks you to use your regression line to forecast the daily sales when there is 20 hours of sunshine. Give **two** reasons why it would be inappropriate to do this. *(2 marks)*

7 The volume, X millilitres, of hand cream in tubs is normally distributed with mean μ and variance σ^2.

(a) From a random sample of 50 tubs, the following information was determined, where $\bar{x}$ denotes the sample mean.

$$\sum x = 25\,065 \quad \text{and} \quad \sum(x - \bar{x})^2 = 384.16$$

(i) Construct a 99% confidence interval for μ, giving the limits to two decimal places. *(6 marks)*

(ii) State why, in answering part (a) (i), you did **not** need to use the Central Limit Theorem. *(1 mark)*

(b) It is proposed that, from a second random sample of 50 tubs, **both** a 99% confidence interval and a 90% confidence interval for μ be constructed.

State the probability that **neither** of these confidence intervals will contain μ. *(1 mark)*

(c) It is also proposed that, from a third random sample of 50 tubs, a 99% confidence interval for μ be constructed and that, from a fourth, independent, random sample of 50 tubs, a 90% confidence interval for μ be constructed.

Find the probability that **neither** of these confidence intervals will contain μ. *(2 marks)*

7 Coursework guidance

This chapter is for students taking the S1A unit.
The S1B unit does not contain coursework.
If you are unsure which unit you are taking, you should ask your teacher.

In this chapter, you will find:

- ✦ A clear description of how to tackle your Statistics coursework
- ✦ A strand by strand breakdown of the marking grid
- ✦ Useful tips and hints from experienced moderators
- ✦ Answers to some frequently asked questions
- ✦ A final checklist

7.1 Introduction

You might ask yourself: 'Why do I need to do coursework for A-level Maths?'

Indeed you may already have completed a piece of data handling coursework at GCSE level.

Applying your statistical knowledge is important, whether it is in other subjects such as biology, psychology or business studies, or in a future work situation where you may be, for example, conducting important tests for quality control.

In your Statistics coursework you will have an opportunity to demonstrate the skills that you have acquired in the S1A unit. You will need to design a given task, collect some data, perform some relevant calculations and interpret your results.

This chapter is to help you with the coursework process right from the starting point to handing in your completed piece of work. There will be useful hints and tips from experienced moderators who work for the Examination Board as well as a clear and full description of the marking grid that will be used to assess your piece of work.

For your S1A coursework you will need to submit one task. This is worth $4\frac{1}{6}\%$ of the A level marks available (or $8\frac{1}{3}\%$ if offered at AS level).

The coursework process can be an enjoyable and rewarding experience. Hopefully these guidelines will help you to produce a piece of work that you will be proud of. It will also help you to revise some of the topics that will appear on the final written paper.

7.2 Choosing a task

The Examination Board will provide a list of tasks that are appropriate for your S1A coursework. Your teacher may decide to offer you one particular task or provide you with a number of choices. It is important to choose a task that you feel comfortable with and which gives you the scope to use your statistical skills fully.

Your teacher may provide some time in class to discuss various ideas and approaches that you might take when tackling your task.

A good starting point is to have a brainstorming session.

- Write down your ideas
- Discuss these with others in your class
- Adapt and modify your ideas and reject as necessary.

> Listen carefully to the advice of your teacher.
> ***Do not*** start a task that has not been approved by your teacher.

7.3 The coursework process

Your coursework can be broken down into a number of stages:

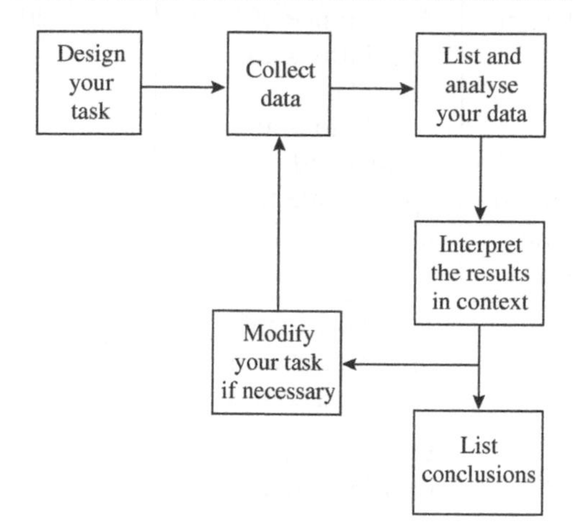

> The process will help you to clarify your thinking and ensure that you use a logical approach.

You should try to follow this process when conducting your coursework task.

7.4 Assessment criteria

Statistics coursework is marked under four strands:

- Design
- Data collection and statistical analysis
- Interpretation and validation
- Communication

There are 80 marks in total. The marking grid on page 194 shows how the marks are broken down.

The following section will discuss in detail the four strands that you will be assessed on. Reference will be made to the marking grid to help you understand exactly what is expected of you.

Marking grid for Statistics S1

Strand	0–8 marks	9–15 marks	16–20 marks	Mark awarded
1. Design	Problem defined and understood. Aims and objectives discussed. Some discussion of how the sample was obtained.	The approach to the task is coherent. The strategies to be employed are appropriate. Clear explanation of how sample was obtained. Some discussion of the statistical theories or distributions used.	A well-balanced and coherent approach. Clear discussion and justification of the statistical theories or distributions used in relation to the task.	/20
2. Data Collection and Statistical Analysis	Adequate data collected. Raw data clearly set out. Some relevant calculations are correct.	A range of relevant statistical calculations are used. Most calculations are correct, and quoted to an appropriate degree of accuracy.	A full range of calculations are used. The calculations are correct and appropriate to the task.	/20
3. Interpretation and Validation	A reasoned attempt is made to interpret the results. Some discussion of how realistic the results are. Some discussion of possible modifications.	Results are interpreted. Attempt to relate the task to the original problem. Clear discussion of possible modifications/improvements which could have been made.	Results are fully interpreted within a statistical context. Outcomes are clearly related to the original task. Clear discussion of the effects of the sampling and data collection methods used.	/20
4. Communication	The report is presented clearly and organised with some explanation. Diagrams are effective and appropriate. Conclusions are stated.	The report is clear and well organised. Other areas of work which could have been investigated are discussed. The report is consistent with a piece of work of 8–10 hours.	Appropriate language and notations used throughout. The report is clear and concise and of sufficient depth and difficulty.	/20
			Total Mark Maximum 80	**/80**

S1

Strand 1: Design

✦ **Candidates must state clear aims and identify their strategies and objectives.** **(4 marks)**

Question: What exactly are you going to do?
It must be clear what the purpose of the piece of work is. It is a good idea to write a short introduction describing the task in your own words with some initial predictions and hypotheses. You will not be given 4 marks for simply copying out the original task as given.

It is useful to consider samples from at least two different populations that will enable meaningful comparisons to be made later.

If comparing word length and sentence length from two books, which two books would you use and why? Maybe look at a children's book against an adult book, or a 19th Century novel against a 21st Century novel.

If comparing heights or reaction times you could compare males against females or different age groups.

✦ **They must clearly define the population being used.** **(2 marks)**

For a full 2 marks you will need to clearly state the population from which you will be sampling.

You could state that 'My population is all the words in the book *Wuthering Heights*'.

✦ **They must explain how their sample was obtained and give details of any questionnaires/experiments used.** **(6 marks)**

You will need to choose some appropriate data to meet your aims. The intention is that you will collect your own data to analyse, but in some cases it may be necessary to collect data in small groups. If this happens, then the final write-up **must** be your own work and you will have to sign a declaration to state that it is.

You must note in your work if the data was collected as a group, and you should state who was in your group.

Question: How are you going to collect your data?
It is important to discuss your sampling method in some detail. Some of these points will need to be considered:

✦ What **sample size** will you use and why?
✦ Are you trying to choose a **random sample** where each member of the population has an equal chance of being selected? If so how are you going to obtain it?

You may need to use a random number generator from a calculator to help you.

If you are unsure about how to use a calculator to obtain random numbers, talk to your teacher. This will not lead to any loss of marks.

If collecting a sample of 50 sentences from a book you could proceed by addressing these questions:

✦ How many pages are there in the book?
✦ How can you use a calculator to obtain random numbers to select a page number?

- Which sentence will you then choose from the pages selected? Do you use more random numbers? If not, why not? Do you choose the first complete sentence on your pages? Is this still random? If not, does it matter?
- Could any problems occur with your method of collecting the sample? What happens if you obtain the same number twice, or the same sentence twice? Do you include it, or ignore it?

All of these issues need to be discussed in your report as there are 6 marks specifically allocated to your sampling method.

If you design a questionnaire or perform an experiment to generate data, then ensure that full details are given in your report. You still need to consider who or what you use in your experiment, and you still need to consider randomness to minimize bias in your sample selection.

Despite using a random method of selecting your sample you can still end up with an unusual sample. All you are ensuring is that your method of selection is random!

- **There should be a clear discussion of which statistical theories or distributions are being used and why. (6 marks)**

Throughout your coursework you will be using various statistical techniques to analyse your data. You need to discuss statistical theories, but only when they arise and in context.

Do not copy out vast chunks of text from a book just because you feel that it might be relevant to your analysis.

Be selective, and express the relevant theory as you understand it using your own words.

If you are producing a confidence interval for μ, the mean length of a chocolate bar, then you will need to use the Central Limit Theorem as well as unbiased estimates of the population mean and variance.

This statement shows good understanding of the underlying statistical theories being used:
'... As the distribution of X, the length of a chocolate bar, is unknown, the Central Limit Theorem needs to be applied. As a sample of over 30 bars has been selected, the distribution of the sample mean, $\overline{X}$, will be approximately normally distributed. ...'

You can make similar statements in context about unbiased estimators. Discuss also how the confidence interval is developed from the sample mean: how do you get the z-values used in the confidence interval?

You could just look the definitions up in a book and state them, but for the highest marks examiners expect you to state why the Central Limit Theorem is necessary for your task.

If you are carrying out a regression task you will need to discuss:

- How well the two variables are correlated, and what this means.
- What is the regression line?

- What does the regression line of y on x minimise and how does that relate to your data?
- If you are calculating residuals for your data from your line, how do you do that? What do the values tell you?

- **Assumptions made should be fully discussed. (2 marks)**

Question: In collecting your data what assumptions or rules are you making?

If you are investigating the number of letters in a word, how will you deal with hyphenated words, acronyms such as NUS or numbers such as 432?

There is no right or wrong answer here. Just try to ensure that your assumptions are sensible.

If you state clearly what you are assuming, then as long as you apply your rules consistently that will satisfy the criteria.

S1

Strand 2: Data Collection and Statistical Analysis

This strand assesses how successful you are in the collection of your data and the quality of the analysis that you have performed on it.

- **Raw data must be recorded and then organized as appropriate. (2 marks)**

There is an expectation that you will list your data in its original raw form. You can put your data in the body of the work or place it in an appendix.

Your data can be arranged into a frequency distribution if appropriate.

- **An adequate amount of data should be collected. (2 marks)**

If you are undertaking a task requiring the Central Limit Theorem then you must collect a sample of size at least 30.

You may feel that a sample size of significantly more than 30 is appropriate to add weight to your argument.

If the Central Limit Theorem is not being applied in your task, a discussion of sample size should take place. You should avoid taking the whole population as your sample, as a sampling technique should be applied.

- **The calculations are correct and appropriate to the statistical model and the content of the unit. (10 marks)**

You are expected to think carefully about the calculations you will be using, and to be selective.

This section is worth 10 marks and is important, but it is not the only skill that is being assessed. Beware of using every statistical technique you have ever heard of, whether relevant or not.

If you are focusing on confidence intervals you may need to calculate for your samples:

- The sample mean.
- The sample variance.
- The unbiased estimator of the population variance.
- The confidence intervals.

Here is an example:

You may have collected some data from which you wish to calculate a 95% confidence interval for the population mean, μ. These are the summary statistics:

$$\sum x = 2259.2$$
$$n = 80$$
$$\sum x^2 = 64\,457.1$$

The sample mean, $\bar{x} = \dfrac{\sum x}{n}$

$$= \frac{2259.2}{80}$$
$$= 28.24$$

S1

Unbiased estimate of population variance,

$$s^2 = \frac{1}{n-1}\left\{\sum x^2 - \frac{(\sum x)^2}{n}\right\}$$
$$= \frac{1}{79}\left\{64\,457.1 - \frac{(2259.2)^2}{80}\right\}$$
$$= 8.320\ldots$$

Therefore, 95% confidence limits for μ are given by:

$$28.24 \pm 1.96\sqrt{\frac{8.320\ldots}{80}}$$
$$= 28.24 \pm 0.632\ldots$$
$$= (27.6, 28.9) \text{ to 3 sf}$$

The mode, median and interquartile range would be unnecessary and inappropriate in an analysis of confidence intervals, and would receive no credit.

Including unnecessary work, such as attempting to show that $\overline{X}$ has a normal distribution by taking sub-samples (when the result is already known from the Central Limit Theorem) would detract significantly from your piece of work.

If you are focusing on correlation and regression you may need to:

- ✦ Draw scatter diagrams.
- ✦ Calculate the correlation coefficient.
- ✦ Calculate the regression line of y on x.
- ✦ Calculate residuals for appropriate points.
- ✦ Make predictions from your line(s).

Your calculations will be marked for accuracy so take care to check your work carefully.

It is not expected that you will try to use other statistical skills outside the content of the S1A unit.

Here is an example:

You may have collected some data from which you can draw a scatter diagram. From the diagram, you can comment on whether you think there is any linear correlation between the two variables.

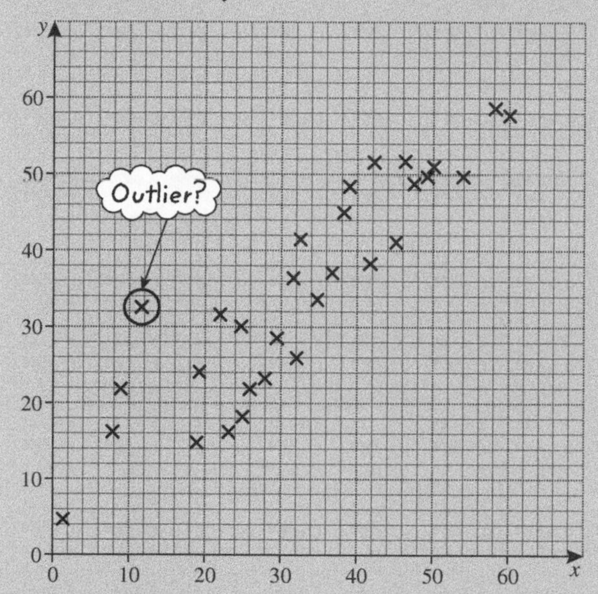

Once you have drawn the diagram and you are satisfied that there is some linear correlation, you can then calculate the product moment correlation coefficient for the data.

Here are the summarised statistics for the original data:

$\sum x = 966$ $\sum y = 1051$ $\sum x^2 = 37\,570$

$\sum y^2 = 42\,669$ $\sum xy = 39\,361$ $n = 30$

So $r = \dfrac{S_{xy}}{\sqrt{S_{xx}S_{yy}}}$

where $S_{xy} = \sum xy - \dfrac{(\sum x)(\sum y)}{n}$

$= 39\,361 - \dfrac{(966)(1051)}{30} = 5518.8$

$S_{xx} = \sum x^2 - \dfrac{(\sum x)^2}{n}$

$= 37\,570 - \dfrac{966^2}{30} = 6464.8$

$S_{yy} = \sum y^2 - \dfrac{(\sum y)^2}{n}$

$= 42\,669 - \dfrac{1051^2}{30} = 5848.967 \ldots$

The diagram may suggest possible outliers for which you may later calculate residuals.

S1

$$r = \frac{5518.8}{\sqrt{6464.8 \times 5848.967\ldots}}$$
$$= 0.897 \text{ (3 sf)}$$

This value of r suggests strong positive linear correlation between the two variables, so it is sensible to calculate the regression line of y on x.

Let $y = a + bx$

$$\text{where } b = \frac{S_{xy}}{S_{xx}}$$
$$= \frac{5518.8}{6464.8}$$
$$= 0.854 \text{ (3 sf)}$$

S1

$$\bar{x} = \frac{\sum x}{n} \qquad \bar{y} = \frac{\sum y}{n}$$
$$= \frac{966}{30} \qquad = \frac{1051}{30}$$

So, as the line passes through the point $(\bar{x}, \bar{y})$ then $\bar{y} = a + b\bar{x}$:

$$\Rightarrow \frac{1051}{30} = a + 0.854\ldots\left(\frac{966}{30}\right)$$
$$\Rightarrow a = 7.55$$

Therefore, the regression line is $y = 7.55 + 0.854x$.

Once this line has been calculated, you could make predictions from within the data (interpolation) or from outside the range of the data (extrapolation), discussing any pitfalls in doing this. Drawing the regression line onto the scatter diagram would also be useful.

You could also see if any points in the original data are significantly far from the line, and what effect these may have had on the calculated line by looking at residuals.
For example, if (11, 33) was one of the original points:

$$\text{Residual} = 33 - 7.55 - 0.854\,(11)$$
$$= 16.1 \text{ (3 sf)}$$

Note that exact values are used in calculations before rounding.

✦ **A sufficient range of relevant calculations and analysis should be used. (4 marks)**

Your analysis should contain enough calculations to ensure that your original aims can be met.

Question: For confidence intervals, have you just used a 95% interval or have you considered other % levels to help with the interpretation?

✦ **Appropriate degrees of accuracy will have been used in the answers given. (2 marks)**

An important consideration is the degree of accuracy you will use in your calculations. For example, if you have collected data to 1 dp, is it appropriate to quote your answers to 2 dp?

Whatever you decide to do, be consistent. If you are consistent, but use inappropriate degrees of accuracy, you will gain some credit.

You might decide to use a greater degree of accuracy during your calculations and then round to a sensible accuracy at the end.

Strand 3: Interpretation and Validation

In this strand you are trying to state what your results show. Do they support your initial ideas?

Remember you are trying to make statements that answer the original questions set in the task.

✦ **Candidates must look at how realistic their final results are, and, if appropriate, give reasons why the answers are not sensible. (6 marks)**

You need to decide how realistic your final results are. You could research whether there are any statistics that could validate your results.

If you are calculating a confidence interval for the average height of year 9 students in a school, you could try to find out the national average from published statistics.

These figures will be based upon a much larger sample size than yours so it would be very useful if this value was inside your interval. Can you offer any reasons if it is not in your interval?

There may not be any relevant national statistics, so you could compare your results with other students who have done the same task at your school or college.

If there is no obvious method of validation then you should discuss your results to satisfy yourself that they are sensible, and that there are no obvious mistakes indicating errors in your calculations.

If you are comparing the average word length of two authors using confidence intervals, you might find that the intervals overlap when you did not expect this to happen.

Try to give possible reasons for this unexpected result: did you notice lots of small words in your data? Why should this be?

✦ **They should give a clear statistical interpretation of their results, along with suitable conclusions. (6 marks)**

For this criterion, you are expected to give a statistical interpretation of your results in context.

If you have calculated a confidence interval for μ, what does the interval mean? If you have calculated intervals for two distributions, do they overlap? What does this indicate about the two population means?

If you have calculated a correlation coefficient between two variables, what does the value indicate? If you then calculate a regression line, what does it tell you about the two variables? How can you use the line to make predictions?

Try to define your confidence intervals using your own words.

✦ **They must relate the outcomes to the original task and discuss the effect of their sampling and data collection methods on their results. (4 marks)**

Question: Do your results support your original hypotheses?

Use specific evidence from your work to support your conclusions.

You should also look back at your original sampling method:

✦ Was it random?
✦ Did you introduce bias into the sample (however unintentionally!)?
✦ How could you have adapted your sampling method to remove any bias?
✦ If you carried out an experiment or collected a questionnaire, was there anything you could have done which would have improved the data collected?

There will be credit given for relating your results back to your original task.

Just stating that you would have used a larger sample size is worthy of little credit.

It is fine to be self-critical in this section.

✦ **They must look at what modifications/improvements could have been made with the benefit of hindsight, (but they should not have to make them unless their analysis is so over-simplified that this becomes necessary). (4 marks)**

This is the opportunity to say if you felt that your design was not everything you hoped it would be!

Question: Could you have improved the quality of the data obtained by changing your original approach?

You only need to suggest alternative approaches, not implement them, unless you have done such a limited analysis that your work lacks depth.

Your teacher will be able to advise you whether you have done sufficient analysis of the task.

Strand 4: Communication

This strand measures how well you have communicated your work in the final write-up. This is a section which credits the good approaches used in the first three strands.

✦ **Candidates must express themselves clearly and concisely using appropriate mathematical language and notation. Graphs and diagrams should be clearly and accurately labelled. (4 marks)**

This is an overall judgement of how clearly you have expressed your ideas. It is important to be concise, and to be efficient in your presentation.

You do not need to include page after page of repetitive calculations, but you must include at least one worked example of all types of calculations that you have used in your coursework.

There is no credit for producing the longest piece of coursework.

Use the appropriate mathematical terms and notation for the specification, for example $\bar{x}$ for the sample mean and μ for the population mean.

Include all appropriate diagrams in your write-up. They should be clearly and appropriately labelled.

✦ **Candidates should indicate other areas of work that could have been investigated further. (2 marks)**

You are expected to suggest other work that could follow from your coursework.

Do not confuse 'further work' with 'modifications'.

Question: Where could you take your research further?

If you are comparing the male and female heights of year 7 and year 9 students, you could then suggest that a weight analysis could follow, to see if the variables are linked.

✦ **The final conclusions should be set out logically. (2 marks)**

Question: What exactly did your analysis indicate?

Do not worry if your analysis is inconclusive, as this is a perfectly valid outcome to your work.

✦ **The overall piece of work should be of sufficient depth and difficulty. (6 marks)**

This section gives credit for all the work that has been done throughout your coursework. Ensure that your approaches have enabled you to generate enough statistics for you to have shown the appropriate skills from the unit. You will receive credit not only for the difficulty of your calculations, but also for the quality and depth of your interpretation and for your overall approach.

It is not expected that you will be looking for ways to make the coursework artificially difficult.

✦ **The investigation should form a coherent whole and should be of a length consistent with a piece of work of 8–10 hours. (6 marks)**

Your investigation should read as a logical piece of writing that should be easy to follow. If you struggle to follow the flow of your arguments when reading the work through, then so will the person marking and assessing it. It is expected that your piece of work will take 8–10 hours to complete. This is an approximate timing and includes data collection and write-up time. It is easy to get carried away with some tasks so be careful that your piece of work does not become too long.

It is not expected that you will use the strands as specific titles in your coursework, although it should be clear to the reader which strand is being addressed.

When complete, read through your work and check your calculations to ensure that you have not made any careless mistakes.

7.5 Frequently asked questions

Here are some questions that are often asked by students.

✦ **Should the coursework be hand-written or word-processed?**

It can be either. If hand-written try to ensure that the work is neat and clear to follow. If word-processed, take care when typing symbols and formulae.

✦ **How long should the piece of work be?**

An appropriate piece of work could vary from 10 sides up to 20 sides including diagrams.

Word-processed pieces tend to be shorter.

✦ **Should I label the page numbers?**

Yes. It is useful when the work is being moderated.

S1

✦ **Can I use secondary data?**

Yes. Secondary data is useful for validation. You will be expected to collect your own data for the initial analysis. This could involve sampling from a large database, many of which are available on the internet.

✦ **Can I use the Internet?**

Yes. The Internet is appropriate to collect secondary data from as well as other information that may be relevant to your task. Always quote any websites used.

Any attempt to copy work from the internet is against Examination Board rules and could lead to serious consequences.

7.6 Checklist

Have you ...?

Strand 1

- Stated your aims **clearly**.
- Defined your population **explicitly**.
- Given **details** of how your sample was collected.
- **Discussed** relevant statistical theories **in context, embedded** in the work as it arises.
- **Discussed** any assumptions made.

Strand 2

- **Listed** your raw data and organized it appropriately.
- **Collected** a large enough amount of data.
- Made **correct** and **appropriate** calculations.
- Used a **sufficient range** of calculations and analysis for your model.
- Used **appropriate** degrees of accuracy in your answers.

Strand 3

- Looked at how **realistic** your final results are, and **if not** have you tried to give reasons.
- Given a **clear statistical** interpretation of your results and made conclusions from them.
- **Related** your results back to the original task **and** discussed if your sampling methods had **any effects** on your results.
- **Discussed** any modifications or improvements that could have been made.

Strand 4

- **Expressed** yourself clearly using **clear** diagrams and appropriate mathematical language and notation.
- **Suggested** other areas of work that could have been considered
- Set out your final **conclusions** clearly.
- Made sure your work is of sufficient **depth and difficulty** (have you made it too simplistic?).
- Made sure your work is **easy to follow** and of **sufficient length**.

And finally …

- **Make sure that you are aware of the deadline set by your teacher and work to it.**

Answers

Unless inappropriate, or requested in the question, or otherwise stated, all decimal answers are given to 3 significant figures.

Chapter 1

Check in

2 a) 15 b) 11.5 c) 7.4

Exercise 1A

1 a) 8 b) 8 c) 7.4 **2** 4.54 m **3** £11.96 **4** 90.61, 91.24 kg (to 2 dp) **5** 46.5 **6** a) 31.6 b) 31

7 a) 9.73 b) 10 c) 10 **8** A small proportion of people have fewer than 2 legs

Exercise 1B

1 36.5 **2** 1240 **3** 9.81 **4** 6 **5** 15.4

Exercise 1C

1 0.39 **2** 1.2 **3** a) 3.97 b) 4 **4** a) 114 miles b) 80– miles **5** a) 26.4 b) 21–25 **6** b) −60 grams

6 c) 46.9 grams d) 46.3 grams **7** b) 3.5 min c) 5.01 min

Exercise 1D

1 a) 15 b) 7 **2** a) 21 b) 13

3

(in seconds)	Q_1	Q_2	Q_3
Experienced	125	128.5	131
Inexperienced	137	145	150.5

4 a)

	Q_1	Q_2	Q_3	IQR
1971	2	3	4	2
2001	1	2	3	2

b) Strong trend to smaller households, many more households of size 1, 2, 3

5 b)

(in years)	Q_1	Q_2	Q_3	IQR
Male	26.4	29.7	34.0	7.6
Female	24.2	27.8	31.9	7.7

c) On average in new marriages the bride is 2 years younger than the groom

Exercise 1E

1 a) 15.2 b) 5.31 **2** a) 12.0 b) 4.00 **3** a) 1.32 kg b) 0.122 $(\text{kg})^2$ **4** 3.05 cm **5** 71.8 $(\text{seconds})^2$

6 a) 83.9 b) 575

Exercise 1F

1 1.86, 0.000186 $(\text{mm})^2$ **2** 1003.1 millibars (to 1 dp) **3** a) 1000001.33 mg b) 10.07 mg (to 2 dp)

Check out

1 a) Mean $\frac{8}{9}$, median 1, mode 0 b) Mean 1, median 1, mode 1 c) Mean 2, median 2.5, mode 3

2 a) Mean 28.75, median 28, modal class 20–30 b) Mean 38.25, median 33.5, modal class 20–30

3 Range 76, IQR 29 **4** 56.4 **5** 9.28, 3.05 **6** 1738, 41.7

Revision exercise 1

1 b) 87.1 minutes, 24.0 minutes c) Essex times more variable **2** a) (80, 1.4) b) 40.0, 17.2

3 a) Q_2 = 52.0 seconds, IQR = 17.7 seconds b) 54.2 seconds, 17.4 seconds c) 53.8 seconds

4 a) Q_2 = 357 days, IQR = 497 days b) Champion better because some machines very reliable

4 c) i) Q_2 = 519 days, IQR = 877 days ii) Makes comparable, though some Champion machines remain very reliable

4 d) Avoid distortion by the few ultra-reliable machines

5 b) i) 14.5 minutes ii) 12.8 (minutes)^2 c) 14.4 minutes d) 13, 15 minutes **6** b) i) 30.6 A ii) 30.9 A iii) 2.23 A

7 b) 28.9 minutes, 5.46 minutes **8** a) Absurdly long c) 2.71 hours, 1.75 hours d) Decrease mean, increase s.d. e) 70%

9 a) £141, £22.5 b) Prop. 1: £147.60, £23.60; Prop 2: £147.80, £23.10 c) Prefer Prop 1: lower total cost

10 a) $Q_2 = 44.1$ s, IQR = 20.4s b) 45.8s, 16.9s c) Grade limits 28s, 64s d) Method B classifies more as poor

11 a) Skewed c) 10.4 minutes, 11.7 minutes

Chapter 2

Check in

1 a) {Head, Tail} b) Score: {1, 2, 3, 4, 5, 6} c) Captain: {Abdel, Ben, Carl, Dai, Ewan} **2** 0.18, 0.32, 0.40, 0.10

Exercise 2A

1 a) $\frac{1}{2}$ b) $\frac{5}{6}$ c) $\frac{1}{3}$ d) $\frac{1}{3}$ **2** a) $\frac{2}{5}$ b) $\frac{4}{15}$ c) $\frac{2}{3}$ **3** $\frac{3}{29}$ **4** a) $\frac{23}{60}$ b) $\frac{1}{60}$ **5** a) 0.9 b) 0.4001 c) 0.0001

5 d) 0.1 e) 0.01 **6** a) $\frac{1}{3}$ b) $\frac{2}{3}$ c) $\frac{7}{30}$ d) $\frac{1}{3}$ e) $\frac{3}{10}$ f) $\frac{3}{5}$ **7** a) $\frac{3}{14}$ b) $\frac{9}{14}$ c) $\frac{5}{14}$ d) $\frac{5}{14}$ e) 1 f) 0

Exercise 2B

1 a) 0.283 b) 0.220 c) 0.660 d) 0.373 e) 0.340 **2** a) $P(A) = \frac{1}{2}, P(B) = \frac{1}{4}, P(C) = \frac{5}{12}, P(D) = \frac{1}{9}, P(E) = \frac{1}{2}$

2 b) i) $\{(A, E), (C, D)\}$ ii) (A, E) **3** a) $P(A) = \frac{1}{2}, P(B) = \frac{1}{3}, P(A \cup B) = \frac{2}{3}, P(A \cap B) = \frac{1}{6}$

3 b) $P(A') = \frac{1}{2}, P(B') = \frac{2}{3}, P(C') = \frac{2}{3}, P(D') = \frac{1}{2}$, c) $(B, C), (C, D)$ d) B, C, D e) 0

4 b) $P(A) = \frac{15}{36}, P(B) = \frac{26}{36}, P(A \cup B) = \frac{30}{36}, P(A \cap B) = \frac{11}{36}$ c) $P(A) = \frac{15}{36}, P(C) = \frac{24}{36}, P(A \cup B) = \frac{33}{36}, P(A \cap B) = \frac{6}{36}$ d) (B, C)

4 e) $P(A') = \frac{7}{12}, P(B') = \frac{5}{18}, P(C') = \frac{1}{3}$, f) $P(A' \cup B) = \frac{8}{9}, P(A \cap B') = \frac{1}{9}, P(B \cup C) = 1, P(B' \cap C') = 0, P(B' \cup C') = \frac{11}{18}$

5 a) $P(A) = \frac{6}{25}, P(B) = \frac{1}{5}, P(C) = \frac{18}{25}$ b) i) (A, C) ii) None

Exercise 2C

1 a) $\frac{13}{36}$ b) $\frac{4}{9}$ c) $\frac{7}{36}$ d) $\frac{3}{4}$ **2** a) $\frac{4}{9}$ b) $\frac{4}{9}$ c) $\frac{1}{9}$ d) $\frac{4}{9}$ e) $\frac{2}{9}$ **3** 0.999 **4** a) $\frac{1}{32}$ b) $\frac{15}{16}$ **5** a) 0.288 b) 0.352

6 b) i) $\frac{1}{4}$ ii) $\frac{17}{24}$ iii) $\frac{1}{24}$ iv) $\frac{1}{3}$ **7** a) $\frac{7}{25}$ b) $\frac{18}{25}$ c) $\frac{14}{75}$ d) $\frac{68}{75}$ e) 0 f) 1 **8** a) 0.395 b) 0.5

9 $P(A) = \frac{1}{64}, P(B) = \frac{3267}{8000}, P(C) = \frac{61}{125}, P(D) = \frac{613}{1600}$

Exercise 2D

1 a) independent b) independent c) not independent **2** a) $\frac{2}{3}$ b) $\frac{1}{2}$ **3** a) $\frac{1}{36}$ b) $\frac{1}{6}$ c) $\frac{1}{3}$ d) $\frac{11}{36}$ e) $\frac{1}{36}$ f) $\frac{1}{2}$

Check out

1 $\frac{1}{4}$ **2** The face showing is not a multiple of 3 **4** a) $\frac{2}{3}$ b) i) 1 ii) 0 c) 0.8 **5** a) 0.9 b) i) 0.5 ii) 0

6 $\frac{1}{16}$ **7** $\frac{3}{4}$

Revision exercise 2

1 a) 0.144 b) 0.384 c) 0.272 **2** a) $\frac{1}{31}$ b) $\frac{1}{961}$ c) $\frac{1}{961}$ d) $\frac{870}{961}$ **3** a) i) 0.33 ii) 0.26 iii) 0.53 iv) $\frac{26}{53} = 0.491$

3 b) $\frac{28}{127} = 0.220$ **4** a) 0.096 b) 0.336 c) 0.488 d) $\frac{12}{61} = 0.197$ **5** a) i) $\frac{1}{3}$ ii) 0.4 iii) 0.4 b) i) (W, X)

5 ii) (V, W): $P(V \cap W) > 0$ and $P(V \mid W) = \frac{5}{24} \neq P(V) = \frac{1}{3}$ **6** a) 0.504 b) 0.049 c) 0.099 d) 0.742

7 a) i) 0.28 iii) 0.33 b) i) 0.154 ii) 0.0525 **8** a) i) $\frac{1}{16}$ ii) $\frac{3}{8}$ b) i) $\frac{14}{33} = 0.424$ ii) $\frac{28}{55} = 0.509$ iii) $\frac{85}{99} = 0.859$

9 a) $\frac{8}{273} = 0.029$ b) $\frac{82}{273} = 0.300$ c) $\frac{35}{82} = 0.427$ d) $\frac{47}{273} = 0.172$ e) $\frac{1}{2}$ **10** a) 0.144 b) 0.226 c) $\frac{41}{113} = 0.363$

Chapter 3

Check in

1 a) $(B, D), (A, C)$ b) (B, D) **3** a) 0.0081 b) 0.0164 c) 0.0230 **4** a) (7, 8) b) (0, 1, 2) c) (4, 5) d) (4, 5, 6, 7)

Exercise 3A

1

x	0	1	2
p(x)	$\frac{3}{28}$	$\frac{15}{28}$	$\frac{10}{28}$

2

x	0	1	2
p(x)	$\frac{9}{64}$	$\frac{30}{64}$	$\frac{25}{64}$

3

x	2	3	4	5	6	7	8
p(x)	$\frac{1}{12}$	$\frac{2}{12}$	$\frac{2}{12}$	$\frac{2}{12}$	$\frac{2}{12}$	$\frac{2}{12}$	$\frac{1}{12}$

4

x	0	3	10
p(x)	$\frac{18}{20}$	$\frac{1}{20}$	$\frac{1}{20}$

5

x	1	$\frac{1}{2}$	$\frac{1}{3}$	$\frac{1}{4}$	$\frac{1}{5}$	$\frac{1}{6}$
p(x)	$\frac{1}{6}$	$\frac{1}{6}$	$\frac{1}{6}$	$\frac{1}{6}$	$\frac{1}{6}$	$\frac{1}{6}$

6

x	−5	−4	−3	−2	−1	0	1	2	3	4	5
p(x)	$\frac{1}{36}$	$\frac{2}{36}$	$\frac{3}{36}$	$\frac{4}{146}$	$\frac{5}{36}$	$\frac{6}{36}$	$\frac{5}{36}$	$\frac{4}{36}$	$\frac{3}{36}$	$\frac{2}{36}$	$\frac{1}{36}$

7

x	0	1	2	3	4	5
p(x)	$\frac{3}{18}$	$\frac{5}{18}$	$\frac{4}{18}$	$\frac{3}{18}$	$\frac{2}{18}$	$\frac{1}{18}$

8

x	0.40	1.40	2.40
p(x)	$\frac{1}{400}$	$\frac{38}{400}$	$\frac{361}{400}$

Exercise 3B

1 a) $0 \leqslant x \leqslant 6$ b) $0 \leqslant x \leqslant 12$ c) $0 \leqslant x \leqslant 25$ d) $0 \leqslant x \leqslant n$ e) $0 \leqslant x \leqslant m$ **2** a) $\frac{1}{27}$ b) $\frac{6}{27}$ c) $\frac{12}{27}$ d) $\frac{8}{27}$ e) $\frac{8}{27}$ f) $\frac{12}{27}$

2 g) $\frac{6}{27}$ h) $\frac{1}{27}$ **3** 0.243 **4** a) $\frac{1}{4}$ b) $\frac{3}{8}$; No: outcome of toss is independent of call **5** a) 0.0001 b) 0.9999 **6** 0.336

Exercise 3C

1 a) 0.250 b) 0.311 c) 0.393 d) 0.617 e) 0.711 **2** 0.315 **3** 0.318; telephone polls are usually biased

4 0.844, 0.156 **5** 0.211 **6** a) 0.531 b) 0.984 **7** 0.368 **8** 0.408 **9** 0.275

Exercise 3D

(Answers to this exercise are given to the tabular accuracy of 4 dp)

1 a) 0.9420 b) 0.0013 **2** a) 0.0548 b) 0.1114 c) 0.6331 **3** a) 0.8689 b) 0.7031 **4** 0.7174

5 a) 0.0007 c) 0.0175 **6** 0.7553

Exercise 3E

1 a) 15, 10.5 **2** a) 2, 1.6 b) 1, 0.949 **3** a) $\frac{5}{3}$, $\frac{25}{18}$ b) 0.485 **4** a) 5 b) 0.234 **5** a) 4.2, 1.65 b) 0.653

6 0.167 **7** a) 0.3, 0.7 b) 0.200, 0.037 **8** 15, 0.7 **9** 101

Check out

1 a) $n = 4$, Independence, constant p b) No c) $n = 10, p = 0.25$ (approx) **2** a) 24 b) 6 c) 15 d) 6

3 a) 0.138 b) 0.201 **4** a) 0.8791 b) 0.0947 c) 0.4890 **5** a) 1.2, 1.08 b) 16, 1.79

Revision exercise 3

(Probability answers to this exercise are given to the tabular accuracy of 4 dp)

1 a) 0.0644 b) 0.9956 c) 0.0190 **2** a) 0.2894 b) 0.2011 c) 0.1465 **3** a) 0.1099 b) 0.8801

4 a) i) 0.9790 ii) 0.2645 b) 0.1954 **5** a) 0.1101 b) 0.8943 **6** a) 0.4437 b) 0.6235

7 a) A: p not constant; B: $n = 10, p = 0.18$; C: p not constant b) i) 0.9345 ii) 0.9125 iii) B(1000, 0.136)

8 a) i) 0.3823 ii) 0.3669 b) 4, 1.55 c) i) 3.92, 3.17 ii) Variance too high **9** a) 0.1712 b) 0.8139 c) 26.5, 12.5

10 a) i) 0.1734 ii) 0.9245 iii) 0.3990 b) 48, 6.5

Chapter 4

Check in

1 a) 0– b) 100– **2** a) 0.92 b) 0.00625 **3** a) $x = 2, y = 4$ b) $x = 4, y = -1$ c) $x = 6, y = 2$ d) $\mu = 3, \sigma = 0.5$

3 e) $\mu = 20.3, \sigma = 4.94$

Exercise 4A

1 a) Discrete b) Continuous c) Discrete d) Continuous e) Continuous

Exercise 4B

(Answers to **1–5** are given to the tabular accuracy of 5 dp)

1 a) 0.884 93 b) 0.035 93 c) 0.080 76 d) 0.211 86 **2** a) 0.011 34 b) 0.540 35 c) 0.384 81 **3** 0.890 40

4 a) 0.823 81 b) 0.103 83 c) 0.079 27 d) 0.698 47 **5** a) 0.000 66 b) 0.999 85 c) 0.002 26 d) 0.996 74

6 a) 1.40 b) −0.40 c) −1.20 d) 2.60 e) 1.90 f) −1.80 **7** 0.60

Exercise 4C

1 a) 0.159 b) 0.945 c) 0.109 d) 0.808 **2** a) 0.804 b) 0.341 c) 0.268 d) 0.097 **3** a) 0.788 b) 0.045

3 c) 0.543 d) 0.367 **4** a) 0.212 b) 0.228 c) 0.186 d) 0.884 **5** a) 0.425 b) 0.698 c) 0.277 d) 0.167

6 a) 0.719 b) 0.527 c) 0.125 d) 0.478 **7** a) 0.106 b) 0.599 c) 0.691 d) 0.227 **8** a) 88.5% b) 21.2%

8 c) 34.5% d) 96.4% e) 28.8% f) 84.9% g) 30.9% **9** 63 grams

Exercise 4D

1 a) 1.881 b) 1.645 c) −3.090 d) −2.326 e) 2.748 f) 2.457 **2** a) 29.4 b) 28.2 c) 6.74 d) 8.37 e) 34.4 f) 32.9

3 101.6 grams **4** 19.4 cm **5** 1004 grams **6** a) 411.6 grams b) 432.8 grams

Exercise 4E

1 a) 6.47 **2** −0.0369 **3** 24.4 **4** 5.63 **5** 3.08, 3.66 **6** 260 min **7** 6.08; $\sigma < 6.08$ **8** 2.07 m, 0.458 m

9 507.07 m, 7.34 m **10** 3.62 cm, 0.002 56 cm^2

Check out

2 a) 0.977 25 b) 0.769 86 c) 0.405 17 d) 0.923 64 **3** a) 0.841 34 b) 0.818 59 c) 0.691 46 **4** a) 0.4677 b) 11.75

5 mean = 3.17, variance = 16.9

Revision exercise 4

1 0.773 **2** a) i) 0.0548 ii) 0.645 b) 25.46 kg **3** a) 68.3% b) 151 grams **4** a) 19.8% b) 67.5 grams

5 a) 0.159 b) 34 mg **6** a) i) 0.977 ii) 0.203 b) 150 miles **7** a) i) 0.833 ii) 33.4 minutes b) 2.4 minutes

7 c) X **8** a) 0.629 b) i) 118 grams ii) 123 grams c) 93.3 grams, 18.2 grams **9** a) i) 0.919 ii) 1226 mm

9 b) 1212.8 mm, 5.9 mm **10** a) i) 0.006 21 ii) 0.562 b) 7.49 m c) 0.27 m d) B: Greater probability of reaching 8.0 m

11 a) 0.787 b) 327 seconds c) 216 seconds d) i) 5.94 seconds ii) s.d. unrealistically small

12 a) i) 0.841 ii) 154.5 b) 181, 10

Chapter 5

Check in

1 a) 11.2, 12.0, 3.47 b) 8, 20.4, 4.51 c) 7, 27.2, 5.22 **2** a) 0.06681 b) 0.87467 c) 9.93

Exercise 5A

1 a) 90.1 grams b) 70.4 (grams)^2 c) 2.97 grams **2** a) 11.3 grams b) 12.2 (grams)^2

3 a) Random sample from all 16-year old girls b) i) 15.6 ii) 14.3

Exercise 5B

1 a) 12, $\frac{1}{9}$ b) 0.0668 **2** a) 90, $\frac{2}{5}$, soldiers on aircraft are random sample from population of soldiers b) 0.886

3 a) N(90, 4) b) 0.0455 **4** 401

Exercise 5C

1 a) N(15, $\frac{5}{14}$); 0.453 **2** a) 0.923 b) 0.988 **3** 0.977

Exercise 5D

(Answers are given to 2 dp)

1 a) (6.34, 10.06) b) (5.76, 10.64) **2** (28.36, 32.48) kg **3** (1.81, 1.83) kg

Exercise 5E

(Answers are given to 2 dp)

1 a) (10.33, 11.01) b) (10.27, 11.08) **2** a) (2.55, 2.86) b) (2.48, 2.93) **3** (51.5, 58.9) mins

Exercise 5F

1 (460.39, 462.01) grams (2 dp): Reject claim that mean = 460.3 grams

2 a) (5.58, 5.78) mins (2 dp) b) Not reasonable to suppose mean = 5.82 mins

3 a) (93.9, 99.3) days (1 dp) b) Does not appear to be a change in average lifetime

4 a) (68.57, 69.67) grams (2 dp) b) Reject claim that mean weight = 70.0 grams

5 (905.1, 965.9) words (1 dp): Accept truth of rumour that average length = 960 words

Check out

1 a) 11.7, 55.0 b) 9.55, 134 c) 9.33, 10.7 **2** a) 1.66 b) 2.99 c) 1.33 **3** N(5, $\frac{25}{49}$) **4** (81.6, 83.2)

5 (4.08, 5.12) **6** No

Revision exercise 5

2 b) 800 **3** a) 50.5 kg, 14.4 kg^2 b) Random sample c) 0.284 **4** a) 0.894 b) Volume is normally distributed

5 a) 0.960 b) CLT, large sample **6** a) 25.0 b) i) 0.632 minutes ii) 0.0571 **7** b) (92.01, 93.19) cm

7 c) Random sample **8** a) X has normal distribution b) (176.1, 179.9) mm **9** a) i) 0.599 ii) 0.146

9 b) (17.7, 38.3) minutes c) 0.255 **10** a) (330.51, 332.05) ml b) CLT, large sample **11** a) 0.00820 b) 49.7 grams

11 c) i) (52.32, 52.60) grams ii) CLT, large sample **12** (80.4, 81.2) grams

Chapter 6

Check in

2 17.5 **3** 39, 295 **4** 999774.3

Exercise 6A

(pmccs are given to 3 dp)

1 a) −0.952 b) Strong evidence that moisture content decreases with depth **2** b) −0.552: moderate negative correlation

3 b) 0.049: Little relation between the extent to which a species is widespread and its abundance

4 b) 0.570 c) Larger towns have larger numbers of both housing types d) Same proportion of each housing type in each region

5 b) 0.906 c) Strong evidence that violent districts have more robberies per capita

Exercise 6B

(pmccs are given to 3 dp)

1 a) −0.616 b) (1896, 64) c) i) −0.974 ii) Strong evidence that larger engines result in lower fuel economy

2 b) −0.155: Little relation between the two types of spending

3 a) The points nearly lie on a straight line b) 0.999: The prices of both models vary with age in the same way

4 b) 0.647 c) High rates of one crime are generally associated with high rates of the other

5 −0.610: Natural gas use has risen at a time when herring stocks have generally declined

6 b) 0.945 c) Strong positive correlation d) Strong evidence that the ratio of killed to seriously injured is nearly constant

7 b) 0.900 c) Strong evidence that larger books are generally more expensive

8 b) 0.882 c) Strong evidence that people with longer arms tend to have bigger hand spans

Exercise 6C

1 b) (1.25, 8.19) c) $a = 3.21, b = 3.98$ **2** b) (54.6, 43.9) c) $h = 67.8 - 0.437g$

3 b) (0.0132, 350) c) $w = 406 - 4270z$ **4** b) (13.8, 10.8) c) $y = 3.48 + 0.531s$

5 (3.50, 69.8) c) $w = 4.53 + 18.7t$ **6** b) (22.6, 2.60) c) $y = 1.00 + 0.0706x$

Exercise 6D

1 b) $y = -7.34 + 12.6x$ c) 36.9 **2** b) $v = -0.459 + 0.204x$ d) 1.38 **3** b) $y = 11.3 - 0.156x$ d) 9.33

4 c) $y = -2280 + 1.64x$ d) M: $y = 5530 + 0.468x$, F: $y = 6385 + 0.219x$ e) £7760 **5** a) p c) 0.682

5 d) $p = 3.66 + 0.0315d$ f) 0 is unlikely, $p(50) = 5.23$, $p(100) = 6.81$, 200 would require extrapolation

Exercise 6E

1 b) (171, 19.5), $t = 20.6 - 0.0257x$ **2** b) $y = -179 + 2.78x$, largest residual = 1280 c) $y = -265 + 2.69x$

3 a) Russia b) $y = 7.32 + 1.10x$, 1880 c) Original data: $r = 0.815$, Reduced data $r = 0.780$

Exercise 6F

1 a) 0.792, 0.0000880, 20.0 b)

x_s	4.905	11.225	14.293	40.624	17.264	12.26	13.903
y_s	0.03	1.31	1.90	3.90	1.54	2.26	3.14

1 d) $y_s = 0.572 + 0.0880x_s$ e) $y = 33.4, y_s = 3.43\ (= y - 30)$

2 a) $-0.0839, y = 7.93 - 0.0103x$ b)

x	2.68	3.03	2.80	0.28	0.31	5.00	2.87	1.85	1.89
y	44.6	35.6	46.4	50.0	53.6	51.8	48.2	48.2	28.4

2 d) $y_s = 46.3 - 0.470x$ e) $y = 7.11, y_s = 44.8\ (= 1.8y + 32)$

3 a) $-0.998, y = 78.0 - 0.669x$ b)

x	113	105	97	88.6	80.5	72.5	64.4	56.4
y	13.6	14.6	16.1	17.1	18.9	20.4	21.8	23.5

3 d) $y_s = 33.2 - 0.176x_s$ e) $y = 42.6, y_s = 18.1\ (= 0.425y)$ f) 78.0: extrapolation error (true value will be 0)

Check out

1 662, 29.8, 4.42 **2** 0.863 **3** a) Response: number, explanatory: time b) Response: pay, explanatory: weight

4 a) $y = 1.21 + 0.564x$ b) $y = -4.32 + 3.90x$ **5** a) 235 b) (20, 40) or, perhaps, (15, 45)

Revision exercise 6

1 a) -0.8 b) 0.4 c) -0.8 **2** a) Rising to a plateau b) The plateau will mislead

3 a) Definitely incorrect, r impossible b) probably incorrect, expect positive r c) probably incorrect, expect negative r

4 -0.392 **5** -0.962 **6** a) 0.151 b) Little relation between the scores

7 a) i) 0.929 ii) Larger towns have more solicitors and more stolen cars

7 b) Table gives no information about number (or occupation) of car thieves

8 b) $y = 8.97 - 0.0586x$ c) Petrol consumption with no students d) F: the largest negative residual.

9 b) $y = -5.53 + 0.642x$ c) 5.30 d) i) 27.8 ii) A fair comment since this value is 6.2 greater than expected

10 b) $l = 210.6 + 0.153m$ c) i) Increase in length (in mm per gram) ii) Length when no mass added d) 266 mm e) String breaks

11 b) $y = 20.6 + 1.72x$ c) Linear with positive slope

11 d) i) Average time per item ordered ii) Not possible – no items to pack means no parcel

11 e) $-6.80, -8.63, -6.40$ f) i) 41.2 minutes ii) 33.9 minutes

MS1A Practice Paper

1 (a) $r = 0.850$ (b) (i) r does not match householder's expectation (ii) outside temperature may be an influential factor

2 (a) 0.733 (b) 32.3 mins

3 (a) (i) $\frac{26}{85}$ (ii) $\frac{4}{85}$ (iii) $\frac{27}{34}$ (iv) $\frac{4}{35}$ (b) A student aged 16 to 17 years or a student who replied 'too high', or both

4 (a) (i) 0.117 (ii) 0.755 (b) not a fixed number of trials (c) (i) 12, 1.74 (ii) 12, 4.8

4 (iii) the observed mean is as expected, but there is less variability observed than would be expected with a random selection

5 (b) $y = 121 + 25.3x$ (c) (i) 39.1 (ii) -87.1 (d) Second day: largest negative residual

5 (e) Yorkshire does not get 20 hours of daylight at any time of year; the prediction involves extrapolating well beyond the range of data

6 (a) (i) (500.28, 502.32) (ii) distribution of X is normal (b) 0.01 (c) 0.001

MS1B Practice Paper

1 (a) $r = 0.850$ (b) (i) r does not match householder's expectation (ii) outside temperature may be an influential factor

2 (a) 0.209 (b) 0.839 (c) 0.690

3 (a) 151–155 cm (b) 158 cm, 12.4 cm (c) 170 cm for example, to allow more customers to buy the skirts

4 (a) (i) 0.04 (ii) 0.197 (b) (i) 0.57 (ii) 0.15 (iii) 0.2

5 (a) 0.733 (b) 32.3 mins (c) (i) 0.097 (ii) Unlikely since probability ≈ 0.1

6 (b) $y = 121 + 25.3x$ (c) (i) 39.1 (ii) -87.1 (d) Second day: largest negative residual

6 (e) Yorkshire does not get 20 hours of daylight at any time of year; the prediction involves extrapolating well beyond the range of data

7 (a) (i) (500.28, 502.32) (ii) distribution of X is normal (b) 0.01 (c) 0.001

Appendices

CUMULATIVE BINOMIAL DISTRIBUTION FUNCTION (Table 1)

The tabulated value is $P(X \leqslant x)$, where X has a binomial distribution with parameters n and p.

p	**0.01**	**0.02**	**0.03**	**0.04**	**0.05**	**0.06**	**0.07**	**0.08**	**0.09**	**0.10**	**0.15**	**0.20**	**0.25**	**0.30**	**0.35**	**0.40**	**0.45**	**0.50**	p
x	$n = 2$																		x
0	0.9801	0.9604	0.9409	0.9216	0.9025	0.8836	0.8649	0.8464	0.8281	0.8100	0.7225	0.6400	0.5625	0.4900	0.4225	0.3600	0.3025	0.2500	**0**
1	0.9999	0.9996	0.9991	0.9984	0.9975	0.9964	0.9951	0.9936	0.9919	0.9900	0.9775	0.9600	0.9375	0.9100	0.8775	0.8400	0,7975	0.7500	**1**
2	1.0000	1.0000	1.0000	1.0000	1.0000	1.0000	1.0000	1.0000	1.0000	1.0000	1.0000	1.0000	1.0000	1.0000	1.0000	1.0000	1.0000	1.0000	**2**
	$n = 3$																		
0	0.9703	0.9412	0.9127	0.8847	0.8574	0.8306	0.8044	0.7787	0.7536	0.7290	0.6141	0.5120	0.4219	0.3430	0.2746	0.2160	0.1664	0.1250	**0**
1	0.9997	0.9988	0.9974	0.9953	0.9928	0.9896	0.9860	0.9818	0.9772	0.9720	0.9393	0.8960	0.8438	0.7840	0.7183	0.6480	0.5748	0.5000	**1**
2	1.0000	1.0000	1.0000	0.9999	0.9999	0.9998	0.9997	0.9995	0.9993	0.9990	0.9966	0.9920	0.9844	0.9730	0.9571	0.9360	0.9089	0.8750	**2**
3				1.0000	1.0000	1.0000	1.0000	1.0000	1.0000	1.0000	1.0000	1.0000	1.0000	1.0000	1.0000	1.0000	1.0000	1.0000	**3**
	$n = 4$																		
0	0.9606	0.9224	0.8853	0.8493	0.8145	0.7807	0.7481	0.7164	0.6857	0.6561	0.5220	0.4096	0.3164	0.2401	0.1785	0.1296	0.0915	0.0625	**0**
1	0.9994	0.9977	0.9948	0.9909	0.9860	0.9801	0.9733	0.9656	0.9570	0.9477	0.8905	0.8192	0.7383	0.6517	0.5630	0.4752	0.3910	0.3125	**1**
2	1.0000	1.0000	0.9999	0.9998	0.9995	0.9992	0.9987	0.9981	0.9973	0.9963	0.9880	0.9728	0.9492	0.9163	0.8735	0.8208	0.7585	0.6875	**2**
3			1.0000	1.0000	1.0000	1.0000	1.0000	1.0000	0.9999	0.9999	0.9995	0.9984	0.9961	0.9919	0.9850	0.9744	0.9590	0.9375	**3**
4									1.0000	1.0000	1.0000	1.0000	1.0000	1.0000	1.0000	1.0000	1.0000	1.0000	**4**
	$n = 5$																		
0	0.9510	0.9039	0.8587	0.8154	0.7738	0.7339	0.6957	0.6591	0.6240	0.5905	0.4437	0.3277	0.2373	0.1681	0.1160	0.0778	0.0503	0.0313	**0**
1	0.9990	0.9962	0.9915	0.9852	0.9774	0.9681	0.9575	0.9456	0.9326	0.9185	0.8352	0.7373	0.6328	0.5282	0.4284	0.3370	0.2562	0.1875	**1**
2	1.0000	0.9999	0.9997	0.9994	0.9988	0.9980	0.9969	0.9955	0.9937	0.9914	0.9734	0.9421	0.8965	0.8369	0.7648	0.6826	0.5931	0.5000	**2**
3		1.0000	1.0000	1.0000	1.0000	0.9999	0.9999	0.9998	0.9997	0.9995	0.9978	0.9933	0.9844	0.9692	0.9460	0.9130	0.8688	0.8125	**3**
4						1.0000	1.0000	1.0000	1.0000	1.0000	0.9999	0.9997	0.9990	0.9976	0.9947	0.9898	0.9815	0.9688	**4**
5											1.0000	1.0000	1.0000	1.0000	1.0000	1.0000	1.0000	1.0000	**5**
	$n = 6$																		
0	0.9415	0.8858	0.8330	0.7828	0.7351	0.6899	0.6470	0.6064	0.5679	0.5314	0.3771	0.2621	0.1780	0.1176	0.0754	0.0467	0.0277	0.0156	**0**
1	0.9985	0.9943	0.9875	0.9784	0.9672	0.9541	0.9392	0.9227	0.9048	0.8857	0.7765	0.6554	0.5339	0.4202	0.3191	0.2333	0.1636	0.1094	**1**
2	1.0000	0.9998	0.9995	0.9988	0.9978	0.9962	0.9942	0.9915	0.9882	0.9842	0.9527	0.9011	0.8306	0.7443	0.6471	0.5443	0.4415	0.3438	**2**
3		1.0000	1.0000	1.0000	0.9999	0.9998	0.9997	0.9995	0.9992	0.9987	0.9941	0.9830	0.9624	0.9295	0.8826	0.8208	0.7447	0.6563	**3**
4					1.0000	1.0000	1.0000	1.0000	1.0000	0.9999	0.9996	0.9984	0.9954	0.9891	0.9777	0.9590	0.9308	0.8906	**4**
5										1.0000	1.0000	0.9999	0.9998	0.9993	0.9982	0.9959	0.9917	0.9844	**5**
6												1.0000	1.0000	1.0000	1.0000	1.0000	1.0000	1.0000	**6**
	$n = 7$																		
0	0.9321	0.8681	0.8080	0.7514	0.6983	0.6485	0.6017	0.5578	0.5168	0.4783	0.3206	0.2097	0.1335	0.0824	0.0490	0.0280	0.0152	0.0078	**0**
1	0.9980	0.9921	0.9829	0.9706	0.9556	0.9382	0.9187	0.8974	0.8745	0.8503	0.7166	0.5767	0.4449	0.3294	0.2338	0.1586	0.1024	0.0625	**1**
2	1.0000	0.9997	0.9991	0.9980	0.9962	0.9937	0.9903	0.9860	0.9807	0.9743	0.9262	0.8520	0.7564	0.6471	0.5323	0.4199	0.3164	0.2266	**2**
3		1.0000	1.0000	0.9999	0.9998	0.9996	0.9993	0.9988	0.9982	0.9973	0.9879	0.9667	0.9294	0.8740	0.8002	0.7102	0.6083	0.5000	**3**
4				1.0000	1.0000	1.0000	1.0000	0.9999	0.9999	0.9998	0.9988	0.9953	0.9871	0.9712	0.9444	0.9037	0.8471	0.7734	**4**
5								1.0000	1.0000	1.0000	0.9999	0.9996	0.9987	0.9962	0.9910	0.9812	0.9643	0.9375	**5**
6											1.0000	1.0000	0.9999	0.9998	0.9994	0.9984	0.9963	0.9922	**6**
7													1.0000	1.0000	1.0000	1.0000	1.0000	1.0000	**7**
	$n = 8$																		
0	0.9227	0.8508	0.7837	0.7214	0.6634	0.6096	0.5596	0.5132	0.4703	0.4305	0.2725	0.1678	0.1001	0.0576	0.0319	0.0168	0.0084	0.0039	**0**
1	0.9973	0.9897	0.9777	0.9619	0.9428	0.9208	0.8965	0.8702	0.8423	0.8131	0.6572	0.5033	0.3671	0.2553	0.1691	0.1064	0.0632	0.0352	**1**
2	0.9999	0.9996	0.9987	0.9969	0.9942	0.9904	0.9853	0.9789	0.9711	0.9619	0.8948	0.7969	0.6785	0.5518	0.4278	0.3154	0.2201	0.1445	**2**
3	1.0000	1.0000	0.9999	0.9998	0.9996	0.9993	0.9987	0.9978	0.9966	0.9950	0.9786	0.9437	0.8862	0.8059	0.7064	0.5941	0.4770	0.3633	**3**
4			1.0000	1.0000	1.0000	1.0000	0.9999	0.9999	0.9997	0.9996	0.9971	0.9896	0.9727	0.9420	0.8939	0.8263	0.7396	0.6367	**4**
5							1.0000	1.0000	1.0000	1.0000	0.9998	0.9988	0.9958	0.9887	0.9747	0.9502	0.9115	0.8555	**5**
6											1.0000	0.9999	0.9996	0.9987	0.9964	0.9915	0.9819	0.9648	**6**
7												1.0000	1.0000	0.9999	0.9998	0.9993	0.9983	0.9961	**7**
8														1.0000	1.0000	1.0000	1.0000	1.0000	**8**

CUMULATIVE BINOMIAL DISTRIBUTION FUNCTION (Table 1 continued)

p	**0.01**	**0.02**	**0.03**	**0.04**	**0.05**	**0.06**	**0.07**	**0.08**	**0.09**	**0.10**	**0.15**	**0.20**	**0.25**	**0.30**	**0.35**	**0.40**	**0.45**	**0.50**	*p*
x	$n = 9$																		*x*
0	0.9135	0.8337	0.7602	0.6925	0.6302	0.5730	0.5204	0.4722	0.4279	0.3874	0.2316	0.1342	0.0751	0.0404	0.0207	0.0101	0.0046	0.0020	**0**
1	0.9966	0.9869	0.9718	0.9522	0.9288	0.9022	0.8729	0.8417	0.8088	0.7748	0.5995	0.4362	0.3003	0.1960	0.1211	0.0705	0.0385	0.0195	**1**
2	0.9999	0.9994	0.9980	0.9955	0.9916	0.9862	0.9791	0.9702	0.9595	0.9470	0.8591	0.7382	0.6007	0.4628	0.3373	0.2318	0.1495	0.0898	**2**
3	1.0000	1.0000	0.9999	0.9997	0.9994	0.9987	0.9977	0.9963	0.9943	0.9917	0.9661	0.9144	0.8343	0.7297	0.6089	0.4826	0.3614	0.2539	**3**
4			1.0000	1.0000	1.0000	0.9999	0.9998	0.9997	0.9995	0.9991	0.9944	0.9804	0.9511	0.9012	0.8283	0.7334	0.6214	0.5000	**4**
5						1.0000	1.0000	1.0000	1.0000	0.9999	0.9994	0.9969	0.9900	0.9747	0.9464	0.9006	0.8342	0.7461	**5**
6										1.0000	1.0000	0.9997	0.9987	0.9957	0.9888	0.9750	0.9502	0.9102	**6**
7												1.0000	0.9999	0.9996	0.9986	0.9962	0.9909	0.9805	**7**
8													1.0000	1.0000	0.9999	0.9997	0.9992	0.9980	**8**
9															1.0000	1.0000	1.0000	1.0000	**9**
	$n = 10$																		
0	0.9044	0.8171	0.7374	0.6648	0.5987	0.5386	0.4840	0.4344	0.3894	0.3487	0.1969	0.1074	0.0563	0.0282	0.0135	0.0060	0.0025	0.0010	**0**
1	0.9957	0.9838	0.9655	0.9418	0.9139	0.8824	0.8483	0.8121	0.7746	0.7361	0.5443	0.3758	0.2440	0.1493	0.0860	0.0464	0.0233	0.0107	**1**
2	0.9999	0.9991	0.9972	0.9938	0.9885	0.9812	0.9717	0.9599	0.9460	0.9298	0.8202	0.6778	0.5256	0.3828	0.2616	0.1673	0.0996	0.0547	**2**
3	1.0000	1.0000	0.9999	0.9996	0.9990	0.9980	0.9964	0.9942	0.9912	0.9872	0.9500	0.8791	0.7759	0.6496	0.5138	0.3823	0.2660	0.1719	**3**
4			1.0000	1.0000	0.9999	0.9998	0.9997	0.9994	0.9990	0.9984	0.9901	0.9672	0.9219	0.8497	0.7515	0.6331	0.5044	0.3770	**4**
5					1.0000	1.0000	1.0000	1.0000	0.9999	0.9999	0.9986	0.9936	0.9803	0.9527	0.9051	0.8338	0.7384	0.6230	**5**
6									1.0000	1.0000	0.9999	0.9991	0.9965	0.9894	0.9740	0.9452	0.8980	0.8281	**6**
7											1.0000	0.9999	0.9996	0.9984	0.9952	0.9877	0.9726	0,9453	**7**
8												1.0000	1.0000	0.9999	0.9995	0.9983	0.9955	0.9893	**8**
9														1.0000	1.0000	0.9999	0.9997	0.9990	**9**
10																1.0000	1.0000	1.0000	**10**
	$n = 11$																		
0	0.8953	0.8007	0.7153	0.6382	0.5688	0.5063	0.4501	0.3996	0.3544	0.3138	0.1673	0.0859	0.0422	0.0198	0.0088	0.0036	0.0014	0.0005	**0**
1	0.9948	0.9805	0.9587	0.9308	0.8981	0.8618	0.8228	0.7819	0.7399	0.6974	0.4922	0.3221	0.1971	0.1130	0.0606	0.0302	0.0139	0.0059	**1**
2	0.9998	0.9988	0.9963	0.9917	0.9848	0.9752	0.9630	0.9481	0.9305	0.9104	0.7788	0.6174	0.4552	0.3127	0.2001	0.1189	0.0652	0.0327	**2**
3	1.0000	1.0000	0.9998	0.9993	0.9984	0.9970	0.9947	0.9915	0.9871	0.9815	0.9306	0.8389	0.7133	0.5696	0.4256	0.2963	0.1911	0.1133	**3**
4			1.0000	1.0000	0.9999	0.9997	0.9995	0.9990	0.9983	0.9972	0.9841	0.9496	0.8854	0.7897	0.6683	0.5328	0.3971	0.2744	**4**
5					1.0000	1.0000	1.0000	0.9999	0.9998	0.9997	0.9973	0.9883	0.9657	0.9218	0.8513	0.7535	0.6331	0.5000	**5**
6								1.0000	1.0000	1.0000	0.9997	0.9980	0.9924	0.9784	0.9499	0.9006	0.8262	0.7256	**6**
7											1.0000	0.9998	0.9988	0.9957	0.9878	0.9707	0.9390	0.8867	**7**
8												1.0000	0.9999	0.9994	0.9980	0.9941	0.9852	0.9673	**8**
9													1.0000	1.0000	0.9998	0.9993	0.9978	0.9941	**9**
10															1.0000	1.0000	0.9998	0.9995	**10**
11																	1.0000	1.0000	**11**
	$n = 12$																		
0	0.8864	0.7847	0.6938	0.6127	0.5404	0.4759	0.4186	0.3677	0.3225	0.2824	0.1422	0.0687	0.0317	0.0138	0.0057	0.0022	0.0008	0.0002	**0**
1	0.9938	0.9769	0.9514	0.9191	0.8816	0.8405	0.7967	0.7513	0.7052	0.6590	0.4435	0.2749	0.1584	0.0850	0.0424	0.0196	0.0083	0.0032	**1**
2	0.9998	0.9985	0.9952	0.9893	0.9804	0.9684	0.9532	0.9348	0.9134	0.8891	0.7358	0.5583	0.3907	0.2528	0.1513	0.0834	0.0421	0.0193	**2**
3	1.0000	0.9999	0.9997	0.9990	0.9978	0.9957	0.9925	0.9880	0.9820	0.9744	0.9078	0.7946	0.6488	0.4925	0.3467	0.2253	0.1345	0.0730	**3**
4		1.0000	1.0000	0.9999	0.9998	0.9996	0.9991	0.9984	0.9973	0.9957	0.9761	0.9274	0.8424	0.7237	0.5833	0.4382	0.3044	0.1938	**4**
5				1.0000	1.0000	1.0000	0.9999	0.9998	0.9997	0.9995	0.9954	0.9806	0.9456	0.8822	0.7873	0.6652	0.5269	0.3872	**5**
6							1.0000	1.0000	1.0000	0.9999	0.9993	0.9961	0.9857	0.9614	0.9154	0.8418	0.7393	0.6128	**6**
7										1.0000	0.9999	0.9994	0.9972	0.9905	0.9745	0.9427	0.8883	0.8062	**7**
8											1.0000	0.9999	0.9996	0.9983	0.9944	0.9847	0.9644	0.9270	**8**
9												1.0000	1.0000	0.9998	0.9992	0.9972	0.9921	0.9807	**9**
10														1.0000	0.9999	0.9997	0.9989	0.9968	**10**
11															1.0000	1.0000	0.9999	0.9998	**11**
12																	1.0000	1.0000	**12**
	$n = 13$																		
0	0.8775	0.7690	0.6730	0.5882	0.5133	0.4474	0.3893	0.3383	0.2935	0.2542	0.1209	0.0550	0.0238	0.0097	0.0037	0.0013	0.0004	0.0001	**0**
1	0.9928	0.9730	0.9436	0.9068	0.8646	0.8186	0.7702	0.7206	0.6707	0.6213	0.3983	0.2336	0.1267	0.0637	0.0296	0.0126	0.0049	0.0017	**1**
2	0.9997	0.9980	0.9938	0.9865	0.9755	0.9608	0.9422	0.9201	0.8946	0.8661	0.6920	0.5017	0.3326	0.2025	0.1132	0.0579	0.0269	0.0112	**2**
3	1.0000	0.9999	0.9995	0.9986	0.9969	0.9940	0.9897	0.9837	0.9758	0.9658	0.8820	0.7473	0.5843	0.4206	0.2783	0.1686	0.0929	0.0461	**3**
4		1.0000	1.0000	0.9999	0.9997	0.9993	0.9987	0.9976	0.9959	0.9935	0.9658	0.9009	0.7940	0.6543	0.5005	0.3530	0.2279	0.1334	**4**
5				1.0000	1.0000	0.9999	0.9999	0.9997	0.9995	0.9991	0.9925	0.9700	0.9198	0.8346	0.7159	0.5744	0.4268	0.2905	**5**
6						1.0000	1.0000	1.0000	0.9999	0.9999	0.9987	0.9930	0.9757	0.9376	0.8705	0.7712	0.6437	0.5000	**6**
7									1.0000	1.0000	0.9998	0.9988	0.9944	0.9818	0.9538	0.9023	0.8212	0.7095	**7**
8											1.0000	0.9998	0.9990	0.9960	0.9874	0.9679	0.9302	0.8666	**8**
9												1.0000	0.9999	0.9993	0.9975	0.9922	0.9797	0.9539	**9**
10													1.0000	0.9999	0.9997	0.9987	0.9959	0.9888	**10**
11														1.0000	1.0000	0.9999	0.9995	0.9983	**11**
12																1.0000	1.0000	0.9999	**12**
13																		1.0000	**13**

CUMULATIVE BINOMIAL DISTRIBUTION FUNCTION (Table 1 continued)

p	0.01	0.02	0.03	0.04	0.05	0.06	0.07	0.08	0.09	0.10	0.15	0.20	0.25	0.30	0.35	0.40	0.45	0.50	p
x	$n = 14$																		x
0	0.8687	0.7536	0.6528	0.5647	0.4877	0.4205	0.3620	0.3112	0.2670	0.2288	0.1028	0.0440	0.0178	0.0068	0.0024	0.0008	0.0002	0.0001	0
1	0.9916	0.9690	0.9355	0.8941	0.8470	0.7963	0.7436	0.6900	0.6368	0.5846	0.3567	0.1979	0.1010	0.0475	0.0205	0.0081	0.0029	0.0009	1
2	0.9997	0.9975	0.9923	0.9833	0.9699	0.9522	0.9302	0.9042	0.8745	0.8416	0.6479	0.4481	0.2811	0.1608	0.0839	0.0398	0.0170	0.0065	2
3	1.0000	0.9999	0.9994	0.9981	0.9958	0.9920	0.9864	0.9786	0.9685	0.9559	0.8535	0.6982	0.5213	0.3552	0.2205	0.1243	0.0632	0.0287	3
4		1.0000	1.0000	0.9998	0.9996	0.9990	0.9980	0.9965	0.9941	0.9908	0.9533	0.8702	0.7415	0.5842	0.4227	0.2793	0.1672	0.0898	4
5				1.0000	1.0000	0.9999	0.9998	0.9996	0.9992	0.9985	0.9885	0.9561	0.8883	0.7805	0.6405	0.4859	0.3373	0.2120	5
6						1.0000	1.0000	1.0000	0.9999	0.9998	0.9978	0.9884	0.9617	0.9067	0.8164	0.6925	0.5461	0.3953	6
7									1.0000	1.0000	0.9997	0.9976	0.9897	0.9685	0.9247	0.8499	0.7414	0.6047	7
8											1.0000	0.9996	0.9978	0.9917	0.9757	0.9417	0.8811	0.7880	8
9												1.0000	0.9997	0.9983	0.9940	0.9825	0.9574	0.9102	9
10													1.0000	0.9998	0.9989	0.9961	0.9886	0.9713	10
11														1.0000	0.9999	0.9994	0.9978	0.9935	11
12															1.0000	0.9999	0.9997	0.9991	12
13																1.0000	1.0000	0.9999	13
14																		1.0000	14
	$n = 15$																		
0	0.8601	0.7386	0.6333	0.5421	0.4633	0.3953	0.3367	0.2863	0.2430	0.2059	0.0874	0.0352	0.0134	0.0047	0.0016	0.0005	0.0001	0.0000	0
1	0.9904	0.9647	0.9270	0.8809	0.8290	0.7738	0.7168	0.6597	0.6035	0.5490	0.3186	0.1671	0.0802	0.0353	0.0142	0.0052	0.0017	0.0005	1
2	0.9996	0.9970	0.9906	0.9797	0.9638	0.9429	0.9171	0.8870	0.8531	0.8159	0.6042	0.3980	0.2361	0.1268	0.0617	0.0271	0.0107	0.0037	2
3	1.0000	0.9998	0.9992	0.9976	0.9945	0.9896	0.9825	0.9727	0.9601	0.9444	0.8227	0.6482	0.4613	0.2969	0.1727	0.0905	0.0424	0.0176	3
4		1.0000	0.9999	0.9998	0.9994	0.9986	0.9972	0.9950	0.9918	0.9873	0.9383	0.8358	0.6865	0.5155	0.3519	0.2173	0.1204	0.0592	4
5			1.0000	1.0000	0.9999	0.9999	0.9997	0.9993	0.9987	0.9978	0.9832	0.9389	0.8516	0.7216	0.5643	0.4032	0.2608	0.1509	5
6					1.0000	1.0000	1.0000	0.9999	0.9998	0.9997	0.9964	0.9819	0.9434	0.8689	0.7548	0.6098	0.4522	0.3036	6
7								1.0000	1.0000	1.0000	0.9994	0.9958	0.9827	0.9500	0.8868	0.7869	0.6535	0.5000	7
8											0.9999	0.9992	0.9958	0.9848	0.9578	0.9050	0.8182	0.6964	8
9											1.0000	0.9999	0.9992	0.9963	0.9876	0.9662	0.9231	0.8491	9
10												1.0000	0.9999	0.9993	0.9972	0.9907	0.9745	0.9408	10
11													1.0000	0.9999	0.9995	0.9981	0.9937	0.9824	11
12														1.0000	0.9999	0.9997	0.9989	0.9963	12
13															1.0000	1.0000	0.9999	0.9995	13
14																	1.0000	1.0000	14
	$n = 20$																		
0	0.8179	0.6676	0.5438	0.4420	0.3585	0.2901	0.2342	0.1887	0.1516	0.1216	0.0388	0.0115	0.0032	0.0008	0.0002	0.0000	0.0000	0.0000	0
1	0.9831	0.9401	0.8802	0.8103	0.7358	0.6605	0.5869	0.5169	0.4516	0.3917	0.1756	0.0692	0.0243	0.0076	0.0021	0.0005	0.0001	0.0000	1
2	0.9990	0.9929	0.9790	0.9561	0.9245	0.8850	0.8390	0.7879	0.7334	0.6769	0.4049	0.2061	0.0913	0.0355	0.0121	0.0036	0.0009	0.0002	2
3	1.0000	0.9994	0.9973	0.9926	0.9841	0.9710	0.9529	0.9294	0.9007	0.8670	0.6477	0.4114	0.2252	0.1071	0.0444	0.0160	0.0049	0.0013	3
4		1.0000	0.9997	0.9990	0.9974	0.9944	0.9893	0.9817	0.9710	0.9568	0.8298	0.6296	0.4148	0.2375	0.1182	0.0510	0.0189	0.0059	4
5			1.0000	0.9999	0.9997	0.9991	0.9981	0.9962	0.9932	0.9887	0.9327	0.8042	0.6172	0.4164	0.2454	0.1256	0.0553	0.0207	5
6				1.0000	1.0000	0.9999	0.9997	0.9994	0.9987	0.9976	0.9781	0.9133	0.7858	0.6080	0.4166	0.2500	0.1299	0.0577	6
7						1.0000	1.0000	0.9999	0.9998	0.9996	0.9941	0.9679	0.8982	0.7723	0.6010	0.4159	0.2520	0.1316	7
8								1.0000	1.0000	0.9999	0.9987	0.9900	0.9591	0.8867	0.7624	0.5956	0.4143	0.2517	8
9										1.0000	0.9998	0.9974	0.9861	0.9520	0.8782	0.7553	0.5914	0.4119	9
10											1.0000	0.9994	0.9961	0.9829	0.9468	0.8725	0.7507	0.5881	10
11												0.9999	0.9991	0.9949	0.9804	0.9435	0.8692	0.7483	11
12												1.0000	0.9998	0.9987	0.9940	0.9790	0.9420	0.8684	12
13													1.0000	0.9997	0.9985	0.9935	0.9786	0.9423	13
14														1.0000	0.9997	0.9984	0.9936	0.9793	14
15															1.0000	0.9997	0.9985	0.9941	15
16																1.0000	0.9997	0.9987	16
17																	1.0000	0.9998	17
18																		1.0000	18

CUMULATIVE BINOMIAL DISTRIBUTION FUNCTION (Table 1 continued)

p	0.01	0.02	0.03	0.04	0.05	0.06	0.07	0.08	0.09	0.10	0.15	0.20	0.25	0.30	0.35	0.40	0.45	0.50	p
x	$n = 25$																		x
0	0.7778	0.6035	0.4670	0.3604	0.2774	0.2129	0.1630	0.1244	0.0946	0.0718	0.0172	0.0038	0.0008	0.0001	0.0000	0.0000	0.0000	0.0000	0
1	0.9742	0.9114	0.8280	0.7358	0.6424	0.5527	0.4696	0.3947	0.3286	0.2712	0.0931	0.0274	0.0070	0.0016	0.0003	0.0001	0.0000	0.0000	1
2	0.9980	0.9868	0.9620	0.9235	0.8729	0.8129	0.7466	0.6768	0.6063	0.5371	0.2537	0.0982	0.0321	0.0090	0.0021	0.0004	0.0001	0.0000	2
3	0.9999	0.9986	0.9938	0.9835	0.9659	0.9402	0.9064	0.8649	0.8169	0.7636	0.4711	0.2340	0.0962	0.0332	0.0097	0.0024	0.0005	0.0001	3
4	1.0000	0.9999	0.9992	0.9972	0.9928	0.9850	0.9726	0.9549	0.9314	0.9020	0.6821	0.4207	0.2137	0.0905	0.0320	0.0095	0.0023	0.0005	4
5		1.0000	0.9999	0.9996	0.9988	0.9969	0.9935	0.9877	0.9790	0.9666	0.8385	0.6167	0.3783	0.1935	0.0826	0.0294	0.0086	0.0020	5
6			1.0000	1.0000	0.9998	0.9995	0.9987	0.9972	0.9946	0.9905	0.9305	0.7800	0.5611	0.3407	0.1734	0.0736	0.0258	0.0073	6
7					1.0000	0.9999	0.9998	0.9995	0.9989	0.9977	0.9745	0.8909	0.7265	0.5118	0.3061	0.1536	0.0639	0.0216	7
8						1.0000	1.0000	0.9999	0.9998	0.9995	0.9920	0.9532	0.8506	0.6769	0.4668	0.2735	0.1340	0.0539	8
9								1.0000	1.0000	0.9999	0.9979	0.9827	0.9287	0.8106	0.6303	0.4246	0.2424	0.1148	9
10										1.0000	0.9995	0.9944	0.9703	0.9022	0.7712	0.5858	0.3843	0.2122	10
11											0.9999	0.9985	0.9893	0.9558	0.8746	0.7323	0.5426	0.3450	11
12											1.0000	0.9996	0.9966	0.9825	0.9396	0.8462	0.6937	0.5000	12
13												0.9999	0.9991	0.9940	0.9745	0.9222	0.8173	0.6550	13
14												1.0000	0.9998	0.9982	0.9907	0.9656	0.9040	0.7878	14
15													1.0000	0.9995	0.9971	0.9868	0.9560	0.8852	15
16														0.9999	0.9992	0.9957	0.9826	0.9461	16
17														1.0000	0.9998	0.9988	0.9942	0.9784	17
18															1.0000	0.9997	0.9984	0.9927	18
19																0.9999	0.9996	0.9980	19
20																1.0000	0.9999	0.9995	20
21																	1.0000	0.9999	21
22																		1.0000	22
	$n = 30$																		
0	0.7397	0.5455	0.4010	0.2939	0.2146	0.1563	0.1134	0.0820	0.0591	0.0424	0.0076	0.0012	0.0002	0.0000	0.0000	0.0000	0.0000	0.0000	0
1	0.9639	0.8795	0.7731	0.6612	0.5535	0.4555	0.3694	0.2958	0.2343	0.1837	0.0480	0.0105	0.0020	0.0003	0.0000	0.0000	0.0000	0.0000	1
2	0.9967	0.9783	0.9399	0.8831	0.8122	0.7324	0.6487	0.5654	0.4855	0.4114	0.1514	0.0442	0.0106	0.0021	0.0003	0.0000	0.0000	0.0000	2
3	0.9998	0.9971	0.9881	0.9694	0.9392	0.8974	0.8450	0.7842	0.7175	0.6474	0.3217	0.1227	0.0374	0.0093	0.0019	0.0003	0.0000	0.0000	3
4	1.0000	0.9997	0.9982	0.9937	0.9844	0.9685	0.9447	0.9126	0.8723	0.8245	0.5245	0.2552	0.0979	0.0302	0.0075	0.0015	0.0002	0.0000	4
5		1.0000	0.9998	0.9989	0.9967	0.9921	0.9838	0.9707	0.9519	0.9268	0.7106	0.4275	0.2026	0.0766	0.0233	0.0057	0.0011	0.0002	5
6			1.0000	0.9999	0.9994	0.9983	0.9960	0.9918	0.9848	0.9742	0.8474	0.6070	0.3481	0.1595	0.0586	0.0172	0.0040	0.0007	6
7				1.0000	0.9999	0.9997	0.9992	0.9980	0.9959	0.9922	0.9302	0.7608	0.5143	0.2814	0.1238	0.0435	0.0121	0.0026	7
8					1.0000	1.0000	0.9999	0.9996	0.9990	0.9980	0.9722	0.8713	0.6736	0.4315	0.2247	0.0940	0.0312	0.0081	8
9							1.0000	0.9999	0.9998	0.9995	0.9903	0.9389	0.8034	0.5888	0.3575	0.1763	0.0694	0.0214	9
10								1.0000	1.0000	0.9999	0.9971	0.9744	0.8943	0.7304	0.5078	0.2915	0.1350	0.0494	10
11										1.0000	0.9992	0.9905	0.9493	0.8407	0.6548	0.4311	0.2327	0.1002	11
12											0.9998	0.9969	0.9784	0.9155	0.7802	0.5785	0.3592	0.1808	12
13											1.0000	0.9991	0.9918	0.9599	0.8737	0.7145	0.5025	0.2923	13
14												0.9998	0.9973	0.9831	0.9348	0.8246	0.6448	0.4278	14
15												0.9999	0.9992	0.9936	0.9699	0.9029	0.7691	0.5722	15
16												1.0000	0.9998	0.9979	0.9876	0.9519	0.8644	0.7077	16
17													0.9999	0.9994	0.9955	0.9788	0.9286	0.8192	17
18													1.0000	0.9998	0.9986	0.9917	0.9666	0.8998	18
19														1.0000	0.9996	0.9971	0.9862	0.9506	19
20															0.9999	0.9991	0.9950	0.9786	20
21															1.0000	0.9998	0.9984	0.9919	21
22																1.0000	0.9996	0.9974	22
23																	0.9999	0.9993	23
24																	1.0000	0.9998	24
25																		1.0000	25

CUMULATIVE BINOMIAL DISTRIBUTION FUNCTION (Table 1 continued)

p	**0.01**	**0.02**	**0.03**	**0.04**	**0.05**	**0.06**	**0.07**	**0.08**	**0.09**	**0.10**	**0.15**	**0.20**	**0.25**	**0.30**	**0.35**	**0.40**	**0.45**	**0.50**	p
x	$n = 40$																		x
0	0.6690	0.4457	0.2957	0.1954	0.1285	0.0842	0.0549	0.0356	0.0230	0.0148	0.0015	0.0001	0.0000	0.0000	0.0000	0.0000	0.0000	0.0000	**0**
1	0.9393	0.8095	0.6615	0.5210	0.3991	0.2990	0.2201	0.1594	0.1140	0.0805	0.0121	0.0015	0.0001	0.0000	0.0000	0.0000	0.0000	0.0000	**1**
2	0.9925	0.9543	0.8822	0.7855	0.6767	0.5665	0.4625	0.3694	0.2894	0.2228	0.0486	0.0079	0.0010	0.0001	0.0000	0.0000	0.0000	0.0000	**2**
3	0.9993	0.9918	0.9686	0.9252	0.8619	0.7827	0.6937	0.6007	0.5092	0.4231	0.1302	0.0285	0.0047	0.0006	0.0001	0.0000	0.0000	0.0000	**3**
4	1.0000	0.9988	0.9933	0.9790	0.9520	0.9104	0.8546	0.7868	0.7103	0.6290	0.2633	0.0759	0.0160	0.0026	0.0003	0.0000	0.0000	0.0000	**4**
5		0.9999	0.9988	0.9951	0.9861	0.9691	0.9419	0.9033	0.8535	0.7937	0.4325	0.1613	0.0433	0.0086	0.0013	0.0001	0.0000	0.0000	**5**
6		1.0000	0.9998	0.9990	0.9966	0.9909	0.9801	0.9624	0.9361	0.9005	0.6067	0.2859	0.0962	0.0238	0.0044	0.0006	0.0001	0.0000	**6**
7			1.0000	0.9998	0.9993	0.9977	0.9942	0.9873	0.9758	0.9581	0.7559	0.4371	0.1820	0.0553	0.0124	0.0021	0.0002	0.0000	**7**
8				1.0000	0.9999	0.9995	0.9985	0.9963	0.9919	0.9845	0.8646	0.5931	0.2998	0.1110	0.0303	0.0061	0.0009	0.0001	**8**
9					1.0000	0.9999	0.9997	0.9990	0.9976	0.9949	0.9328	0.7318	0.4395	0.1959	0.0644	0.0156	0.0027	0.0003	**9**
10						1.0000	0.9999	0.9998	0.9994	0.9985	0.9701	0.8392	0.5839	0.3087	0.1215	0.0352	0.0074	0.0011	**10**
11							1.0000	1.0000	0.9999	0.9996	0.9880	0.9125	0.7151	0.4406	0.2053	0.0709	0.0179	0.0032	**11**
12									1.0000	0.9999	0.9957	0.9568	0.8209	0.5772	0.3143	0.1285	0.0386	0.0083	**12**
13										1.0000	0.9986	0.9806	0.8968	0.7032	0.4408	0.2112	0.0751	0.0192	**13**
14											0.9996	0.9921	0.9456	0.8074	0.5721	0.3174	0.1326	0.0403	**14**
15											0.9999	0.9971	0.9738	0.8849	0.6946	0.4402	0.2142	0.0769	**15**
16											1.0000	0.9990	0.9884	0.9367	0.7978	0.5681	0.3185	0.1341	**16**
17												0.9997	0.9953	0.9680	0.8761	0.6885	0.4391	0.2148	**17**
18												0.9999	0.9983	0.9852	0.9301	0.7911	0.5651	0.3179	**18**
19												1.0000	0.9994	0.9937	0.9637	0.8702	0.6844	0.4373	**19**
20													0.9998	0.9976	0.9827	0.9256	0.7870	0.5627	**20**
21													1.0000	0.9991	0.9925	0.9608	0.8669	0.6821	**21**
22														0.9997	0.9970	0.9811	0.9233	0.7852	**22**
23														0.9999	0.9989	0.9917	0.9595	0.8659	**23**
24														1.0000	0.9996	0.9966	0.9804	0.9231	**24**
25															0.9999	0.9988	0.9914	0.9597	**25**
26															1.0000	0.9996	0.9966	0.9808	**26**
27																0.9999	0.9988	0.9917	**27**
28																1.0000	0.9996	0.9968	**28**
29																	0.9999	0.9989	**29**
30																	1.0000	0.9997	**30**
31																		0.9999	**31**
32																		1.0000	**32**

CUMULATIVE BINOMIAL DISTRIBUTION FUNCTION (Table 1 continued)

p	0.01	0.02	0.03	0.04	0.05	0.06	0.07	0.08	0.09	0.10	0.15	0.20	0.25	0.30	0.35	0.40	0.45	0.50	p
x	$n = 50$																		x
0	0.6050	0.3642	0.2181	0.1299	0.0769	0.0453	0.0266	0.0155	0.0090	0.0052	0.0003	0.0000	0.0000	0.0000	0.0000	0.0000	0.0000	0.0000	**0**
1	0.9106	0.7358	0.5553	0.4005	0.2794	0.1900	0.1265	0.0827	0.0532	0.0338	0.0029	0.0002	0.0000	0.0000	0.0000	0.0000	0.0000	0.0000	**1**
2	0.9862	0.9216	0.8108	0.6767	0.5405	0.4162	0.3108	0.2260	0.1605	0.1117	0.0142	0.0013	0.0001	0.0000	0.0000	0.0000	0.0000	0.0000	**2**
3	0.9984	0.9822	0.9372	0.8609	0.7604	0.6473	0.5327	0.4253	0.3303	0.2503	0.0460	0.0057	0.0005	0.0000	0.0000	0.0000	0.0000	0.0000	**3**
4	0.9999	0.9968	0.9832	0.9510	0.8964	0.8206	0.7290	0.6290	0.5277	0.4312	0.1121	0.0185	0.0021	0.0002	0.0000	0.0000	0.0000	0.0000	**4**
5	1.0000	0.9995	0.9963	0.9856	0.9622	0.9224	0.8650	0.7919	0.7072	0.6161	0.2194	0.0480	0.0070	0.0007	0.0001	0.0000	0.0000	0.0000	**5**
6		0.9999	0.9993	0.9964	0.9882	0.9711	0.9417	0.8981	0.8404	0.7702	0.3613	0.1034	0.0194	0.0025	0.0002	0.0000	0.0000	0.0000	**6**
7		1.0000	0.9999	0.9992	0.9968	0.9906	0.9780	0.9562	0.9232	0.8779	0.5188	0.1904	0.0453	0.0073	0.0008	0.0001	0.0000	0.0000	**7**
8			1.0000	0.9999	0.9992	0.9973	0.9927	0.9833	0.9672	0.9421	0.6681	0.3073	0.0916	0.0183	0.0025	0.0002	0.0000	0.0000	**8**
9				1.0000	0.9998	0.9993	0.9978	0.9944	0.9875	0.9755	0.7911	0.4437	0.1637	0.0402	0.0067	0.0008	0.0001	0.0000	**9**
10					1.0000	0.9998	0.9994	0.9983	0.9957	0.9906	0.8801	0.5836	0.2622	0.0789	0.0160	0.0022	0.0002	0.0000	**10**
11						1.0000	0.9999	0.9995	0.9987	0.9968	0.9372	0.7107	0.3816	0.1390	0.0342	0.0057	0.0006	0.0000	**11**
12							1.0000	0.9999	0.9996	0.9990	0.9699	0.8139	0.5110	0.2229	0.0661	0.0133	0.0018	0.0002	**12**
13								1.0000	0.9999	0.9997	0.9868	0.8894	0.6370	0.3279	0.1163	0.0280	0.0045	0.0005	**13**
14									1.0000	0.9999	0.9947	0.9393	0.7481	0.4468	0.1878	0.0540	0.0104	0.0013	**14**
15										1.0000	0.9981	0.9692	0.8369	0.5692	0.2801	0.0955	0.0220	0.0033	**15**
16											0.9993	0.9856	0.9017	0.6839	0.3889	0.1561	0.0427	0.0077	**16**
17											0.9998	0.9937	0.9449	0.7822	0.5060	0.2369	0.0765	0.0164	**17**
18											0.9999	0.9975	0.9713	0.8594	0.6216	0.3356	0.1273	0.0325	**18**
19											1.0000	0.9991	0.9861	0.9152	0.7264	0.4465	0.1974	0.0595	**19**
20												0.9997	0.9937	0.9522	0.8139	0.5610	0.2862	0.1013	**20**
21												0.9999	0.9974	0.9749	0.8813	0.6701	0.3900	0.1611	**21**
22												1.0000	0.9990	0.9877	0.9290	0.7660	0.5019	0.2399	**22**
23													0.9996	0.9944	0.9604	0.8438	0.6134	0.3359	**23**
24													0.9999	0.9976	0.9793	0.9022	0.7160	0.4439	**24**
25													1.0000	0.9991	0.9900	0.9427	0.8034	0.5561	**25**
26														0.9997	0.9955	0.9686	0.8721	0.6641	**26**
27														0.9999	0.9981	0.9840	0.9220	0.7601	**27**
28														1.0000	0.9993	0.9924	0.9556	0.8389	**28**
29															0.9997	0.9966	0.9765	0.8987	**29**
30															0.9999	0.9986	0.9884	0.9405	**30**
31															1.0000	0.9995	0.9947	0.9675	**31**
32																0.9998	0.9978	0.9836	**32**
33																0.9999	0.9991	0.9923	**33**
34																1.0000	0.9997	0.9967	**34**
35																	0.9999	0.9987	**35**
36																	1.0000	0.9995	**36**
37																		0.9998	**37**
38																		1.0000	**38**

NORMAL DISTRIBUTION FUNCTION (Table 3)

The table gives the probability p that a normally distributed random variable Z, with mean = 0 and variance = 1, is less than or equal to z.

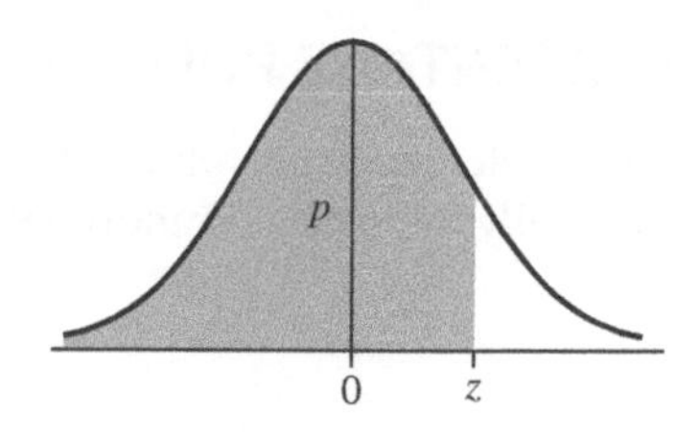

z	0.00	0.01	0.02	0.03	0.04	0.05	0.06	0.07	0.08	0.09	z
0.0	0.50000	0.50399	0.50798	0.51197	0.51595	0.51994	0.52392	0.52790	0.53188	0.53586	**0.0**
0.1	0.53983	0.54380	0.54776	0.55172	0.55567	0.55962	0.56356	0.56749	0.57142	0.57535	**0.1**
0.2	0.57926	0.58317	0.58706	0.59095	0.59483	0.59871	0.60257	0.60642	0.61026	0.61409	**0.2**
0.3	0.61791	0.62172	0.62552	0.62930	0.63307	0.63683	0.64058	0.64431	0.64803	0.65173	**0.3**
0.4	0.65542	0.65910	0.66276	0.66640	0.67003	0.67364	0.67724	0.68082	0.68439	0.68793	**0.4**
0.5	0.69146	0.69497	0.69847	0.70194	0.70540	0.70884	0.71226	0.71566	0.71904	0.72240	**0.5**
0.6	0.72575	0.72907	0.73237	0.73565	0.73891	0.74215	0.74537	0.74857	0.75175	0.75490	**0.6**
0.7	0.75804	0.76115	0.76424	0.76730	0.77035	0.77337	0.77637	0.77935	0.78230	0.78524	**0.7**
0.8	0.78814	0.79103	0.79389	0.79673	0.79955	0.80234	0.80511	0.80785	0.81057	0.81327	**0.8**
0.9	0.81594	0.81859	0.82121	0.82381	0.82639	0.82894	0.83147	0.83398	0.83646	0.83891	**0.9**
1.0	0.84134	0.84375	0.84614	0.84849	0.85083	0.85314	0.85543	0.85769	0.85993	0.86214	**1.0**
1.1	0.86433	0.86650	0.86864	0.87076	0.87286	0.87493	0.87698	0.87900	0.88100	0.88298	**1.1**
1.2	0.88493	0.88686	0.88877	0.89065	0.89251	0.89435	0.89617	0.89796	0.89973	0.90147	**1.2**
1.3	0.90320	0.90490	0.90658	0.90824	0.90988	0.91149	0.91309	0.91466	0.91621	0.91774	**1.3**
1.4	0.91924	0.92073	0.92220	0.92364	0.92507	0.92647	0.92785	0.92922	0.93056	0.93189	**1.4**
1.5	0.93319	0.93448	0.93574	0.93699	0.93822	0.93943	0.94062	0.94179	0.94295	0.94408	**1.5**
1.6	0.94520	0.94630	0.94738	0.94845	0.94950	0.95053	0.95154	0.95254	0.95352	0.95449	**1.6**
1.7	0.95543	0.95637	0.95728	0.95818	0.95907	0.95994	0.96080	0.96164	0.96246	0.96327	**1.7**
1.8	0.96407	0.96485	0.96562	0.96638	0.96712	0.96784	0.96856	0.96926	0.96995	0.97062	**1.8**
1.9	0.97128	0.97193	0.97257	0.97320	0.97381	0.97441	0.97500	0.97558	0.97615	0.97670	**1.9**
2.0	0.97725	0.97778	0.97831	0.97882	0.97932	0.97982	0.98030	0.98077	0.98124	0.98169	**2.0**
2.1	0.98214	0.98257	0.98300	0.98341	0.98382	0.98422	0.98461	0.98500	0.98537	0.98574	**2.1**
2.2	0.98610	0.98645	0.98679	0.98713	0.98745	0.98778	0.98809	0.98840	0.98870	0.98899	**2.2**
2.3	0.98928	0.98956	0.98983	0.99010	0.99036	0.99061	0.99086	0.99111	0.99134	0.99158	**2.3**
2.4	0.99180	0.99202	0.99224	0.99245	0.99266	0.99286	0.99305	0.99324	0.99343	0.99361	**2.4**
2.5	0.99379	0.99396	0.99413	0.99430	0.99446	0.99461	0.99477	0.99492	0.99506	0.99520	**2.5**
2.6	0.99534	0.99547	0.99560	0.99573	0.99585	0.99598	0.99609	0.99621	0.99632	0.99643	**2.6**
2.7	0.99653	0.99664	0.99674	0.99683	0.99693	0.99702	0.99711	0.99720	0.99728	0.99736	**2.7**
2.8	0.99744	0.99752	0.99760	0.99767	0.99774	0.99781	0.99788	0.99795	0.99801	0.99807	**2.8**
2.9	0.99813	0.99819	0.99825	0.99831	0.99836	0.99841	0.99846	0.99851	0.99856	0.99861	**2.9**
3.0	0.99865	0.99869	0.99874	0.99878	0.99882	0.99886	0.99889	0.99893	0.99896	0.99900	**3.0**
3.1	0.99903	0.99906	0.99910	0.99913	0.99916	0.99918	0.99921	0.99924	0.99926	0.99929	**3.1**
3.2	0.99931	0.99934	0.99936	0.99938	0.99940	0.99942	0.99944	0.99946	0.99948	0.99950	**3.2**
3.3	0.99952	0.99953	0.99955	0.99957	0.99958	0.00060	0.00061	0.00002	0.99904	0.99905	**3.3**
3.4	0.99966	0.99968	0.99969	0.99970	0.99971	0.99972	0.99973	0.99974	0.99975	0.99976	**3.4**
3.5	0.99977	0.99978	0.99978	0.99979	0.99980	0.99981	0.99981	0.99982	0.99983	0.99983	**3.5**
3.6	0.99984	0.99985	0.99985	0.99986	0.99986	0.99987	0.99987	0.99988	0.99988	0.99989	**3.6**
3.7	0.99989	0.99990	0.99990	0.99990	0.99991	0.99991	0.99992	0.99992	0.99992	0.99992	**3.7**
3.8	0.99993	0.99993	0.99993	0.99994	0.99994	0.99994	0.99994	0.99995	0.99995	0.99995	**3.8**
3.9	0.99995	0.99995	0.99996	0.99996	0.99996	0.99996	0.99996	0.99996	0.99997	0.99997	**3.9**

PERCENTAGE POINTS OF THE NORMAL DISTRIBUTION (Table 4)

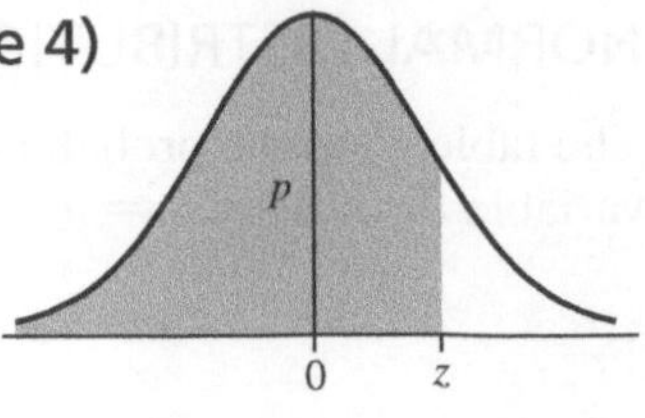

The table gives the values of z satisfying $P(Z \leq z) = p$, where Z is the normally distributed random variable with mean = 0 and variance = 1.

p	**0.00**	**0.01**	**0.02**	**0.03**	**0.04**	**0.05**	**0.06**	**0.07**	**0.08**	**0.09**	p
0.5	0.0000	0.0251	0.0502	0.0753	0.1004	0.1257	0.1510	0.1764	0.2019	0.2275	**0.5**
0.6	0.2533	0.2793	0.3055	0.3319	0.3585	0.3853	0.4125	0.4399	0.4677	0.4958	**0.6**
0.7	0.5244	0.5534	0.5828	0.6128	0.6433	0.6745	0.7063	0.7388	0.7722	0.8064	**0.7**
0.8	0.8416	0.8779	0.9154	0.9542	0.9945	1.0364	1.0803	1.1264	1.1750	1.2265	**0.8**
0.9	1.2816	1.3408	1.4051	1.4758	1.5548	1.6449	1.7507	1.8808	2.0537	2.3263	**0.9**
p	**0.000**	**0.001**	**0.002**	**0.003**	**0.004**	**0.005**	**0.006**	**0.007**	**0.008**	**0.009**	p
0.95	1.6449	1.6546	1.6646	1.6747	1.6849	1.6954	1.7060	1.7169	1.7279	1.7392	**0.95**
0.96	1.7507	1.7624	1.7744	1.7866	1.7991	1.8119	1.8250	1.8384	1.8522	1.8663	**0.96**
0.97	1.8808	1.8957	1.9110	1.9268	1.9431	1.9600	1.9774	1.9954	2.0141	2.0335	**0.97**
0.98	2.0537	2.0749	2.0969	2.1201	2.1444	2.1701	2.1973	2.2262	2.2571	2.2904	**0.98**
0.99	2.3263	2.3656	2.4089	2.4573	2.5121	2.5758	2.6521	2.7478	2.8782	3.0902	**0.99**

RANDOM NUMBERS (Table 13)

8956	29927	66187	80784	37542	62446	13481	72730	48511	42315
4451	62506	22780	30720	79338	68358	62765	33401	82758	42929
1323	83752	10664	12193	88766	76763	90977	46881	59089	39648
1916	75703	27522	79504	06662	25468	92407	19626	61173	52793
3727	99617	59120	33554	32904	95312	61763	68868	94179	73442
1966	17490	64900	12690	95474	53849	64791	35843	44832	01296
7355	02384	16680	76637	42437	27994	24718	09566	43821	89315
8802	44031	51668	85907	22683	06119	25360	35480	91334	01522
6134	94058	36466	99717	57651	02512	98785	86491	76812	10324
7217	88783	77127	95783	40666	82539	84224	94354	41979	32823
7895	33380	47444	02936	57303	31458	28669	22538	66884	38370
9108	95198	41684	89066	17963	39042	50791	44683	15134	19909
9310	03183	62706	65531	47767	42347	51899	33582	28098	43168
4447	26623	00550	52329	90292	37508	97310	92049	47365	80242
2737	57929	14290	08118	95473	91586	58953	74998	73950	54662
5269	49103	92150	78211	27762	18135	43479	61698	77768	00223
6198	98634	31870	56839	60478	62129	87149	60240	09079	38567
5823	90593	76248	60379	98204	59254	51616	41091	11818	11001
9611	68604	90298	38595	52048	95137	73363	53307	37914	27903
2205	72711	43441	87108	82155	43650	81967	56348	19878	75813
4513	08193	05302	11352	48369	55731	81158	21037	29534	98074
9851	74829	51695	51682	97660	97110	69540	69776	22736	54635
0349	25900	81265	25339	43875	38563	43530	36289	78810	18959
9871	42417	50106	24752	94664	11611	05720	77091	96338	68507
1268	32291	57653	42135	36440	79427	11660	15666	55682	25449
7468	24096	57419	35611	91179	51464	94284	92449	97347	22184
4454	50344	22824	09193	98771	30963	02876	97671	56397	91677
1503	76672	52872	48610	31314	21545	23601	18278	93530	02142
7261	50385	70112	26897	00077	04803	98326	88933	17710	75750
4852	64222	95920	80534	55090	04105	01415	11376	20709	78887
1198	11602	06891	07924	42959	73124	36830	70559	55739	73191
0818	87962	92071	13405	05057	85947	73043	94208	52829	88272
7297	41595	07611	36646	70863	57797	82033	19236	74608	14324
4648	34917	58038	47230	38817	70605	62771	02851	23195	20204
9898	50622	76133	54065	34055	13961	07604	30260	92240	40736
5060	14422	58282	73673	04535	03557	40036	85475	16021	77173
4300	48254	71043	44942	12252	59557	53013	26170	21980	18582
2710	59322	65251	84379	05985	45765	38349	68661	18129	29338
1352	04224	19593	72554	54239	44870	38726	51297	82412	65799
5076	17264	41154	16019	70481	97716	53185	53901	89036	01253
2445	09632	07182	78111	19253	12414	73496	24090	54974	48941
6267	54282	74626	40866	91371	44589	31478	58842	71961	38487
9681	80207	43497	37079	53974	20241	62576	15660	68105	57002
1884	93899	94309	56732	59858	28457	74546	45424	92496	71035
0038	46869	52284	00000	42554	58770	83458	58425	60956	21595
5342	61693	10160	27212	91407	61420	55196	32064	99083	45348
7696	88047	21252	52766	88011	96661	77691	78801	05384	92340
5749	27087	84246	04208	37579	54270	94698	86310	06727	88176
5251	34691	89127	51214	38276	27601	02422	77625	02017	13801
4230	48467	55548	84036	63668	20271	26235	76671	51372	35552

Formulae

This section lists formulae which relate to the Statistics module S1, and which are included in the AQA formulae booklet.

Probability

$$P(A \cup B) = P(A) + P(B) - P(A \cap B)$$
$$P(A \cap B) = P(A)P(B \mid A)$$

Binomial distribution

When $X \sim B(n, p)$

$$P(X = x) = \binom{n}{x} p^x (1-p)^{n-x}$$

Mean $= np$

Variance $= np(1-p)$

Sampling distributions

For a random sample $x_1, x_2, \ldots, x_n$ of n independent observations from a distribution having mean μ and variance σ^2, the corresponding random variables are $X_1, X_2, \ldots, X_n$ with

$$\overline{X} = \frac{1}{n}(X_1 + X_2 + \ldots + X_n)$$

$\overline{X}$ is an unbiased estimator of μ, with $\text{Var}(\overline{X}) = \dfrac{\sigma^2}{n}$

S^2 is an unbiased estimator of σ^2, where $S^2 = \dfrac{\sum(X_i - \overline{X})^2}{n-1}$

For a random sample of n observations from $N(\mu, \sigma^2)$, $\dfrac{\overline{X} - \mu}{\frac{\sigma}{\sqrt{n}}} \sim N(0, 1)$

Correlation and regression

For a set of n pairs of values (x_i, y_i)

$$S_{xx} = \sum(x_i - \bar{x})^2 = \sum x_i^2 - \frac{(\sum x_i)^2}{n}$$

$$S_{yy} = \sum(y_i - \bar{y})^2 = \sum y_i^2 - \frac{(\sum y_i)^2}{n}$$

$$S_{xy} = \sum(x_i - \bar{x})(y_i - \bar{y}) = \sum x_i y_i - \frac{(\sum x_i)(\sum y_i)}{n}$$

The product moment correlation coefficient is

$$r = \frac{S_{xy}}{\sqrt{S_{xx}S_{yy}}} = \frac{\sum(x_i - \bar{x})(y_i - \bar{y})}{\sqrt{\{\sum(x_i - \bar{x})^2\}\{\sum(y_i - \bar{y})^2\}}} = \frac{\sum x_i y_i - \frac{(\sum x_i)(\sum y_i)}{n}}{\sqrt{\left(\sum x_i^2 - \frac{(\sum x_i)^2}{n}\right)\left(\sum y_i^2 - \frac{(\sum y_i)^2}{n}\right)}}$$

The regression coefficient of y on x is $b = \dfrac{S_{xy}}{S_{xx}} = \dfrac{\sum(x_i - \bar{x})(y_i - \bar{y})}{\sum(x_i - \bar{x})^2}$

Least squares regression line of y on x is $y = a + bx$ where $a = \bar{y} - b\bar{x}$

Candidates should learn the following formula, which is **not** included in the AQA formulae booklet, but which may be required to answer questions:

$(\text{residual})_i = y_i - a - bx_i$

Notation

$A, B, C, \ldots$	events
$A \cup B$	union of the events A and B
$A \cap B$	intersection of the events A and B
$\mathrm{P}(A)$	probability of the event A
A'	complement of the event A
$\mathrm{P}(A \mid B)$	probability of the event A conditional on the event B
$X, Y, R, \ldots$	random variables
$x, y, r, \ldots$	values of the random variables $X, Y, R, \ldots$
$x_1, x_2, \ldots$	observations
$f_1, f_2, \ldots$	frequencies with which the observations $x_1, x_2, \ldots$ occur
$p(x)$	probability function $\mathrm{P}(X = x)$ of the discrete random variable X
$p_1, p_2, \ldots$	probabilities of the values $x_1, x_2, \ldots$ of the discrete random variable X
$\mathrm{f}(x), \mathrm{g}(x), \ldots$	the value of the probability density function of the continuous random variable X.
$\mathrm{F}(x), \mathrm{G}(x), \ldots$	the value of the cumulative distribution function $\mathrm{P}(X \leqslant x)$ of the continuous random variable X
$\mathrm{E}(X)$	expectation of the random variable X
$\mathrm{E}[\mathrm{g}(X)]$	expectation of $\mathrm{g}(X)$
$\mathrm{Var}\,(X)$	variance of the random variable X
$\mathrm{B}(n, p)$	binomial distribution with parameters n and p
$\mathrm{N}(\mu, \sigma^2)$	normal distribution with a mean of μ and a variance of σ^2
μ	population mean
σ^2	population variance
σ	population standard deviation
$\bar{x}$	sample mean
s^2	unbiased estimate of population variance from a sample, $s^2 = \dfrac{1}{n-1}\Sigma(x_i - \bar{x})^2$
z	value of the standard normal variable with distribution $\mathrm{N}(0, 1)$
$\Phi(z)$	corresponding (cumulative) distribution function
ρ	product moment correlation coefficient for a population
r	product moment correlation coefficient for a sample
a	intercept with the vertical axis in the linear regression equation
b	gradient in the linear regression equation

Index